Y0-DHB-951

Advances in
PARASITOLOGY

VOLUME 26

Editorial Board

W. H. R. Lumsden University of Dundee Animal Services Unit, Ninewells Hospital and Medical School, P.O. Box 120, Dundee DD1 9SY, UK

P. Wenk Tropenmedizinisches Institut, Universität Tübingen, D7400 Tübingen 1, Wilhelmstrasse 31, Federal Republic of Germany

C. Bryant Department of Zoology, Australian National University, G.P.O. Box 4, Canberra, A.C.T. 2600, Australia

E. J. L. Soulsby Department of Clinical Veterinary Medicine, University of Cambridge, Madingley Road, Cambridge CB3 0ES, UK

K. S. Warren Director for Health Sciences, The Rockefeller Foundation, 1133 Avenue of the Americas, New York, N.Y. 10036, USA

J. P. Kreier Department of Microbiology, College of Biological Sciences, Ohio State University, 484 West 12th Avenue, Columbus, Ohio 43210–1292, USA

M. Yokogawa Department of Parasitology, School of Medicine, Chiba University, Chiba, Japan

QH
547
.A38
v.26

Advances in PARASITOLOGY

Edited by

J. R. BAKER

Cambridge, England

and

R. MULLER

CAB International Institute of Parasitology
St. Albans, England

VOLUME 26

1987

ACADEMIC PRESS

Harcourt Brace Jovanovich, Publishers

London Orlando San Diego New York Austin
Boston Sydney Tokyo Toronto

ACADEMIC PRESS INC. (LONDON) LTD
24/28 Oval Road
LONDON NW1

United States Edition published by
ACADEMIC PRESS INC.
Orlando, Florida 32887

Copyright © 1987, by
ACADEMIC PRESS INC. (LONDON) LTD

All Rights Reserved
No part of this book may be reproduced in any form by photostat, microfilm, or any other means, without written permission from the publishers

ISBN 0-12-031726-5
ISSN 0065-308X

Typeset by Latimer Trend and
Company Ltd, Plymouth, England
Printed in Great Britain by Galliard (Printers) Ltd, Great Yarmouth

CONTRIBUTORS TO VOLUME 26

J. M. BEHNKE, *MRC Experimental Parasitology Group, Department of Zoology, University of Nottingham, University Park, Nottingham NG7 2RD, UK*

A. D. IRVIN*, *International Laboratory for Research on Animal Diseases, PO Box 30709, Nairobi, Kenya*

D. F. METTRICK, *Department of Zoology, University of Toronto, Ontaria, Canada M5S 1A1*

W. P. ROGERS, *Department of Physiology, Waite Agricultural Research Institute, Glen Osmond, South Australia, Australia 5001*

R. I. SOMMERVILLE, *Department of Zoology, University of Adelaide, Adelaide, South Australia, Australia 5001*

M. V. K. SUKHDEO, *Department of Zoology, University of Toronto, Ontario, Canada M5S 1A1*

P. T. K. WOO, *Department of Zoology, College of Biological Science, University of Guelph, Guelph, Ontario, Canada N1G 2W1*

**Present address:* Overseas Development Administration, Eland House, Stag Place, London SW1E 5DH.

PREFACE

Once again we present a mixture of topics containing, we hope, something for every one of our readers. Two papers deal with communication, neural communication in helminths (by M. V. K. Sukhdeo and D. F. Mettrick) and, a broader field, chemical communication between hosts and parasites (by R. I. Sommerville and W. P. Rogers). Two papers concern protozoa, the economically important Theileriidae (by A. D. Irvin) and the less well known, but perhaps equally important, Cryptobiidae or trypanoplasms of fish (by P. T. K. Woo). The remaining paper (by J. M. Behnke) reviews a topic of ever increasing relevance, the mechanisms adopted by parasites (in this example, nematodes) to evade their hosts' immune responses. The antigenic variation practised by trypanosomes and malaria parasites, and the antigenic disguise adopted by schistosomes, have been extensively (though not yet exhaustively) studied; now it is the turn of the roundworms to come under scrutiny in this respect. Only by fully understanding these mechanisms, *inter alia*, will it become possible (if indeed it does become possible) to engineer effective anti-parasite vaccines.

1987

J. R. Baker
R. Muller

CONTENTS

Cryptobia and Cryptobiosis in Fishes

P. T. K. WOO

The Nature and Action of Host Signals

R. I. SOMMERVILLE AND W. P. ROGERS

Evasion of Immunity by Nematode Parasites Causing Chronic Infections

J. M. BEHNKE

MRC Experimental Parasitology Group, Department of Zoology, University of Nottingham, University Park, Nottingham NG7 2RD, England

ADVANCES IN PARASITOLOGY VOL. 26
ISBN 0-12-031726-5

Copyright © 1987 Academic Press Inc. (London) Ltd.
All rights of reproduction in any form reserved.

I. Introduction

It is well recognized that human nematode infections are long-lasting (chronic) and that people living in endemic areas may become infected in early childhood and carry worms for the remainder of their lives (Croll *et al.*, 1982; Anderson and Medley, 1985). Nematodes are among the most common and widespread of all the invasive organisms affecting mankind, especially in the tropics, where >90% prevalence with *Ascaris lumbricoides*, hookworms (*Necator americanus* and *Ancylostoma duodenale*), *Trichuris trichiura* and filarial species are not uncommon in rural communities (Croll *et al.*, 1982; Kirkwood *et al.*, 1983; Anderson and May, 1982; Martin *et al.*, 1983). The extremely high overall prevalence of infection and the relatively stable age-intensity of infection profiles, suggest that infections are borne throughout life (Nawalinski *et al.*, 1978; Anderson, 1982) and that host protective immune responses have a minor role, if any, in controlling such parasites (Mitchell, 1979a; Anderson and May, 1985). Among the important questions which are raised by these observations and to which this review will be addressed are the following: (1) Do nematode parasites causing chronic infection possess the capacity to elicit host protective immune responses; (2) Are the worms sufficiently robust to tolerate the range of protective effector mechanisms available to the host; (3) Have these parasites evolved alternative mechanisms by which host immune responses are avoided?

Strategies adopted by parasites to circumvent host defences have been intensively studied during the last decade and considerable progress has been made in our understanding of such mechanisms as antigenic variation, immunodepression, and antigenic disguise (Ogilvie and Wilson, 1977; Bloom, 1979; Cohen, 1982; Parkhouse, 1984) but to date there is no satisfactory immunological explanation for the longevity of nematode parasites and the apparent impunity with which their survival is accomplished, in hosts that seem otherwise (i.e. prior to infection) to be fully immunocompetent.

There are reasons why progress in our understanding of the immunological interactions between host and parasite in infections caused by chronic nematode parasites (CNP) has been so slow. It is obvious that human parasites should take priority in research programmes, but it is seldom possible to conduct immunological studies on human CNP because all the species mentioned earlier are highly specific to man and cannot be transmitted to laboratory rodents consistently enough to make *in vivo* experimentation possible (a few exceptions to this rule are listed in Table 1). Furthermore, where rodents have been found to be susceptible to human CNP, the resulting infections often follow a course which is quite distinct from that in man. More often than not, the host species involved is a rodent which is still poorly characterized in immunological terms, e.g. jird (*Meriones unguiculatus*), hamster (*Mesocricetus auratus*), multimammate rat (*Mastomys natalensis*) or cotton rat (*Sigmodon hispidus litoralis*). The alternative approach of using natural parasites of rodents is restricted by the scarcity of rodent nematodes with host/parasite relationships closely resembling their human counterparts. Only two rodent filariae have been widely studied (*Dipetalonema viteae* and *Litomosoides carinii*) and only one model has been popular in the study of chronic gastrointestinal infection (*Nematospiroides dubius* = *Heligmosomoides polygyrus*).

In this review I will consider those aspects of the immunological relationship between host and parasite, in field and laboratory studies, which are pertinent to an understanding of the mechanisms by which immunity is avoided and thus chronicity of infection achieved. A discourse on the range of immunologically-mediated effector mechanisms available to resist infection is, therefore, beyond the scope of the present paper and the reader is directed to the following articles for further information: Wakelin, 1978b, 1984; Mitchell, 1979a,b; Mitchell and Anders, 1982; Befus and Bienenstock, 1982; Capron *et al.*, 1982; Miller, 1984; Immunological Reviews, 1982.

II. Evidence for the Longevity of Nematode Parasites

A. Definition of Terms

In medical and veterinary science the term chronic is generally applied to prolonged infections in which there is gradual onset of symptoms and deterioration of the host over a period of several weeks if not months. In acute infections, symptoms appear rapidly and are followed by an episode of severe ill health, during which mortality may ensue. In parasitology, the terms chronic and acute are used to distinguish between long-lived parasites and those species which elicit rapid host protective responses. It is in this latter sense that the terms chronic/acute are used here.

A further point which may engender controversy is how long must an infection survive to be designated chronic? This question is easier to answer for laboratory rodents than for other host species. Mice and rats, depending on strain, have the capacity to generate responses which eliminate *Trichinella spiralis*, *Nippostrongylus brasiliensis*, *Trichuris muris* and *Strongyloides ratti* within 5 weeks of infection (Wakelin, 1978a). These therefore are acute nematode infections. A parasite which survives for more than 5 weeks following infection in the rodent intestine must be doing so despite the host's capacity to respond with a spontaneous cure response within this period and hence causes a chronic infection.

During epidemics with *T. spiralis* in man, symptoms of gastroenteritis can become evident within 2 days and in some patients may last until week 12 (Gould, 1945; Pawlowski, 1983). If these symptoms are analogous to the pathophysiological/inflammatory changes which occur during expulsion of *T. spiralis* from rodents, the human host is considerably more variable and a 3-month cut-off point would be necessary to distinguish between acute and chronic nematode parasites of man. All the human nematodes listed earlier persist for well in excess of 3 months in infected individuals living under conditions of continual re-exposure.

The distinction between chronic and acute nematodes parasitizing ruminants is equally difficult to establish because the duration of primary infections is highly variable and seldom studied because of the problems of reinfection while grazing on pasture. Even within breeds of sheep, individuals can behave quite differently; some resist infection whilst others may be totally susceptible (R. L. Coop and F. Jackson, personal communication). It is also pertinent to note that experiments on ruminants are generally conducted using numbers of larvae which are several orders of magnitude higher than corresponding infections in laboratory animals. Sheep grazing on endemic pasture may accumulate very high intestinal nematode burdens, with total worm counts in the range 10 000–20 000 being commonly encountered (Morgan *et al.*, 1951; Thomas and Boag, 1972; Boag and Thomas, 1977; Thomas and Waller, 1979). In some studies, naturally acquired worm burdens of considerably higher magnitude have been reported, e.g. 111 648 *Nematodirus battus*, 66 700 *Ostertagia circumcincta*, 25 338 *Trichostrongylus vitrinus* by Taylor and Cawthorne (1972) and 35 000 *O. circumcincta* by Reid and Armour (1975). For this reason, experimental infections attempt to reproduce the same parasite numbers in order to assess their influence on growth, pathology, etc.

Many commonly encountered gastrointestinal nematodes of ruminants survive for less than 3–4 months during a primary infection, although a residual, non-egg producing population of worms may persist after the spontaneous cure response. Three-month-old Suffolk Greyface lambs given 300 000 larvae of *N. battus* eliminated 90% of the worm burden by day 34 (Mapes *et al.*, 1973; Lee and Martin 1976) although lambs given only 2000 larvae harboured a stable worm burden for at least 74 days. In 6-month-old Blackface sheep given 100 000 *O. circumcincta* larvae, expulsion commenced 16–21 days after infection but worms were not completely eliminated until day 60 (Armour *et al.*, 1966; see Fig. 3b). Fourteen-week-old Dorset Horn lambs given 3000 larvae harboured a stable worm burden until about day 45, after which worms were lost at an exponential rate (Hong *et al.*, 1986). Lambs given 10 000 or 33 000 larvae had shorter stable pre-expulsion phases, corresponding to approximately 38 and 26 days respectively, but in all three groups, worm burdens in excess of 300 were still present on day 77 post infection (Hong *et al.*, 1986). Ayrshire calves given 100 000 (Ritchie *et al.*, 1966) or 300 000 (Murray *et al.*, 1970) *O. ostertagi* larvae began to expel worms 16–21 days after infection, but in both studies residual worms persisted until the last autopsy (days 90 and 70 respectively). Some species are longer-lived in primary infections, e.g. *Haemonchus placei* in calves (Harness *et al.*, 1971), *Trichostrongylus colubriformis* and *T. vitrinus* infections in lambs last for 12–16 weeks (R. L. Coop and F. Jackson, personal communication). These representative data suffice to emphasize that the ruminant intestine has the capacity to mount a protective immune response within 4 months, although there is considerable variation between individual animals, species of parasites and hosts. None of the above species can therefore be considered to be truly chronic, despite the fact that some survive considerably longer than others. Factors which influence the onset of worm expulsion may include the intensity of infection (Lee and Martin, 1976), site occupied, pathology, repertoire of antigens as well as a varying capacity to immunomodulate (see Section VIII). The only species for which there is irrefutable evidence of extreme longevity is *Haemonchus contortus* (see Section II E2).

B. EPIDEMIOLOGICAL STUDIES

1. *Age-intensity curves*

People living in endemic areas are continually exposed to infection by parasites. The individual is likely to make daily contact with small numbers of infective stages, although on occasion large quantities may be encountered (Schad *et al.*, 1983). Under these circumstances it is difficult to judge precisely how long-lived an individual parasite may be.

The Onchocerciasis Control Programme in West Africa presented an opportunity for probably one of the most comprehensive epidemiological surveys ever conducted. Kirkwood *et al.* (1983) studied a total of 18 778 persons and their data (Fig. 1a,b) clearly show that children become infected with *Onchocerca volvulus* in their early teens. By about 20–25 years the intensity of infection, as measured by microfilariae (mf)/skin snip, reaches a point of stability which remains high with no sign of reduction in the older age groups. Although these findings do not establish the longevity of individual worms, the data emphasize that host immune responses, if indeed responsible for any beneficial effect, operate at a high threshold and that in the field, the disease is chronic in nature, although the worms may not be.

Several horizontal studies of *A. lumbricoides* and hookworms revealed the

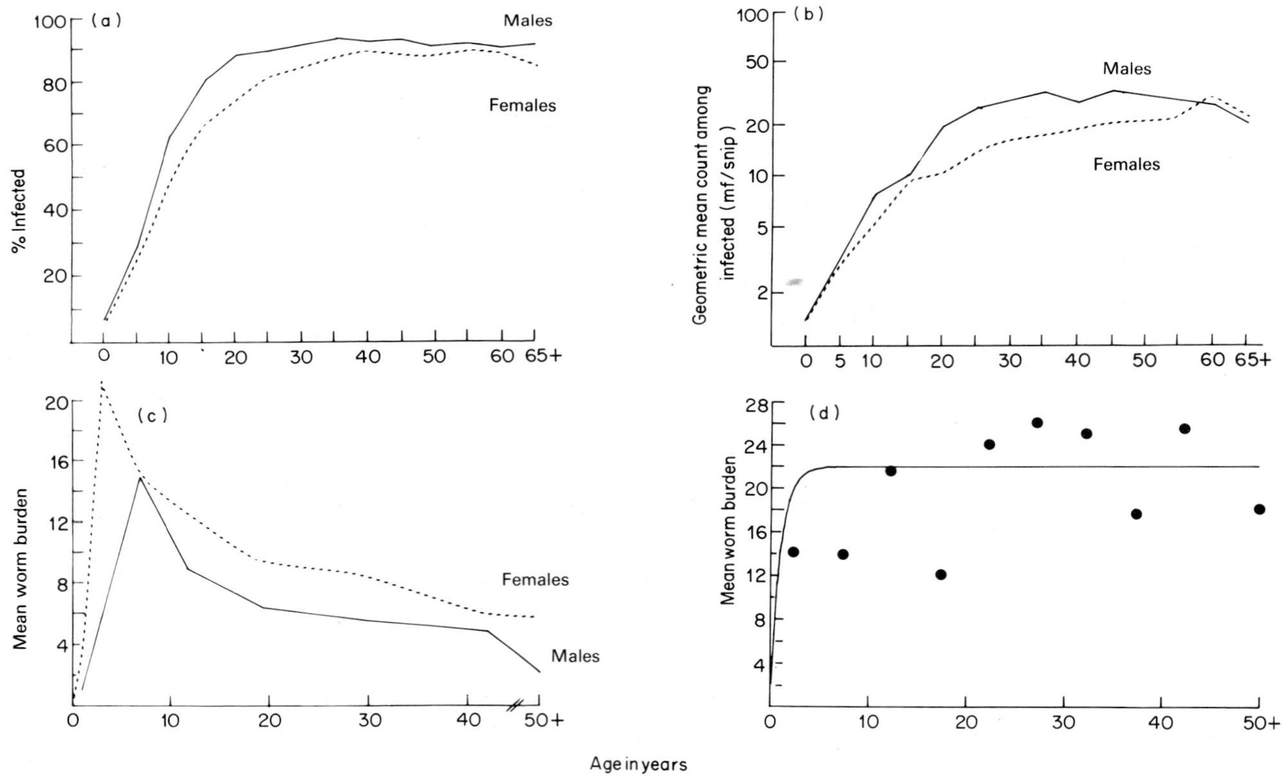

FIG. 1. Some examples of age-prevalence, age-intensity profiles with human nematode parasites. (a) Prevalence of *Onchocerca volvulus* in the Onchocerciasis Control Programme (OCP) area by age and sex (Kirkwood *et al.*, 1983). (b) Intensity of infection with *O. volvulus* in the OCP area by age and sex (Kirkwood *et al.*, 1983). (c) Intensity of infection with *Ascaris lumbricoides* in India, by age and sex (Elkins *et al.*, 1986). (d) Intensity of infection with *A. lumbricoides* in Iran. Combined data for both sexes. Symbols are for observed values and solid line is for the predictions of the model defined by Anderson (1985). Data from Croll *et al.* (1982). (Fig. from Anderson, 1982).

same pattern, with infections commencing in childhood and with relative stability after attainment of the peak in the age–intensity curve in the mid teens–early twenties (Anderson, 1980, 1982; Croll *et al.*, 1982; Schad *et al.*, 1983). However, epidemiological data from other surveys has produced convex curves, with the intensity of infection falling off in older individuals (Fig. 1c; Thein-Hlaing *et al.*, 1984; Anderson and May, 1985; Elkins *et al.*, 1986). These latter observations raise the possibility that acquired immunity may be involved after prolonged, continual exposure or, alternatively, that changing patterns of behaviour minimizing contact with infective stages contribute to lower levels of infection in older individuals. Since both patterns are well documented, it would be extremely interesting to conduct a combined immunological/parasitological study comparing two communities exhibiting markedly different age–intensity profiles.

There can be little doubt that transmission rates are high in endemic areas. The rapidity with which anthelmintic-treated individuals become reinfected points to the continuous availability of ample infective stages in the environment, and to poor acquired immunity in the affected populations. In Croll and Ghadirian's (1981) study in Iran, *A. lumbricoides* eggs were passed within one month of chemotherapy, increasing steadily to reach pretreatment levels of infection within 12 months; these findings concur with observations made by Seo *et al.* (1980) in Korea and by Thein-Hlaing (1985) in Burma. Bundy *et al.* (1985) reported that following treatment for trichuriasis Jamaican children became reinfected to pretreatment levels within 7 months. However, density-dependent restraints must operate to prevent the uncontrolled build-up of adult parasites and to cause the levelling off of the age–intensity curve (Anderson, 1982, 1985). The extent to which immunological and non-immunological mechanisms interact in bringing about the plateau in the curve is a subject of considerable debate and much remains to be done before the issue is fully resolved (Anderson and May, 1985). Among the most intriguing questions awaiting solution are the following: How long do adult worms survive under field conditions, in individuals carrying low and high level infections? What proportion of invading larvae are lost in between infection and patency in individuals with light/heavy infections and after the original infection has been cleared by chemotherapy? Does the presence of adult worms impair or enhance larval establishment? Is the stability and possibly subsequent slow decline in age–intensity curves, the consequence of a balance between the rate of worm loss and acquisition of new parasites, or do the original worms predominate in the parasite populations, excluding incoming larvae by processes analogous to concomitant immunity (Smithers and Terry, 1969)? If adult worms survive by local immunomodulatory activity, the waning of their efficacy in old age may allow such worms to be rejected by local immune responses within the intestine and to be replaced by

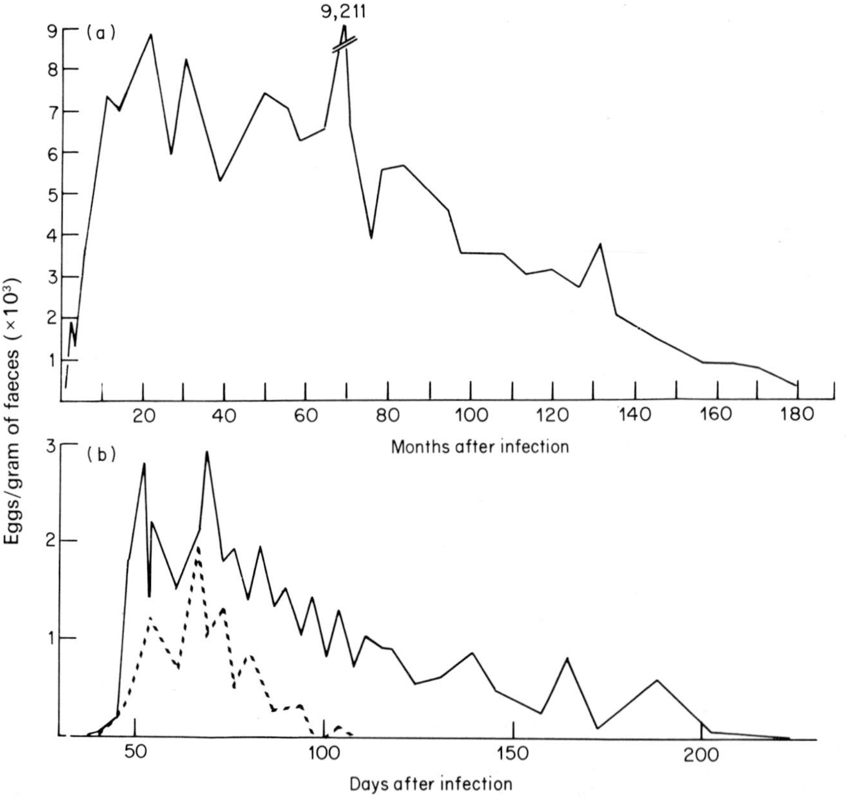

FIG. 2. The longevity of *Necator americanus* in (a) self-infected human volunteer (Palmer, 1955). (b) Male (——) and female (– – –) DSN hamsters infected with 70 larvae when 2–3 days old (Behnke, unpublished data).

new individuals which can shield themselves by means of their immunomodulatory factors (Pritchard and Behnke, 1985; see Sections V.C and VIII).

2. *Following successful termination of transmission*

In filarial infections, which are transmitted by insects, human reinfections are curtailed after vector control programmes. Only the stages parasitic in man remain alive and since chemotherapeutic treatment has not always been possible to reinforce vector control, opportunities have been created for monitoring the longevity of the parasites under field conditions where reinfection has been abolished.

Roberts *et al.* (1967) followed the successful interruption in the transmis-

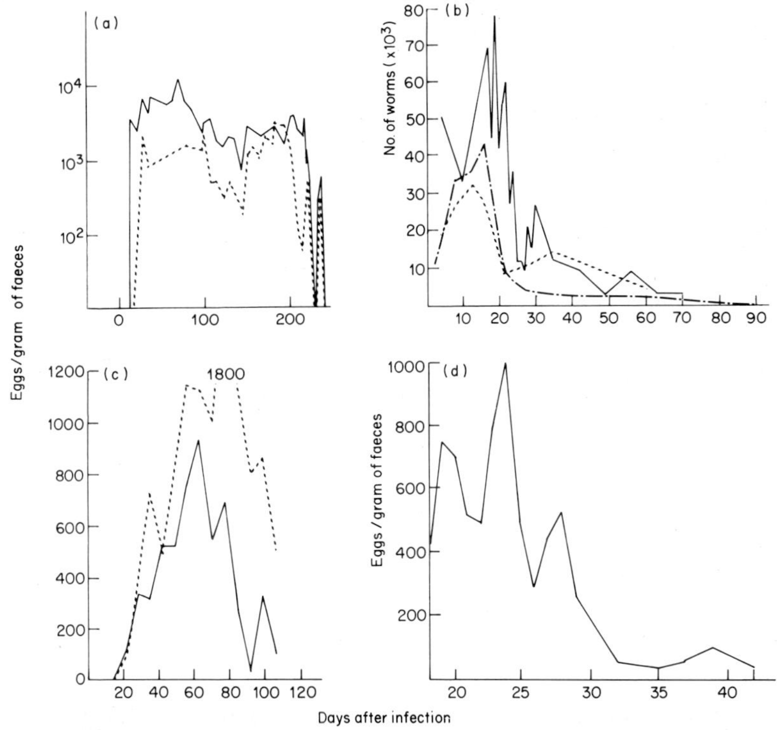

FIG. 3. The time course of infection with various gastrointestinal nematodes of domestic animals. (a) *Haemonchus contortus* in sheep given 10 000 larvae, grazing on parasite free pasture (——) or on endemic pasture (– – – –) (Allonby and Urqhart, 1973). (b) *Ostertagia circumcincta* in sheep given 100 000 larvae (– – – –) (Armour *et al.*, 1966); *O. ostertagi* in calves given 300 000 larvae (——) (Murray *et al.*, 1970) or 100 000 larvae (—·—) (Ritchie *et al.*, 1966). (c) *Trichostrongylus vitrinus* in two representative sheep given 2500 larvae daily (Coop *et al.*, 1979). (d) *O. ostertagi* in calves infected with 300 000 larvae (Murray *et al.*, 1970).

sion of onchocerciasis in Kenya in 1946–1956 with regular examinations of the indigenous population. They concluded that the worms live for at least 11 years, probably as long as 16 years, but die within 18 years. In more recent years, the persistence of the control programme in West Africa has been rewarded by evidence that transmission of onchocerciasis by the *Simulium* vectors has been severely restricted (WHO, 1984). However, the adult worms persist in the indigenous populations although the prevalence and intensity of infection are declining as a result of the gradual death of adult worms. Regression lines calculated on the basis of periodic examinations converge at zero at a time point situated around 11 years after the cessation of transmission (WHO, 1984). These are probably unique examples because there is no drug available which is sufficiently effective and safe to be used for large-scale selective population chemotherapy (WHO, 1984). In other species, ethical considerations would necessitate the employment of chemotherapy alongside vector control.

C. EMIGRATION OF INFECTED INDIVIDUALS TO NON-ENDEMIC REGIONS

Visitors to and inhabitants of endemic areas who subsequently emigrate to regions where transmission does not occur, can provide useful information on the longevity of parasitic infections. Several examples are recorded in the literature, with *Wuchereria bancrofti* being perhaps the most thoroughly documented species in this context. During the Second World War, thousands of American servicemen became infected whilst serving in the Pacific; upon confirmation of diagnosis they were evacuated home where representative cases were followed for varying periods of time (Wartman, 1947; Trent, 1963; Beaver, 1970). In some cases the symptoms of infection persisted for 16 years, possibly caused by long-lasting obstructions of the lymphatics and gonads by worms which had died earlier (Trent, 1963). In the majority of war veterans, microfilaraemia was extremely short-lived (Trent, 1963; Beaver, 1970), although examples of microfilaraemia lasting for 7.5 years have been reported (Conn and Greenslit, 1952). Natives who emigrate from endemic areas have long-lasting patterns of microfilaraemia, with reports ranging from 5–8 years (Leeuwin, 1962; Mahoney and Aiu, 1970; Guptavanij and Harinasuta, 1971). However, Carme and Laigret (1979) described an interesting case of a Tahitian female who left Polynesia in 1935 to live in France. When she returned in 1975, microfilariae (mf) were detected in her circulation, using a concentration method which yielded 2 mf in 5 ml of venous blood. Therefore, under some circumstances *W. bancrofti* can maintain microfilaraemia for up to 40 years. Other studies have variously estimated adult worm longevity at 10–17 years (Manson-Bahr, 1959; Nelson, 1966).

Reports concerning other species include *Loa loa*—10 years (Nelson, 1966), *Brugia malayi*—7 years (Guptavanij and Harinasuta, 1971), *Ancylostoma duodenale*—18 months (Saint-Martin and Dussault, 1957)—4 and 6 years (Boycott, 1911) and hookworms (both species)—8 years (Chandler, 1926, 1935). Presumably, many cases of helminth infections are diagnosed among immigrants to non-endemic countries, but are seldom reported. Indeed, hookworm and *Ascaris* infections are so frequently encountered among Asian women in the U.K., that it has almost become standard practice for faecal examinations to be made during prenatal examinations in hospitals dealing with immigrant communities.

D. THE LONGEVITY OF MICROFILARIAE FOLLOWING THE DEATH OF ADULT WORMS BY CHEMOTHERAPY

The survival of the microfilariae (mf) of *O. volvulus* has been observed in two patients treated with the macrofilaricidal drug Mel W which does not affect mf (Duke, 1968). Both patients lived in the Cameroons and were employed as nightwatchmen in an area where an effective *Similium* control scheme was operating. Mf counts fell by 35% within 6 months of treatment, but were not entirely cleared until 30 months, indicating that mf have a maximum life span of about 2.5 years.

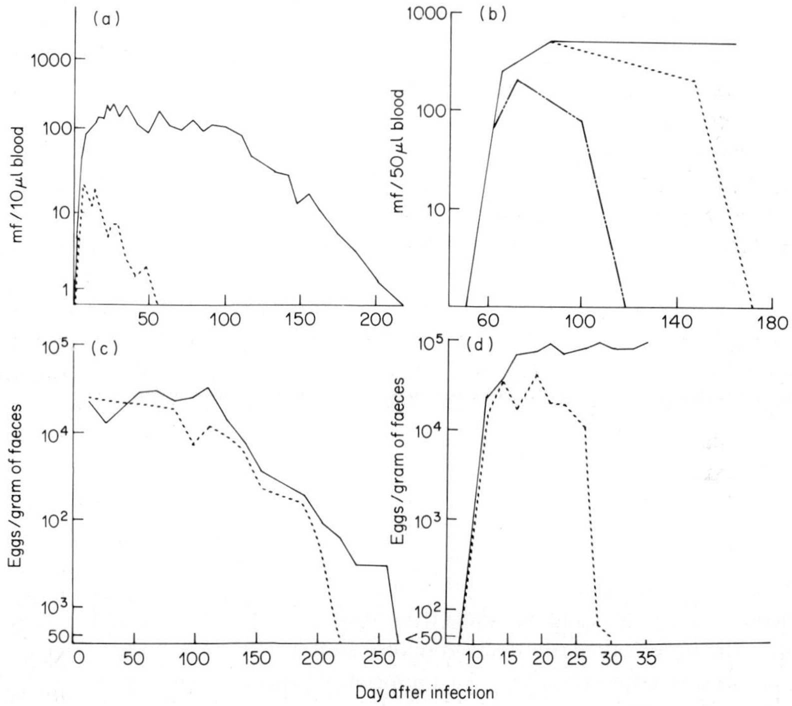

FIG. 4. The time course of infection with filarial and gastrointestinal nematodes of laboratory animals. (a) *Dipetalonema viteae* microfilaraemia in BALB/b (——) and $C_{57}BL_{10}$ (– – –) mice, following transplantation of five female worms (Storey *et al.*, 1985). (b) *D. viteae* microfilaraemia in LSH and CB (——), LCH and MHA (– – –) and LVG and PD4 (—— - - ——) hamsters following infection with third stage larvae (Neilson, 1978). (c) *Nematospiroides dubius* in $C_{57}BL_{10}$ (——) and NIH (– – –) mice following infection with 200 larvae (Behnke and Robinson, 1985). (d) *N. dubius* in CFLP mice (——) and jirds (– – –) following infection with 150 larvae (Hannah and Behnke, 1982).

E. EXPERIMENTAL INFECTIONS

1. *In human volunteers*

Experiments under the last heading must surely represent self sacrifice in the cause of science. Understandably, few experiments are on record, but there are several notable examples. Palmer (1955) reported the case of a 21-year-old white male living in North America who was infected with an undetermined number of larvae of *N. americanus*. The pattern of faecal egg production was monitored for 15 years before faecal egg counts became negative. Shorter experiments were reported by Ball and Bartlett (1969), who found that *N. americanus* persisted in a volunteer for 2.5 years despite several challenge infections administered after the initial inoculum. Faecal egg counts indicated that challenge infection worms became superimposed, with no signs of worm loss or reduction in fecundity. Ogilvie *et al.* (1978) subjected a volunteer to four separate infections with *N. americanus*, each terminated by anthelmintic prior to re-exposure. Again, there was no evidence of acquired immunity and the fourth infection was shown to be stable for 12 months before termination by chemotherapy.

Kendrick (1934) reported that prisoners experimentally infected with *A. duodenale* and *N. americanus* passed hookworm eggs for up to 81 and 64 months respectively, whilst Nawalinski and Schad (1974) found evidence for arrested development of *A. duodenale* following self-infection with a strain from West Bengal. The parasites did not mature until 9 months after primary exposure and faecal egg production was monitored until week 56.

2. *In laboratory and domestic animals*

Details of laboratory experiments in which the longevity of primary infections has been determined are summarized in Table 1. Mice given a single pulse primary infection of 100–250 larvae of *Nematospiroides dubius* continue to produce eggs for up to 300 days (Ehrenford, 1954; Behnke and Robinson, 1985). The time course of infection is very similar (Fig. 4c) in the majority of mouse strains commonly used in immunological research (e.g. CBA, C_3H and BALB/c). The few strains which have the capacity to reject primary infection worms (e.g. SJL, SWR) are relatively little studied (Sections VII B and VIII A).

Dipetalonema viteae is a natural filarial parasite of the jird *Meriones libycus* and is infective to *M. unguiculatus* (Worms *et al.*, 1961). In both species a low level infection is long-lasting, with a progressively rising microfilaraemia which can exceed 1000 mf/10 μl of blood and may last for over 18 months (Weiss, 1970). The parasite will also develop in hamsters, although microfila-

TABLE 1
Chronic nematode infections in intact laboratory and domestic animals

Parasite	Host	Longevity (wks)	References
Nematospiroides dubius	Mice	34	Ehrenford, 1954
		30–38	Behnke and Robinson, 1985
Trichostrongylus colubriformis	Jirds	9	Lewis (personal communication)
Obeliscoides cuniculi	Rabbits	20+	Watkins and Fernando, 1986
Necator americanus	Hamsters	16	Sen, 1972
		32+	Behnke, unpublished
Ancylostoma duodenale	Dogs	13	Schad, 1979
Ancylostoma ceylanicum	Dogs	36+	Carroll and Grove, 1984
Trichuris muris	DBA/2 mice	15	Worley *et al.*, 1962
	Schofield mice	15	Wakelin and Selby, 1974
Dipetalonema viteae	Jirds	Adults > 104 Microfilaraemia > 104	Johnson *et al.*, 1974
	Multimammate rats	Adults > 37 Microfilaraemia > 37	Sanger et al., 1981
Litomosoides carinii	Cotton rats	Adults > 60	Bertram, 1966
		Microfilaraemia until 70	Williams, 1984
	Multimammate rats	Adults > 45 Microfilaraemia > 45	Sanger *et al.*, 1981
Brugia pahangi	Cats	Adults > 104 Microfilaraemia > 104	Denham *et al.*, 1972; Wilson and Ramachandran, 1971
	Jirds	Adults > 78 Microfilaraemia > 104	Ash, 1973
Brugia malayi	Jirds	Adults > 78 Microfilaraemia > 104	Ash, 1973
	Ferrets (*Mustela putorius furo*)	Microfilaraemia > 52	Thompson *et al.*, 1985

raemia is generally transient, with mf counts falling by week 17. However, Neilson (1978a) reported that LSH and CB hamsters follow the jird pattern and fail to clear mf. Adult worms are particularly long-lived, surviving for many months in hamsters which have become amicrofilaraemic (Neilson and Forrester, 1975). These worms still continue to produce mf, despite the absence of a blood microfilaraemia (Neilson, 1978b; Haque *et al.*, 1978).

The infective larvae of *D. viteae* do not mature in mice, but the development of a proxy model involving the implantation of adult female worms into subcutaneous pockets in recipient mice, has presented an opportunity for the investigation of chronic microfilaraemia in mice (Thompson *et al.*, 1979; Haque *et al.*, 1980a). Two strains of mice, BALB/c and CBA/N (a mutant strain with a deficient IgM response), sustain a high and persistent microfilaraemia which lasts for 180–>200 days (Thompson *et al.*, 1969; Haque *et al.*, 1980a; Philipp *et al.*, 1984a; Storey *et al.*, 1985).

Of the nematode parasites which affect domestic ruminants, only *Haemonchus contortus* can be considered to be chronic. This species is a voracious blood sucker and is pathogenic in sheep in relatively low level infections (Dargie and Allonby, 1975). In comparison to the heavy infections generally used for other species (> 50 000; see Section VII A), primary infections with *H. contortus* have been studied in animals given < 10 000 larvae. Six to seven-month-old Merino ewes carried a primary infection of 5000 larvae for 55 weeks (Adams and Beh, 1981). A 4500 larval infection lasted in 7–9-month-old Merino ewes for more than 16 weeks (Adams, 1981) and Allonby and Urquhart (1973) found that 10 000 larvae infections lasted for over 30 weeks in 2-year-old Merino ewes. Nevertheless, primary infections with *H. contortus* are subject to abrupt termination by a spontaneous cure response which can follow a large challenge infection (Dargie and Allonby, 1975) or after grazing on fresh pasture (Allonby and Urquhart, 1973).

Among recent developments in this area are reports of three new models for the study of chronic intestinal nematode infections. Jirds are susceptible to infection with *T. colubriformis*, and adult worms persist for over 60 days following a primary infection; this is considerably longer than in guinea-pigs (D. Lewis, personal communication). Neonatal hamsters were shown to be susceptible to infection with *N. americanus* by Sen (1972) and Behnke *et al.* (1986); recent unpublished experiments have confirmed that despite some worm loss in the first 15 weeks of infection, faecal egg counts remain positive for periods in excess of 32 weeks. Finally, Carroll and Grove (1984) found that *Ancylostoma ceylanicum* survived in dogs infected by 2000 larvae for more than 36 weeks, causing hookworm disease very similar to that seen in humans. All three models should provide an opportunity for detailed laboratory investigations of the mechanisms which allow nematodes to cause chronic intestinal infections.

III. Evidence that Nematodes do not lack Intrinsic Immunogenicity

Prior to the advent of modern sensitive analytical techniques it was assumed that parasites which cause chronic infections lacked intrinsic immunogenicity, as a consequence of continuous selection for ability to survive in the host (Sprent, 1959). All the nematodes which have been carefully examined are now known to possess surface, somatic and excretory/secretory (ES) antigens which to a greater or lesser extent elicit appropriate antibody and/or cell-mediated responses. However, not all hosts recognize the same antigens, nor do all hosts mount identical responses under similar circumstances.

A. The Nematode Cuticle and Other Possible Sources of Immunogens

The nematode cuticle is the obvious target for immune responses because its outermost layer represents the interface between host and parasite. The cuticle is a complex, multi-layered structure which has inbuilt rigidity and yet is flexible enough to allow movement. It has been considered in the past to be a relatively inert structure, resistant to attack and impermeable to large molecules (Bird, 1971; Pappas and Reid, 1975; Inglis, 1983). It is certainly considerably different from the live, metabolically active, syncytial cytoplasm which constitutes the tegument of platyhelminth parasites such as tapeworms and schistosomes (Smyth, 1972; Hockley, 1973).

Recent studies have indicated that the nematode cuticle may be more active than had been realized by earlier workers. Filarial nematodes such as *Brugia*, which are tissue dwelling, have poorly developed intestines and can take up amino acids and sugars from the surrounding environment through the cuticle (Howells and Chen, 1981; Howells *et al.*, 1983). Intestinal nematodes as well as tissue dwelling species possess prominent surface antigens which are species and even stage specific (Maizels *et al.*, 1982). These antigens elicit antibody responses during the course of infection and can be precipitated from supernatant fractions of centrifuged worm homogenate by appropriate infection sera. Mouse strains vary in their ability to recognize the full spectrum of surface antigens on *N. dubius* and *T. spiralis* (Jungery and Ogilvie, 1982; Wakelin, 1985) and the recognition of particular antigens on the latter species by NIH mice has been linked to the rapid responder status of this mouse strain. C_3H mice which take considerably longer to reject *T. spiralis* do not "see" all the antigens until 30 days post infection (Jungery and Ogilvie, 1982). Surface cuticular antigens on intestinal nematodes are shed *in vitro* (Philipp *et al.*, 1980; Pritchard *et al.*, 1985) as well as *in vivo*. When surface labelled *N. dubius* were implanted into the mouse intestine, radioactivity was subsequently detected in internal organs such as the spleen and liver (D. I. Pritchard and J. M. Behnke, unpublished observations). However, the source of these antigens is not known. Are they continually being replaced on the cuticular surface and, if so, from where? The secretory glands such as the stichosome of trichuroid species may represent a potential source and indeed there are molecules of similar molecular weight in ES and surface cuticular preparations (Silberstein and Despommier, 1984; Grencis *et al.*, 1986). It is a strong possibility that in *T. spiralis* and *T. muris* which live in intracellular burrows and in *T. colubriformis* which penetrates the mucosa, anteriorly secreted molecules move backwards in the narrow confines between the host and parasite and that some adhere to the parasite cuticle. Gut lumen dwelling species such as *N. dubius* and *N. americanus* are continually washed by intestinal contents and it is less likely that anteriorly secreted material binds to the surface.

Beside oral and anal openings, nematodes have prominent secretory glands, excretory pores and genital openings (Bird, 1971). A wide range of substances emanate from these sources as well as from the surface and in practice it is difficult to collect the products of a particular source separately. Thus, the incubation products of nematodes maintained *in vitro* contain waste material as well as secretions for as yet poorly understood, but presumably strategically important, functions; these are collectively referred to as excretory/secretory (ES) products. Pritchard *et al.* (1985) have described a technique involving the use of the cationic detergent CTAB, by which the surface antigens can be removed and collected in relatively pure form, uncontaminated by other ES products and somatic proteins. *Trichinella spiralis* antigens prepared in this way were shown to be immunogenic and were used to successfully vaccinate mice against challenge infection (Grencis *et al.*, 1986).

One group of ES products which has received particular attention are the acetylcholinesterases. These enzymes are secreted in comparatively large amounts by many species of intestinal parasites including *Nematodirus battus*, *N. americanus*, *N. dubius* and *N. brasiliensis* (Ogilvie *et al.*, 1973; McLaren *et al.*, 1974; Lee and Martin, 1976) but not by *T. spiralis*, nor *T. muris* (D. Wakelin, personal observation). It is believed that acetylcholinesterases play an important role in allowing parasites to maintain their position in the intestine, by slowing intestinal movements in the vicinity of the worms (Lee, 1970; Ogilvie and Jones, 1971). This function has been questioned by Philipp (1984) who pointed out that acetylcholinesterase has an inhibitory effect on mucosal mucus secretion and since mucus is an important component of the processes which culminate in worm expulsion (Miller *et al.*, 1981; Lee and Ogilvie, 1982), the secretion of the enzymes may be primarily to delay the host effector mechanism and hence to prolong parasite survival.

The adults of *Ancylostoma caninum* and *A. duodenale* secrete a protease with a molecular weight of 37 000 which has anticoagulant activity and which probably helps to liquify and degrade the bolus of host mucosa which is taken into the buccal capsule by the worms (Hotez and Cerami, 1983; Hotez *et al.*, 1985). The ES products of adult *N. americanus* also contain proteolytic activity (D. I. Pritchard, A. Carr and P. G. McKean, unpublished observations), as do the infective larvae of *A. caninum* (Hotez *et al.*, 1985); in the latter, the enzyme probably aids percutaneous invasion. Dogs repeatedly infected with *A. caninum* develop antibodies which neutralize the proteolytic enzyme activity in eosophageal extracts of the parasite (Thorson, 1956) and it is therefore conceivable that such antibodies, if host protective, may prevent the success of larval establishment and cause starvation of adult worms by blocking antihaemostatic and digestive mechanisms (Hotez and Cerami, 1983).

In nematodes such as *N. dubius* which survive by immunomodulation, ES products are probably contaminated by immunomodulatory factors. It may therefore be relevant that the ES products of *N. brasiliensis*, *T. muris* and *T. spiralis*, all species expelled by rodents, are powerful host protective immunogens (Day *et al.*, 1979; Despommier, 1981; Mitchell and Anders, 1982; Jenkins and Wakelin, 1983). In contrast, the ES products of *N. dubius*, while equally complex in molecular diversity, cannot be used to vaccinate mice against challenge infection (Day *et al.*, 1979; Hurley *et al.*, 1980; Mitchell and Anders, 1982).

B. NEMATODE ANTIGENS AS TARGETS FOR HOST PROTECTIVE EFFECTOR MECHANISMS

The sequence of events culminating in the destruction of tissue dwelling parasites is initiated by the accumulation and antibody dependent/independent adhesion of leukocytes to the parasite surface, leading eventually to restriction of movement. This is followed by degranulation, the release of cytotoxic mediators and the encapsulation of the parasite in a granulomatous response which ultimately kills the organism. The cellular and antibody-mediated processes involved have been reviewed by Butterworth (1984). Despite these responses, many nematode parasites can survive in highly inflamed tissue sites for prolonged periods of time (Behnke and Parish, 1979b; Piessens and Mackenzie, 1982; Büttner, 1985).

The infective larvae of *N. dubius* generate particularly vigorous granulomatous reactions in immune mice (Jones and Rubin, 1974; Prowse *et al.*,

1979). In the first 3 days of infection the site of worm development is invaded by macrophages and neutrophils and thereafter by increasing numbers of eosinophils (Jones and Rubin, 1974; Sukhdeo *et al.*, 1984), all of which have been observed at close apposition to live and dead worms. It is not clear which larval stage is the main target for host responses *in vivo*, although *in vitro* antibody dependent cellular adhesion (ADCA) reactions have been reported for both L_3 and L_4 stages (Penttila *et al.*, 1983; Pritchard *et al.*, 1983). Furthermore L_4s express a stage-specific surface antigen which is recognized by immune serum but not by primary infection serum (Pritchard *et al.*, 1984c); this suggests that this antigen may be involved in host protective immune responses. The host protective activity present in immune serum is almost exclusively accounted for by IgG_1 antibody (Pritchard *et al.*, 1983), a murine immunoglobin isotype which is known to have the capacity to collaborate with eosinophils in mediating ADCA reactions (Ramalho-Pinto *et al.*, 1979). The presence of eosinophils in granulomata, the coincidence in mouse strains of the capacity to mount vigorous eosinophilic and acquired immune responses (Hurley and Vadas, 1983) and the protective activity in IgG_1 antibodies all point to the IgG_1–eosinophil mediated ADCA reaction as an important element of protective immunity to *N. dubius*.

In vitro experiments have established that L_3 larvae can be damaged by leukocytes other than eosinophils. Macrophages bind to L_3s in the presence and absence of antibodies and following *in vitro* incubation of L_3s in the presence of macrophages and antibody, infectivity is seriously impaired (Chaicumpa and Jenkin, 1978; Chaicumpa *et al.*, 1977). Similar experiments have revealed that peripheral blood eosinophils and neutrophils may also reduce larval infectivity (Penttila *et al.*, 1983, 1984a). The critical importance of neutrophils in protective immunity in mice, has been emphasized by the demonstration of a synergistic interaction between immune serum and neutrophils from infected mice in transferring immunity to naive recipients (Penttila *et al.*, 1984b) and by the observation that neutrophil-specific monoclonal antibodies impair resistance to *N. dubius* in treated mice (Penttila *et al.*, 1985).

However, the vigorous granulomatous response observed in the initial stages of a challenge infection does not necessarily kill all the larvae. Jones and Rubin (1974) noted that by day 10 many granulomata lacked worms within and this coincided with an overall reduction in worm numbers. Expulsion of worms, which complete their development despite the host response, has been confirmed by experiments in my laboratory (Behnke and Wakelin, 1977; Behnke and Robinson, 1985). Furthermore, it is also clear that the larvae can survive for a very long time in the intestinal tissues of immune mice, some worms persisting for more than 3 weeks as arrested or slowly developing larvae (Behnke and Parrish, 1979b). A long period of encapsulation may therefore be required to kill the larvae within the granulomata and even so, some worms escape to the gut lumen, to be subsequently expelled. It is interesting to note that in abnormal hosts such as hamsters and rats, the worms are trapped and killed in intestinal granulomata during the course of a primary infection (Cross, 1960; Cross and Duffy, 1963). Analysis of the cellular processes involved may help to explain why mice cannot mount equally effective responses. Perhaps L_3 and L_4 larvae secrete immunomodulatory factors which protect the worms as the adults do, but only in mice!

It is believed that the surface antigens on microfilariae (mf) are particularly important as targets for mf clearing responses. The protein and/or glycoprotein moieties involved show a wide diversity of molecular sizes among the major human and rodent species and some are species-specific (reviewed by Maizels *et al.*, 1982; Philipp *et al.*, 1984b). Hamsters and mice infected with *D. viteae* develop specific anti-mf surface IgM antibodies during mf clearance. Mouse strains such as BALB/c and CBA/N which cannot produce the relevant response, are unable to clear mf for a long time following the implantation of adult female worms (see Section VII B). In hamsters, IgM antibodies collaborate with neutrophils to bring about mf clearance (Weiss and Tanner, 1979; Rudin *et al.*, 1980; Neilson *et al.*, 1981) but in rats IgE antibody mediates mf killing by macrophages (Haque *et al.*, 1980b).

The primary importance of ES antigens from intestinal nematodes is probably to initiate host protective effector mechanisms which act non-specifically to damage the parasites or to create an environment which is detrimental to survival (reviewed by Miller, 1984). Nevertheless, specific antibody directed at ES and cuticular antigens abounds in the serum and intestinal lumen of immune animals (Befus and Bienenstock, 1982; Miller, 1984). It is possible that such antibody may neutralize parasite secretions or impair sense organs (amphids and plasmids), thereby disorientating the worms sufficiently to initiate their passage through the gut (McLaren, 1976). Serum immunoglobulins have access to the parasites because the intestinal permeability may be severely disrupted in infected animals (Murray *et al.*, 1971; Nawa, 1979; King and Miller, 1984). In *T. spiralis*, antibodies are believed to be important in suppressing worm fecundity (Grencis and Wakelin, 1983), but overall there is still little experimental evidence for direct antibody-mediated damage in nematode infections (Wakelin, 1978b). The intestinal washings from mice infected with *N. dubius* contain specific anti-adult worm antibody (Crandall *et al.*, 1974) and such antibody has been demonstrated bound to the cuticular surface of worms *in vivo*. Despite this the worms survive and seem to be unaffected. In this context it may be particularly interesting to examine intestinal antibody responses to *N. dubius* in mouse strains which reject the primary infection. Expulsion of primary infection adult *N. dubius* from SJL mice is not accompanied by the intense inflammation and mastocytosis observed during the rejection of other species such as *T. spiralis* (S. Dehlawi, J. M. Behnke and D. Wakelin, unpublished data). Furthermore, worm loss occurs over a comparatively long period of time, taking 2 weeks or longer to be completed. It may be that slow attrition is caused by a continually sustained antibody response in the gut lumen.

C. INFECTIONS IN ABNORMAL AND RESPONDER HOSTS

By definition chronic nematodes (CNP) cause longstanding stable infections in their definitive hosts, but are less successful in abnormal hosts. The longevity of parasites in abnormal hosts may be influenced by a range of factors (Mims, 1982) such as physiological/biochemical incompatibility and may be radically curtailed by host protective immune responses (Wakelin, 1978a; Hannah and Behnke, 1982; Philipp *et al.*, 1984a).

The chronicity of primary infections with *N. dubius*, the difficulties encountered in generating acquired immunity and the ability of adult worms to survive in mice immune to larval challenge, raised the possibility that the parasite lacked the capacity to elicit immune responses in mice or that by virtue of its location within the intestinal lumen, an environment from which the host could not be adequately sensitized was being exploited (Bartlett and Ball, 1974; Jacobson *et al.*, 1982). However, primary infections in jirds, in which apparently normal, viable adult worms develop, are relatively short-lived, with complete expulsion occurring within 5 weeks of infection (Jenkins, 1977; Hannah and Behnke, 1982). Worm loss was shown to be a T-cell dependent phenomenon because jirds treated with antithymocyte serum were unable to expel worms and harboured parasites for over 2 months (Hannah, 1983). In this example, *N. dubius* was perfectly capable of surviving provided the immune response was depressed, and hence expulsion was not simply the consequence of physiological incompatibility between host and parasite. The kinetics and characteristics of worm expulsion had all the hallmarks of the spontaneous cure response described for other species (J. Hannah, Ph.D. thesis: University of Nottingham, 1983). It has also become apparent that some mouse strains reject adult *N. dubius* during the course of a primary infection (see Section VIII A). Therefore, unless there are radical differences in the intestinal characteristics of rodents which reject *N. dubius* and those which do not, it must be supposed that the same antigens which elicit protective responses in jirds are also made available to the immune systems of mouse strains which tolerate the worm. The explanation for chronic infections in these latter hosts must lie elsewhere.

This argument can be broadened to other examples. *Dipetalonema viteae* microfilaraemia is chronic in jirds but not in hamsters, which nevertheless cannot rapidly destroy adult worms (Neilson and Forrester, 1975; Haque *et al.*, 1978). Mice kill adult worms within 5 weeks of implantation and most strains clear mf within 10 weeks (see Section VII B). Again, therefore, the antigens capable of eliciting host protective responses are available but fail to trigger appropriate effector mechanisms in some strains/species of hosts. It cannot be argued that parasites survive because they lack intrinsic immunogenicity. It may be, however, that the failure of particular hosts to reject worms may be explicable by a genetically determined inability (see Section VII) to respond to particular types of molecules or the form in which they are presented to the immune system. This hypothesis is testable but requires pure preparations of host protective antigens. If the surface antigens on the mf of *D. viteae* which evoke mf clearance in $C57BL_{10}$ mice could be isolated, their presentation to BALB/c mice would establish whether non-responder strains have the capacity to respond to the antigens *per se*, or whether it is the form in which such antigens are presented which determines whether a response will ensue. It is also possible that particular hosts, while recognizing the important protective antigens, are unable to mount the type of response to which the parasite would be susceptible and hence in these hosts parasite survival is assured.

IV. Evidence that Chronic Nematode Parasites are Susceptible to Host Protective Effector Mechanisms

Our inability to satisfactorily explain long-lasting nematode infections inevitably led to the hypothesis that such species may be particularly robust and tolerant enough not to succumb to the range of available effector mechanisms (Day *et al.*, 1979). However, this hypothesis is difficult to substantiate experimentally and there is little evidence to support it. In order to conclude that a parasite is resistant to an inflammatory response in the intestine for example, it would be necessary to demonstrate that such a response actually took place and that it was capable of expelling parasites known to be sensitive to it (e.g. *T. spiralis*), while at the same time failing to affect the chronic species. It would be extremely difficult, however, to eliminate the possibility that locally, in the immediate vicinity of the parasites, the environment was still as detrimental to parasite survival as elsewhere. If chronic nematode parasites survive by secreting locally-acting immunomodulatory factors, the acute inflammatory reaction may be endured in "safe havens" created by parasite activity and not through intrinsic tolerance of hostile environments (Pritchard and Behnke, 1985).

A. INFECTIONS IN ABNORMAL HOSTS

Ample evidence has already been presented to show that nematodes causing chronic infections in their definitive hosts are susceptible to immune attack in abnormal hosts (see Section III C). Beside the examples listed earlier, *A. lumbricoides* and *Brugia malayi* are both rejected by mice (Mitchell *et al.*, 1976, 1982; Fanning and Kazura, 1983). For other species which infect humans, such as *W. bancrofti* and *O. volvulus*, insufficient information is available to determine whether their failure to grow in laboratory animals can be explained by vigorous immune response or by physiological incompatibility between host and parasite.

B. INFECTIONS IN NORMAL HOSTS

It is perhaps far more relevant to ascertain whether chronic nematodes can be eliminated under particular circumstances from their own normal hosts, in which they would otherwise cause long-lasting infections. Thus, in epidemiological studies, prevalence of infection is never quite 100%. Some individuals remain infection-free despite continual exposure to infective stages (see Section VII A). A proportion of jirds clear the microfilariae of *D. viteae* and do not support a chronic microfilaraemia (Weiss, 1970). There are at least four lines of evidence which support the concept that mice infected with *N. dubius* have the capacity to expel adult worms, but that the relevant effector mechanisms are generally not initiated to terminate primary infections with this species.

1. *Non-specific responses*

(a) Inflammatory reactions induced by heterologous antigens. When NIH mice, infected with 50–100 *N. dubius* were challenged with 250–600 *T. spiralis*, the acute inflammatory response which followed resulted in the expulsion of both species. In some experiments almost the entire *N. dubius* population was eliminated, whereas in others a proportion of worms survived. In those mice which supported a residual *N. dubius* burden, some *T. spiralis* also persisted well beyond their normal period of residence (J. M. Behnke, unpublished observations). One interpretation of these data is that some *N. dubius* are more robust than other species and successfully endure the hostile environment. An alternative hypothesis is that these worms survive because they have created safe pockets in the intestine through the secretion of immunomodulatory factors. The surviving *T. spiralis* may capitalize on these areas of relative safety created by *N. dubius* and thus elude

the host response. It would follow from this hypothesis that *N. dubius* and *T. spiralis* should show an aggregated distribution in the intestine. Interestingly, in concurrently infected $C57BL_{10}$ mice (a strain which rejects *T. spiralis* slowly), a greater proportion of *N. dubius* survive the acute response. Therefore, either $C57BL_{10}$ mice are unable to mount as intense an inflammatory response as NIH mice or, alternatively, this mouse strain is more severely affected by the immunomodulatory activity of *N. dubius* (see Section VIII A).

The important point about these experiments is that both NIH and $C57BL_{10}$ mice have all the components necessary to mount a host-protective inflammatory response to *N. dubius* because when such a response is elicited by *T. spiralis* many *N. dubius* are affected by it. Why then do mice fail to initiate the same effector mechanism in direct response to infection with *N. dubius* alone?

2. *Specific responses*

(a) Infections in responder mouse strains. Reports that SJL, SWR, ($C57BL_{10}$ × NIH) F_1 and LAF_1 mice reject primary infection adult *N. dubius* prove that the adult worms are susceptible to aggressive responses in the normal host (Cypress *et al.*, 1977; Mitchell *et al.*, 1982; Behnke and Robinson, 1985). However, even in these strains the kinetics of worm expulsion are vastly different from those seen during the rejection of *T. spiralis* or *N. brasiliensis*. Once initiated the expulsion of these latter species is completed within several days (Wakelin, 1978a). In contrast, the expulsion of *N. dubius* from SJL mice commences on days 14–28, but is not complete until day 49 (Robinson, 1985). The other strains take even longer and, depending on the worm burden, infections may last for at least 119 days (Robinson, 1985).

(b) Expulsion of adult N. dubius *from immune or repeatedly challenged mice.* Under conditions of repeated challenge certain inbred mouse strains or a proportion of individuals in outbred strains develop resistance to larvae and lose the adult worms persisting from the initial innocula (Prowse *et al.*, 1979; Mitchell and Cruise, 1984). When immune NIH mice were challenged with *N. dubius*, a proportion of the worm burden completed development in the intestinal walls but was subsequently expelled from the lumen (Behnke and Wakelin, 1977; Behnke and Robinson, 1985). However, the worms were severely stunted and it is possible that damage sustained during larval development may have been responsible for their susceptibility to expulsion from the gut.

(c) Expulsion of worms from mice immunized by implanted adult N. dubius. The expulsion of adult worms has been elicited in BALB/c mice by presensitization with ectopically implanted, mature parasites (Day *et al.*, 1979; Hurley *et al.*, 1980). Furthermore, the weak responder strain $C57BL_6$ was induced to reject adult worms by implantation of worms and concurrent administration of minute doses of the adjuvant, pertussigen, derived from *Bordetella pertusis* (Mitchell and Munoz, 1983). This latter phenomenon could not be reproduced in other weak responder mice (C_3H and CBA) and the treatment was actually counterproductive in BALB/c mice (Mitchell and Cruise, 1984). Nevertheless, both experiments established that under particular circumstances (the precise significance of the variables involved is still far from clear), mice which normally tolerate adult *N. dubius* for many months, can be made to express aggressive intestinal responses which dramatically curtail the period of survival.

V. Longlasting Infections by Nematodes Which Normally Cause Acute Infections

Nematode species which are actively expelled by the host within several weeks of infection are not the main concern of this paper, but under certain conditions these parasites may cause long-term infections. Some representative examples are considered here.

A. EXPLOITATION OF NATURALLY ARISING WEAKNESSES IN HOST IMMUNOCOMPETENCE

1. *Infections in neonatal and lactating animals*

Primary infections with *N. brasiliensis* last considerably longer than normal in neonatal and lactating rats (Connan, 1973). Other examples include *T. spiralis* in mice and *N. dubius* in jirds (Ngwenya, 1976; Hannah and Behnke, 1982). Analysis of the rats/*N. brasiliensis* model has revealed that in both cases antibody responses appear to be normal, but that the cellular components which control the final effector mechanism are at fault (Dineen and Kelly, 1973). In lactating rats this has been attributed to the influence of lactogenic hormones, whereas in neonatal rats the slow maturation of the cellular components and the enhanced suppressor cell activity may be responsible for slowing host protective responses (Kelly and Dineen, 1973; Calkins and Stutman, 1978; Strober, 1984). In both situations the adoptive transfer of immune mesenteric lymph node cells brings about active expulsion; thus, the components for mediating expulsion are available but are not activated because of a failure at the level of cellular control (Dineen and Kelly, 1972, 1973).

Prolonged infections and the enhanced susceptibility of neonatal and lactating animals are both phenomena of particular importance in agriculture and possibly also in medicine. Lactating ewes develop high worm burdens in the spring when worms which have overwintered in their intestines as arrested larvae become activated and resume development. Pasture contamination by the infective larvae of species which are resistant to the cold adds to the accumulating adult worm burden (Thomas, 1974) and the subsequent rise in faecal egg counts (spring or postparturient rise) further contaminates the pasture at a time when susceptible lambs begin to graze (Michel, 1976).

2. *Malnourishment*

Animals maintained on protein–calorie deficient diets show weakened cell-mediated responses and this in turn enhances their susceptibility to infection (Chandra, 1975; Koster and Pierce, 1985). Rats kept on protein deficient diets maintain prolonged infections with *N. brasiliensis*. The worldwide distributions of *Ascaris*, hookworms and filarial worms are coincident throughout most of their range with regions in which malnourishment of the human inhabitants is widespread (Crompton, 1984). However, whilst malnourished individuals may show enhanced susceptibility to infection, many have elevated thresholds at which host responses are initiated and hence may tolerate prolonged infections; malnourishment in itself cannot be the sole explanation for the persistence of chronic nematode infections. Many species of chronically persisting nematodes also cause long-lasting infections in well nourished individuals (see Section II C and E).

3. *Concurrent infection*

In nature, it is unusual to find animals which carry only a single species infection; it is conceivable therefore that some of the organisms in concurrently infected hosts interact to enhance each other's survival (Behnke *et al.*, 1978). This phenomenon has been termed interactive protection from expulsion (Mitchell, 1979b). It is best illustrated by experiments in which one parasite is *N. dubius* and the others may be *T. spiralis*, *T. muris*, *Hymenolepis diminuta* or *H. citelli* (see Section VII C). However, there is no evidence that human nematodes interact in this way. Croll and Ghadirian (1981) found that individuals who carried excessive burdens of one nematode species (e.g. *Ascaris*, hookworms, *T. trichiura*, *Trichostrongylus*) were not necessarily predisposed to concurrent high infections by other species. It was concluded by the authors that the absence of heavy infections occurring concurrently argued against "wormy" individuals having increased general susceptibility to infection with other intestinal parasites.

B. SUBTHRESHOLD INFECTIONS

The expulsion of some nematode parasites is dose-dependent, low level infections persisting beyond the usual survival time (Lee and Martin, 1976). *Trichuris muris* is normally expelled by mice within 2–3 weeks of infection, but this particular organism is not fecund until day 32 and survival in nature is therefore unlikely to succeed unless expulsion can be avoided (Behnke and Wakelin, 1973; Behnke *et al.*, 1984). Natural infections in wild mice are mostly low-level (< 10 worms) and the significance of this has been confirmed by laboratory experiments which have established that infections of this intensity survive to patency and are fertile (Behnke and Wakelin, 1973). Worm burdens of fewer than 10 individuals may provide insufficient stimulation to the immune system to elicit a protective response prior to the adult stage, but low-level infections are certainly immunogenic in the long term despite the presence of adult worms because the mice are resistant to reinfection (Wakelin, 1973). The ability of adult *T. muris* to survive is intriguing and the system has much scope for further analysis. For example, nothing is known about the long-term stability of low-level infections with *T. muris* in mice of varying responder status.

The concept of a threshold, a critical intensity of infection required to elicit a host protective response, has received relatively little attention and is consequently still far from clear. The intensity of infection representing the threshold is several orders of magnitude higher in ruminants and possibly also in man than in laboratory animals. Lambs infected with 2000 larvae of *N. battus* produced parasite eggs for considerably longer than animals given higher infection levels (Lee and Martin, 1976) and *O. ostertagi* survived for over 17 weeks when only 8300 larvae were administered (Michel *et al.*, 1978). Other ruminant parasites have seldom been studied at low intensity infections because these would not be of economic value and the necessity to keep animals under reinfection-free conditions for long periods at a time, would make the relevant experiments prohibitively expensive to carry out (see also Section II E).

If the immune response in the intestine operates in a very local manner, worms in low-level infections may simply avoid expulsion by moving on to a fresh location (Miller, 1984). Nematode parasites, especially lumen dwelling species, are mobile within the intestine, migrating with the passage of food and aggregating in relation to reproduction etc. (See Section IX and Croll and Smith, 1977). The canine hookworm *A. caninum* has been observed browsing on the intestinal mucosa for 4–6 hrs at a time before moving on to a new location (Kalkofen, 1970, 1974). An overall spontaneous cure response may therefore require that there are sufficient parasites in the intestine to convert the local effects into a general response of the whole intestine (at the organ level), thereby depriving the worms of the opportunity to avoid immunity locally. However, it must be emphasized that the threshold in the case of *T. muris* is unlikely to operate in this way. The anterior region of *T. muris* is located in intricately constructed intracellular channels and these worms are presumably not as mobile as entirely luminal species (Lee and Wright, 1978). Furthermore low-level infections with *T. spiralis* are expelled with kinetics indistinguishable from those observed in heavy infections (Wakelin and Lloyd, 1976).

C. TRICKLE INFECTIONS

In nature, man and animals are continually exposed to varying quantities of infective larvae and yet the immunology of repeatedly administered antigens is a poorly developed field (Andrew *et al.*, 1984; Saklayen *et al.*, 1984), and it may be particularly relevant to long-lived nematodes that chronic oral presentation of some antigens can induce antigen-specific tolerance (Saklayen *et al.*, 1984). Experimental attempts to mimic natural infections with *N. brasiliensis* by administering five larvae/weekday resulted in the worm burden accumulating and the parasites surviving for more than 12 weeks, which is considerably longer than normal (Jenkins and Phillipson, 1971). However, trickle infections were only successful when initiated in young rats; older animals developed resistance quickly and neonatal unresponsiveness may therefore have been a contributing factor (Jenkins, 1974).

Trickle infections with *T. muris* do not cause stable worm burdens in responder mouse strains such as NIH or CFLP, unless the mice are immunocompromized or concurrently infected with *N. dubius* (Behnke and Wakelin, 1973; Behnke *et al.*, 1984). However, some worms mature successfully in trickle-infected $C57BL_{10}$ mice; eggs appeared on day 34 and egg production lasted until day 90 (Behnke *et al.*, 1984). It may be that in this strain, the immunological threshold is high and hence the larvae from the initial infections have an opportunity to complete development to the adult stage before the immune response begins to operate effectively against subsequent doses of incoming infective stages (Behnke *et al.*, 1984).

Intestinal nematodes can cause severe problems in agriculture, notably to grazing domestic animals and therefore, perhaps not surprisingly, there is a rich literature on management strategies in relation to the epidemiology of helminths which affect animal production (Michel, 1976, 1982, 1985). Pasture contamination with infective larvae can be very high at particular times of the year, exceeding 900 L_3/kg in mid-summer (Thomas, 1974). In consequence, grazing animals may be exposed to several thousands of larvae per day. In experimental studies where cattle are exposed to repeated doses of *Ostertagia ostertagi* larvae, the intestinal worm burden undergoes a continuous turnover, with new worms being acquired as old worms are lost. Adults have a short lifespan under field conditions, with an average of 26 days (Michel, 1970) despite the potential to survive for more than 100 days in single pulse, low-level infections (Michel *et al.*, 1978). It is the brevity of the lifespan which is the principal factor in regulating populations (Michel, 1982). Thus, adult worms are lost continuously and replaced by incoming infective larvae. Resistance to infection increases with continuous exposure, so that gradually incoming larvae are less successful and the rate of replacement falls, accounting for the ultimate decline in worm numbers (Michel, 1970; Donald and Waller, 1982). Although total worm burdens are considerably higher, the kinetics of *O. ostertagi* under repeated infection conditions are very similar to those of *A. lumbricoides* in human populations. Elkins *et al.* (1986) have recently calculated that the longevity of *Ascaris* may be only 12 months, this despite an extremely high prevalence across all age groups in the communities studied. Larval and adult parasites were found throughout the age groups, suggesting that as in *O. ostertagi* a continuous turnover of the worm population was taking place.

A different pattern of events is observed in animals repeatedly infected with *T. vitrinus* or *T. colubriformis*. These worms are not regulated by a turnover of the adult population (Donald and Waller, 1982). In contrast to *O. ostertagi*, when sheep are exposed to daily infection with *Trichostrongylus*, adult worm burdens accumulate until resistance develops to incoming larvae. Even when larval recruitment has been abolished completely, adult worms persist for varying periods of time before they also are ultimately expelled (Donald and Waller, 1982; Jackson *et al.*, 1983). The regulation of *H. contortus* populations in sheep grazing on endemic pasture is more complex and still somewhat controversial (Courtney *et al.*, 1983; Barger *et al.*, 1985). Barger *et al.* (1985) found that in animals given 2400–4800 larvae/week, worms accumulated for the first 4 weeks, after which a plateau was reached, with the establishment of further incoming larvae drastically curtailed. Expulsion of the adult worms followed in weeks 12–14. In contrast, sheep given 600–1200 larvae/week, whilst equally resistant to further larval establishment from week 4 onwards, did not expel the accumulated adult worms within the 15 week experimental period. These results are not compatible with worm turnover of the kind seen in *Ostertagia*, but rather suggest the development of resistance to infection, reflected in reduced establishment and increasing arrest among incoming larvae, the loss of established adults, triggered by the density of the worm population and related to the rate of larval intake, and possibly the age of the host. *Trichostrongylus* and *Haemonchus* infections are similar to *N. dubius* in that adult worms appear to survive in hosts which are immune to reinfection. Thus, immunomodulatory activity by adult worms may enable the survival of adult worms whilst anti-larval immunity develops in the host. Eventually parasite immunomodulatory factors are also neutralized and expulsion of adult worms takes place (Sections VIII B and IX).

Although there are relatively few careful studies of changes in worm burdens in mice repeatedly infected with *N. dubius*, this is an area of growing interest and several groups are currently embarking on appropriate experiments (Keymer, 1985). From the reports which have been published several outcomes appear to be possible. Thus, strong responder mice develop rapid resistance to larvae and expel adult worms (Mitchell and Prowse, 1979; Prowse and Mitchell, 1980). It is not known whether complete resistance is preceded by a period when the intestine is occupied only by adult worms, although this would be predicted. In weak responders such as CBA or C_3H mice, worm burdens accumulate rapidly and reach a plateau or continue climbing, eventually resulting in the death of the host. These mice presumably cannot easily overcome parasite immunomodulatory factors and hence fail to readily develop resistance (Section VIII A).

It is far more difficult although challenging to explain worm turnover in terms of host protection and immunomodulation. A working hypothesis may be as follows: perhaps it is the larvae which are immunomodulatory, keeping host responses at bay until a particularly high threshold of stimulation is exceeded and anti-larval immunity is initiated. There is evidence that the larval stages of *A. lumbricoides* cause immunodepression. Adult *O. ostertagi* and *Ascaris* are both known to have the capacity to survive for considerably longer than the 4 weeks and 12 months respectively, reported under field conditions. Their lifespan may therefore be abbreviated by host responses which operate selectively and ensure continuous loss of mature parasites. Presumably adult worm immunomodulatory factors are less effective in these species.

VI. Disguise by Host Antigens, Antigenic Variation and Stage-Specific Antigens

The incorporation of host molecules and the expression of host-like molecules on the surface of schistosomes, thereby minimizing the antigenic disparity between the host and parasite, are both well known survival strategies which have received considerable attention (Smithers and Doenhoff, 1982). The filariae and the invasive/migratory larvae of gut nematodes come into intimate contact with the host's tissues and it is conceivable that antigenic disguise could be beneficial for these organisms. Attempts to demonstrate host molecules on adult nematodes either directly or indirectly by searching for parasite protective properties have been unsuccessful (McGreevy *et al.*, 1975), although the presence of host immunoglobulins on the parasite surface has been frequently reported (McLaren, 1984). Surface-bound antibodies may represent responses to antigens not involved in host protective immunity or may be antibodies which cannot mediate appropriate host responses, but instead block access to relevant antigens and thus prevent alternative mechanisms from destroying the parasite. There is some experimental evidence to support such a role for surface-bound antibody. Thus, Hayashi *et al.* (1984) incubated *B. malayi* and *B. pahangi* L_3s in immune serum for 2 hours prior to inoculation into BALB/c mice and found that larval recoveries 14 days later were approximately two times higher than in controls. Similarly, Dobson and Cayzer (1982b) showed that preincubation of *N. dubius* L_3s in immune serum enhanced their capacity for survival in recipient mice passively protected with immune serum.

The presence of polysaccharide molecules resembling human blood group substances has been demonstrated on several species of nematodes including *A. lumbricoides*, *N. americanus*, *T. spiralis* and *Toxocara canis* (Oliver-Gonzalez and Torregrosa, 1944; Smith *et al.*, 1983). However, *Ascaris* survives equally well in pigs which produce anti-A isoagglutinin and those which do not, so the importance of these molecules in relation to chronic survival is debatable (Soulsby and Coombs, 1959).

The microfilariae (mf) of *W. bancrofti* and *Loa loa* express human blood group substances A and B on their surface (Ridley and Hedge, 1977) and several recent studies have identified host albumin in association with the mf cuticle (Maizels *et al.*, 1984; Forsyth *et al.*, 1984; Philipp *et al.*, 1984b). The mf of *W. bancrofti* also express human albumin on their surface but curiously those of *B. malayi* do not; since these species have very similar biological relationships with their hosts, the survival value of incorporating host albumin is not clear (Maizels *et al.*, 1984). The mf of *Onchocerca gibsoni* when isolated from the uterus of female worms, reveal a complex profile of proteins on their surface, but these antigens could not be identified on mf isolated from the skin. Instead, skin mf expressed a single protein complex of which albumin was the major component (Forsyth *et al.*, 1984). Fluorescent antibody techniques failed to confirm the presence of albumin on the cuticle of living mf, uterine mf did not adsorb albumin in *in vitro* culture and the surface albumin could not be precipitated by sera specific for protein antigens on the mf cuticle. The authors suggest that albumin may mask all the epitopes on the mf cuticle and hence living skin mf, equipped with a surface coat of albumin, may be able to migrate freely through host tissues without eliciting an inflammatory response (Forsyth *et al.*, 1984).

As discussed earlier (Section III A and B) the surface antigens on nematode parasites show stage-specific moieties and therefore, by expressing a different pattern of surface antigens, each stage may evade the host response evoked by the one before (Wakelin and Denham, 1983). However, as far as is known, the surface antigens on mf and adult worms, which do not moult in the mammalian host, do not change; hence, stage-specific antigens cannot account for long-lasting infections.

Some protozoan parasites prolong their survival in the host by antigenic variation, but nematodes (excepting *Strongyloides* and *Capillaria philippinensis*) do not replicate within the host and therefore new antigenic forms arising from worms already within the host would be of no value in prolonging infection (Cohen, 1982; Turner, 1984). The nearest parallel to antigenic variation in nematodes is the demonstration that adult *N. brasiliensis* developing in immune or trickle-infected rats show phenotypic differences from parasites in primary infections (Ogilvie, 1974; Ogilvie and Love, 1974). These worms are stunted, fecund despite the immune environment, less antigenic than normal worms and secrete a different combination of acetylcholinesterase isoenzymes (Jenkins, 1972). Such immune adapted worms may contribute to the prolonged survival of *N. brasiliensis* in trickle infections, but the phenomenon has not been reported for other nematodes.

VII. The Role of Genetically Based Variation in Immunocompetence in Facilitating Chronic Nematode Infections

A. EPIDEMIOLOGICAL STUDIES

Frequency distribution studies of nematodes in human populations show overdispersion of the parasites, with most individuals carrying light infections and a few harbouring disproportionately heavier worm burdens. Croll and Ghadirian (1981), who studied three villages in Iran found that 2 and 4/80 individuals carried respectively 30% of *A. duodenale* and 38% of *N. americanus* in one village, 1 and 1/40 (not the same individual) carried respectively 11% of *A. duodenale* and 84% of *N. americanus* in a second village. In the third village, 5/111 inhabitants carried 16% of all *A. lumbricoides*. These results are broadly confirmed by other studies (Seo *et al.*, 1979;

Anderson and Schad, 1985; Nwosu and Anderson, unpublished observations) and a reasonable generalization would be that up to 70% of the parasite population may be harboured by fewer than 15% of the host population (Anderson and Medley, 1985).

Numerous phenomena besides genetically based variation in immunological competence, probably contribute to creating heavily infected individuals. Thus behavioural, dietary and professional factors, as well as age and sex, exert a significant influence (Schad *et al.*, 1983). The superimposition of several categories of random events in addition to differences in innate and acquired immunity is involved (Croll and Ghadirian, 1981). In a recent study of *A. lumbricoides* in India, most of the very heavy infections were registered among children 1–20 years of age, although parasite burdens were still overdispersed in older age groups (Elkins *et al.*, 1986). In order to evaluate the role of acquired immunity in determining worm burdens evidence has been sought from studies in which populations were monitored for signs of reinfection at regular intervals following chemotherapy. Several such studies have now been reported and all agree that reinfection is extremely rapid, with precontrol infection levels being restored within 12 months (Seo, 1980; Croll and Ghadirian, 1981; Elkins *et al.*, 1986). Some studies have found no evidence for predisposition to heavy infection (Croll and Ghadirian, 1981; Bundy *et al.*, 1984; Nwosu and Anderson, unpublished observations) whereas others have firmly established that individuals identified as "wormy" prior to treatment, become reinfected more heavily afterwards (Thein-Hliang, 1985; Schad and Anderson, 1985; Nwosu and Anderson, unpublished observations; Elkins *et al.*, in 1986). Overall, it appears likely that human communities contain groups of high and low responders who form, respectively, classes of "non-wormy" (resistant) and "wormy" (susceptible) people (Anderson and Medley, 1985).

Even "non-wormy" individuals, however, may carry light infections and are continually reinfected throughout life. In immunological terms these are both intriguing phenomena, suggesting that there may be a variable threshold at which immunological/non-immunological control is initiated (see Sections V C and II B for relevant discussion). In order to evaluate the importance of immunological phenomena in controlling infections, future epidemiological surveys should be linked to immunological analyses of worm/non-wormy individuals. Routinely employed antibody and/or cell proliferation assays, using relevant antigens, may reveal whether the failure to control parasite numbers is correlated with an inability to respond to particular parasite antigens.

Epidemiological studies of filariasis are complicated because there is no accurate method for measuring adult worm burdens in human tissues, other than at autopsy, and because there are still no drugs with 100% macrofilaricidal efficacy available for general use (WHO, 1984). In populations affected by bancroftian filariasis or onchocerciasis, there is a spectrum of clinical conditions ranging from individuals who are asymptomatic and without blood or skin microfilariae to persons with high microfilarial levels and/or severe symptoms of disease such as blindness. Asymptomatic individuals with intense microfilaraemia and amicrofilaraemic subjects with elephantiasis, the extreme consequence of infection with *W. bancrofti*, are also readily encountered in the field (Nelson, 1970; Ottesen, 1980, 1984; Haque *et al.*, 1983).

Genetic influences on variation in susceptibility to infection and/or development of disease symptoms is suggested by the familial clustering of patients with filariasis (Ottesen *et al.*, 1981), but to date attempts to link clinical manifestations of filariasis and susceptibility to infection to blood group ABO or HLA antigens have been unsuccessful (Ottesen *et al.*, 1981; Gyorkos *et al.*, 1983) or have identified barely significant trends (Chan *et al.*, 1981). The most promising study by Chan *et al.* (1984) found that HLA-B15 was observed in 30% of Sri Lankan patients, compared to 4% in the uninfected controls ($P=0.0058$). Neverthless, despite the evidence that both mf and adult filariae are controlled, a large proportion of the indigenous population carries worms for prolonged periods of time (Kirkwood *et al.*, 1983). In this context it is interesting to note that whilst many of the American servicemen stationed in the Pacific during World War II became infected with *W. bancrofti* and showed clinical symptoms of the disease, very few were microfilaraemic (Beaver, 1970). Furthermore, microfilaraemia is rarely encountered in European or American residents in the Pacific area, and although this may reflect a genetically determined resistance lacking in the indigenous population, the phenomenon has been linked to the fact that European immigrants are unlikely to have been exposed to continuous infection from conception onwards, as have local people (Beaver, 1970; see also Section VIII A).

B. STUDIES IN MODEL SYSTEMS

1. Dipetalonema viteae

Genetic control of immunity to filarial infection has been analysed in greatest detail in the *D. viteae*/mouse system. BALB/c, BALB/b and BALB/k mice, all with the BALB/c background genes but differing H-2 haplotypes ($H\text{-}2^d$, $H\text{-}2^b$ and $H\text{-}2^k$ respectively) develop intense and long-lasting microfilaraemia, whereas mouse strains of various H-2 haplotype but B10 background genes clear microfilaraemia rapidly (Haque *et al.*, 1980a; Storey *et al.*, 1985). Radiation chimaeras involving H-2 matched strains have established that the response phenotype can be altered by transferring bone marrow cells from a congenic strain of opposite response phenotype, e.g. B10 D2/N (resistant phenotype)→BALB/c (susceptible phenotype) (Storey *et al.*, 1985). The ability to clear microfilariae (mf) is not T-cell dependent (Haque *et al.*, 1980a), but demands the capacity to mount an IgM response to antigenic determinants on the mf surface (Thompson *et al.*, 1979; Philipp *et al.*, 1984b; Storey, 1985). Neither BALB/c nor CBA/N mice generate anti mf surface IgM antibodies (Thompson *et al.*, 1979; Storey, 1985), but in both strains temporary clearance of mf can be brought about by injection of post mf clearance serum from B10 donor mice. On cessation of antibody injection, mf return to control levels within 2 days (N. Storey, Ph.D. thesis: University of Nottingham, 1985). Thus, the inability to produce relevant IgM is not the only lesion in BALB/c and CBA/N mice and a second, possibly cellular component is required to bring about permanent clearance. It may be that as in hamsters, IgM antibodies are required to mediate the killing of mf by neutrophils (Weiss and Tanner, 1979; Rudin *et al.*, 1980; Neilson *et al.*, 1981).

2. Nematospiroides dubius

The existence of genetically determined differences in ability to respond to gastrointestinal nematodes is well established and the literature has been reviewed recently (Wakelin, 1978b, 1985; Mitchell *et al.*, 1982; Rosenstreich *et al.*, 1982). Analysis of the genetic/immunological control of chronic infections with *N. dubius* has progressed slowly, partly because infections are so long-lasting and partly because many of the commonly used mouse strains do not readily develop resistance (Liu, 1966; Behnke and Wakelin, 1977; Prowse *et al.*, 1979; Behnke and Robinson, 1985).

Genetic control of liability (susceptibility) to infection with *N. dubius* has been investigated by Dobson *et al.*, who have demonstrated that appropriate selection of outbred or wild mouse strains can lead to lines which show reduced (R) or enhanced (L) liability to primary infection. Mice were selected on the basis of faecal egg counts 3 weeks following infection with 100 larvae and with each generation, selection for resistance for liability increased the inter-line divergence (Brindley and Dobson, 1981, 1982). The divergence between the two lines stopped after seven generations, at which time the worm burdens in R mice were 83% of the mean worm burden in L mice (Brindley and Dobson, 1983). In terms of worm numbers, therefore, the difference between the lines was relatively small, although fecundity (the criterion used for selection) and worm growth were more affected. It would be extremely interesting to determine the stability of primary infections in these mice over a longer period of time. Do fewer worms establish in R mice or are they rejected sooner?

Among the conventional laboratory strains CBA, BALB/c, C_3H, $C57BL_{10}$ and NIH mice all carry long-term primary infections (Behnke and Robinson, 1985). DBA/1, DBA/2 and female C_3H/H_EJ mice lose worms somewhat sooner, although many worms persist for more than 10 weeks (Prowse *et al.*, 1979; Behnke and Robinson, 1985). SJL and SWR mice expel their worms considerably earlier. Mitchell *et al.* (1982) reported that SJL mice lost all worms by day 78. In my laboratory, expulsion is complete in female SJL by day 50 (Robinson, 1985). Three hybrid strains, ($C57BL_{10} \times$ NIH) F_1, (B10G × NIH) F_1 and (A/HE × C57L) F_1 also expel primary infection worms, but in these strains expulsion is dose-dependent (Robinson, 1985) and worms survive longer than in SJL mice (see Section VIII A).

The ability to expel primary infections is inherited as a dominant trait (Prowse and Mitchell, 1980) and in some combinations when two parental strains, neither of which normally expels primary infections, are crossed, the resulting F_1 progeny can reject adult parasites (Cypess *et al.*, 1977; Behnke and Robinson, 1985). Therefore, gene complementation is a feature of this model.

No clear picture has yet emerged about the number and role of the genes which determine the duration of primary infections with *N. dubius*. Brindley and Dobson (1983) suggested that two genetic units control innate immunity, one influencing parasite infectivity and the other interfering with reproduction and growth. In general, mouse strains which expel primary infection worms also develop marked acquired immunity (Behnke and Robinson, 1985) and the analysis of the latter phenomenon has revealed that the response phenotype is influenced by both background and MHC-linked genes (Prowse *et al.*, 1979; Behnke and Robinson, 1985). Nevertheless some strains which develop good acquired immunity cannot rapidly expel primary infections, e.g. NIH, BALB/c (Behnke and Robinson, 1985). Overall, it is perhaps surprising that the possession of genes allowing for resistance to primary infection is restricted to so few mouse strains and that so little is known about strains such as SJL which can overcome *N. dubius* relatively promptly. An explanation of the mechanisms used by SJL mice to reject *N. dubius* may provide pointers for the identification of the strategy used by *N. dubius* to block such responses in other mouse strains (see Section VIII A).

From what little is known about SJL mice, it appears that the strain is sensitive to histamine, is a low IgE producer, but responds to parasitic infection with a vigorous eosinophilia (Mitchell *et al.*, 1982; Sugane and Oshima, 1985). SJL mice also have a defect in their ability to generate antigen-specific suppressor cells (Amagai and Cinader, 1981; Cooke and Hutchings, 1984). There is evidence that *N. dubius* antigen elicits sheep red blood cell (SRBC)-specific suppressor cells when injected intravenously into mice challenged with SRBC (Pritchard *et al.*, 1984a). If suppressor cells are instrumental in preventing the expression of intense inflammatory responses in the intestine, it may follow that the defect in suppressor cells in SJL mice permits inflammatory responses to occur in this strain following infection with *N. dubius*. Wassom *et al.* (personal communication) have recently found that B10S mice which, like SJL, carry the H-2^s haplotype and fail to express I-E products on the surface of antigen-presenting cells, are also strong responders to *N. dubius*. It was suggested that the presentation of otherwise host protective parasite antigens to T-cells in the context of I-E preferentially induces the generation of suppressor T-cells. Strains such as SJL lacking I-E would not therefore be subject to suppression.

VIII. Immunomodulation as a Strategy for Survival

Although epidemiological data implies that parasite survival is disproportionately dependent on a few heavily infected individuals, the majority of inhabitants in endemic areas can expect to carry small worm numbers throughout life, e.g. <5 *A. lumbricoides*, <60 *N. americanus*, <30 *A. duodenale* (Croll and Ghadirian, 1981; Elkins *et al.*, in press). It is possible that parasite burdens are kept low in these individuals by host protective responses. The intriguing question which follows is why does immunity fail to eliminate all the worms? In this section I consider the possibility that nematodes survive by manipulating the host's immune system to block, misdirect or impair potentially protective immune mechanisms.

A. Evidence that Parasite-Induced Immunodepression May Be Beneficial to Nematode Survival

1. *Interference with homologous immunity by filarial parasites*

Central to the whole issue of parasite induced immunodepression is whether the parasite concerned derives any benefit in terms of prolonged survival. This question has received relatively little attention because appropriate *in vivo* experiments are difficult to arrange logistically.

Klei *et al.* (1980) found that jirds carrying a primary infection of *B. pahangi*, instead of resisting a challenge infection developed twice as many worms as the control group. It was proposed that the enhanced susceptibility could have arisen as a result of changes in the structure of the lymphatics caused by the initial worm burden. Dilated lymphatic vessels may have enabled more challenge infection larvae to become established than would otherwise have done so. However, specific hyporesponsiveness to developing larvae initiated by the established parasites has also to be considered as a possibility (Klei *et al.*, 1981; Philipp *et al.*, 1984b).

There is evidence that *Litomosoides carinii* affects the host in a way which benefits the survival of adult worms. Primary infections with *L. carinii* are chronic in cotton rats (Williams, 1948), although challenge infections are resisted, immunity being directed preferentially against the developing larval stages (Scott *et al.*, 1958; Ogilvie and MacKenzie, 1981). Curiously, the surgical implantation of adult worms into naive recipients results in their rapid encapsulation and destruction (Fujita and Kobayashi, 1969; Weiner and Soulsby, 1976; Storey and Al-Mukhtar, 1983). However, when worms are implanted in animals which already harbour adult worms (Weiner and Soulsby, 1976) or have been immunized with irradiated larvae, there is virtually no protective host response. Transplanted worms in the latter two cases survive for over 9 weeks and give rise to viable microfilariae (mf) (Storey and Al-Mukhtar, 1983). Having experienced the developing larval stages of *L. carinii*, cotton and multimammate rats seem to be "conditioned" in some way which prevents a suitable host protective anti-adult response from being mounted. If immunomodulation is involved, it must be the larval L_4 stages which are mainly responsible, because adult worms cannot prolong their own survival following transplantation into naive hosts (Storey and Al-Mukhtar, 1983). Immunodepression directed at shared (L_4 and adult) functional antigens (Philipp *et al.*, 1984), initiated by L_4s but possibly maintained albeit less effectively, by adult worms, may be one explanation. This phenomenon, as far as is known, has no direct parallel in other filarial systems. Adult *D. viteae*, *B. pahangi* and *B. malayi* survive for over 18 months following transplantation to naive jirds (Ash, 1973; Johnson *et al.*, 1974).

Rats are normally resistant to infection with *D. viteae*, but a microfilaraemia of some 120 days duration can be initiated by the surgical implantation of adult worms. The offspring of microfilaraemic female rats born during the period of their mother's microfilaraemia, already harboured mf in their circulation at birth and for some 17 weeks afterwards. Furthermore, these rats were unresponsive to antigens prepared from *D. viteae* and when challenged with L_3s supported the development of the parasite, giving rise to adult worms and a 120 day microfilaraemia (Haque and Capron, 1982). Thus, exposure to mf antigens *in utero* and in neonatal life appears to have alleviated the barriers which normally prevent *D. viteae* from developing to maturity in rats. These experiments have provided particularly exciting results which appear to reflect the field observation that indigenous but not immigrant inhabitants of areas where filariasis is prevalent develop microfilaraemia (Beaver, 1970).

It must be obvious that all three of the models described above are eminently suitable for dissection and that a lot more remains to be accomplished, before the factors involved in chronic survival of adult filariae and mf are understood. It is more than likely that the three models reflect different aspects of survival strategies employed by filarial parasites but detailed knowledge about the mechanism involved in each case would have general and wider ranging implications.

2. *Depression of homologous immunity by* N. dubius

The remarkable ability of adult *N. dubius* to persist even in immune mice and the influence exerted upon other species in concurrent infections prompted the hypothesis that the parasite is immunomodulatory (Hagan and Wakelin, 1982; Behnke *et al.*, 1983). This hypothesis was tested in experiments where mice were infected with normal, irradiated or normal and irradiated larvae. Following exposure to 25 krad of Cobalt 60 irradiation the infective stages of *N. dubius* do not develop to the adult stage but are extremely immunogenic (Hagan *et al.*, 1981; Behnke and Robinson, 1985). However, when irradiated larvae were administered simultaneously with normal larvae, their immunogenicity was severely impaired (Behnke *et al.*, 1983). Indeed, only 55 normal worms were required to completely abolish the immunity that would otherwise have been elicited by concurrently administered irradiated larvae. It was demonstrated that adult worms developing from normal larvae were primarily responsible for the depression of homologous immunity, and it was postulated that the parasites secreted factors which affected the immunocompetence of the local intestinal environment, thereby enabling the worms to evade potentially protective responses (Behnke *et al.*, 1983). Recent experiments from my laboratory have further shown that weak responder strains such as $C57BL_{10}$ mice are considerably more susceptible to parasite-induced homologous immunodepression than strong responder strains such as NIH. Thus 13 adult *N. dubius* caused 84% depression of immunity in $C57BL_{10}$ mice, whereas in NIH mice 104 worms caused a reduction of only 12% (Crawford, Behnke and Pritchard, unpublished observations).

Evidence to support the concept that *N. dubius* is immunomodulatory is available from four other lines of experimentation.

(a) Dose-dependent suppression of immunity. Some strains of strong responder mice (e.g. $(C57BL_{10} \times NIH)\ F_1$) show dose-dependent expulsion of primary infection worms. Approximately 50% of a 50-worm infection was lost by day 49, whereas mice infected with 250 larvae still harboured the full worm burden. The latter group, however, rejected the majority of worms by day 119 (Robinson, 1985). Q strain mice infected with 50 larvae rejected a greater proportion of the established worm burden by day 63 post infection,

than did mice given 400 larvae (Dobson *et al.*, 1985). In contrast, SJL mice were not subject to dose-dependent suppression and following the administration of 100, 200 or 400 larvae, expulsion occurred simultaneously in all groups and was completed by day 49 (Robinson, 1985). In jirds a 25-worm infection was lost by day 25 but a 500-worm infection persisted until day 36 (Hannah and Behnke, 1982). A particularly interesting observation was made by Dobson and Cayzer (1982a) who found that primary infection serum from Q strain mice infected for 3 weeks with 50 *N. dubius* conferred better protection on naive recipients than serum from mice which had received 400 larvae, despite considerably higher anti-adult *N. dubius* antibody titres in the latter ($\log_2 6$ *vs.* $\log_2 10$ respectively). Finally, a recent paper by Sitepu *et al.* (1985) has reported on dose-related suppression in the induction of acquired immunity to *N. dubius*. Mice selected through seven generations for liability to infection with *N. dubius* were more severely affected at lower worm burdens than mice selected for resistance. All these data are compatible with the hypothesis that *N. dubius* is immunomodulatory. A dose-dependent depressive effect on intestinal immunity would have delayed expulsion in heavily infected jirds and F_1 responser mice, slowed the development of protective antibodies in Q mice and suppressed the development of acquired immunity in susceptible strains. SJL mice may be an exception or alternatively this strain may be suppressed by doses in excess of 400 larvae.

It is interesting that some aspects of these experiments have a parallel in *T. spiralis*. Dose-dependent retardation in expulsion has been reported in rats (Bell *et al.*, 1983) and in mice (Bell *et al.*, 1984; Wassom *et al.*, 1984) and in the latter it has been established that H-2 genes exert a marked influence on the phenomenon. Mouse strains expressing $H\text{-}2^q$ or $H\text{-}2^f$ were suppressed at high doses to a greater extent than were mice expressing $H\text{-}2^k$ (Wassom *et al.*, 1984). However, the fast responder NIH mice ($H\text{-}2^q$) did not show dose-dependent delayed expulsion. Infection intensities within the range 100–400 larvae were all expelled by day 12 (Wakelin *et al.*, 1985).

(b) Acquired immunity. Acquired immunity to *N. dubius* has been studied by a variety of experimental protocols with, until recently, little consistency in the approaches adopted by different workers. Surprisingly, superimposed challenge infections, especially when given soon after the primary infection, establish with relatively little worm loss, but primary infections, terminated after 9–14 days by anthelmintic treatment, elicit strong resistance to challenge (Behnke and Robinson, 1985). Thus, in the absence of adult worms, the larval stages of *N. dubius* are immunogenic, but the degree of protection declines if the larvae are given an opportunity to mature (Behnke and Robinson, 1985). The greater the delay to anthelmintic treat-

ment, the weaker the subsequent response to challenge. Cayzer and Dobson (1983) demonstrated that several short infections each terminated by anthelmintic treatment resulted in strong acquired immunity and higher antibody titres than in mice where the infections were not separated by anthelmintic.

(c) Survival of adult worms in immune mice. Adult *N. dubius* seem to be extremely resilient, surviving in animals which are totally refractory to larval challenge. LAF mice immunized by protocols which have made them totally resistant to larval challenge, support transplanted adult worms (Jacobson *et al.*, 1982). However, other studies have shown that transplanted adults may be rejected by strong responder mouse strains, depending on the nature of the immunizing regime used. NIH mice expel transplanted adult worms following immunization by 25 krad-irradiated larvae or the divided primary infection (Behnke and Wakelin, 1977) but not after a 9-day anthelmintic abbreviated infection (M. Robinson, Ph.D. thesis: University of Nottingham, 1985). F_1 hybrids and SJL mice expel transplanted adults even when immunized by the latter protocol (Robinson, Ph.D. thesis). Therefore strong responder strains can overcome adult worms, but the salient point is that under several experimental conditions mice which have been made totally refractory to larval infection seem incapable of expelling adult worms.

Adult *N. dubius* also have an advantage over larval parasites in mice which have been adoptively/passively immunized. Mice treated with immune serum (IS) are protected against challenge only when it is administered within 6 days of infection (Behnke and Parish, 1979a) and even the transfer of immune mesenteric lymph node cells (IMLNC) + IS is ineffective once the worms have matured, despite the capacity of IMLNC + IS to confer 90% protection when given earlier (Behnke and Parish, 1981; H. A. Parish, M.Phil. thesis: University of Nottingham, 1982; Pritchard and Behnke, 1985). It could be argued that immunity is stage-specific, but in fact a substantial component of the protective response acts on worms which have survived their developmental phase in the intestinal tissues and which are subsequently rejected as adults (Behnke and Parish, 1979a, 1981). This is a particularly prominent feature of the passive transfer experiments in which worm loss does not occur until weeks 3–4. It is therefore improbable that transferred antibodies cause expulsion directly. However, if immunomodulation is a central component of the survival strategy employed by *N. dubius*, it would seem reasonable that in order to expel adult worms, the host must first develop protection against parasite immunomodulatory factors (IMF) (Behnke and Parish, 1979a; Mitchell *et al.*, 1982). Treatment with IS prior to infection may equip the mice with sufficient IMF-neutralizing antibodies (in addition to enhancing the tissue response against larvae) to enable the animals to generate their own protective response capable of expelling the stunted adult worms. Where the parasite has had an opportunity to develop to the late L_4/adult stages, the adoptive/passive transfer is ineffective because the worms have already created areas of relative safety into which immune effectors cannot penetrate (Section VIII B).

Experiments with *T. muris* in CBA/Ca mice made tolerant by short-term treatment with cortisone provide curiously similar results. Mice carrying adult worms could not be protected by adoptive transfer of IMLNC, despite the fact that the same cells mediated strong resistance to larvae when given prior to infection (Lee and Wakelin, 1982). *T. muris*, like *N. dubius*, is a parasite which mice cannot remove readily once it has matured (see Section V B and C).

B. MECHANISMS OF IMMUNOMODULATION

Immunomodulation is considered here in its widest context, encompassing all situations in which the immune responses of infected animals depart from normal or fail to operate. There is already a wide literature on non-specific immunodepression (NSID) and antigen-specific immunodepression (ASID) in infected animals (Barriga, 1984; Ottesen, 1984; Philipp *et al.*, 1984a). NSID in particular has received a lot of attention and has been reported both in nematodes which cause acute (*T. spiralis*—Faubert, 1976; Jones *et al.*, 1976; *N. brasiliensis*—Haig *et al.*, 1980; McElroy *et al.*, 1983) and chronic infections (Shimp *et al.*, 1975; Ali and Behnke, 1983, 1984a,b). The capacity of the immune system to mount concurrent immune responses cannot be inexhaustible and when faced with an array of different antigens of parasite origin, the host may be unable to respond with equal vigour to all the antigens involved (Ali and Behnke, 1984a). General systemic NSID may therefore be an epiphenomenon, an inevitable consequence of infection by all helminths and of little direct relevance to parasite survival. It is possible that general NSID creates an environment in the context of which ASID may be initiated to effectively prolong parasite survival. Nevertheless, general NSID is unlikely to be a mechanism of choice because it would leave the host open to infection by other organisms and could lead to the premature death of the host. Some types of general NSID may reflect an unavoidable consequence of local NSID, i.e. general NSID may be a side effect of a mechanism used by the parasite to immunomodulate locally in its immediate micro-environment. In mice infected with *N. dubius*, most of the systemic changes (e.g. in haematology and spleen) observed in the early stages of infection, including general NSID subside once the mesenteric lymph nodes have expanded to maximum capacity in the third week of infection. NSID may therefore simply ensue from the pathological consequences of the early phase of infection or immunomodulatory factors may enter the circulation at this stage, causing systemic changes with subsequent restriction to the intestinal niche occupied by adult worms (Ali and Behnke, 1983, 1984, 1985; Ali *et al.*, 1985).

1. *Specific suppression by circulating blocking factors*

General and specific hypergammaglobulinaemia is a feature of many chronic helminth infections besides filarial (Ottesen, 1980) and gastrointestinal nematodes (Chapman *et al.*, 1979a).

(a) Blocking antibodies in N. dubius *infection.* In mice infected with *N. dubius* the concentration of serum IgG_1 rises within 2 weeks of infection and stabilizes at approximately double the control level (Crandall *et al.*, 1974; Williams and Behnke, 1983). Primary infection sera (PS) contain parasite-specific antibody (Dobson *et al.*, 1982) and in particular parasite-specific IgG_1 (Molinari *et al.*, 1978), but passive transfer studies in my laboratory have not succeeded in transferring immunity to naive recipient mice by using PS (Williams and Behnke, 1983). This contrasts with the work of Dobson (1982) and Dobson and Cayzer (1982a,b) who have shown that 21 days PS from Q strain mice has the capacity to passively immunize naive recipients.

High levels of circulating IgG_1 are characteristic of several chronic helminth infections beside nematodes (Sher *et al.*, 1977; Chapman *et al.*, 1979b) and can be induced experimentally by repeated injections of sheep red blood cells (Chapman *et al.*, 1979a). It may be that the persistent high dose, T-cell-dependent stimulation of the B-cell system, as would occur in a chronic nematode infection, preferentially induces the proliferation of IgG_1 plasma cell precursors (Chapman *et al.*, 1979a). The association of IgG_1 hypergammaglobulinaemia with chronic infection suggested the possible role of this immunoglobulin isotype as a "blocking antibody", preventing the generation and/or expression of a host protective response. The hypothesis that *N. dubius* may avoid expulsion by eliciting blocking antibodies was first suggested by Bartlett and Ball (1974) and has received recent support from Dobson and Cayzer (1982a,b). However, a detailed study by Pritchard *et al.* (1984b) failed to substantiate the hypothesis. Several experimental approaches including *in vivo* and *in vitro* assays were used to test for blocking activity in primary infection sera (PS). IgG_1 was purified from PS, concentrated and injected into naive recipient mice at a concentration of 24 mg/recipient, this being the average amount in IS. However, IgG_1 in PS did not block immunity transferred adoptively by concurrently injected immune mesenteric lymph mode cells (IMLNC). Immune complexes precipitated from PS by polyethylene glycol failed to inhibit the transfer of immunity by treated IMLNC. It is therefore likely that the chronic survival of *N. dubius* is accomplished by mechanisms other than circulating blocking factors.

(b) Blocking-suppressive factors in filarial infection. The immune mechanisms by which microfilariae are cleared from the circulation have been studied by various workers using *in vitro* assays in which antibody-dependent cytoadherence (ADCA) or cytotoxicity (ADCC) was measured. ADCA reactions are associated with most human and experimental filarial infections and are known to involve a variety of mechanisms comprising the different leukocyte types and immunoglobulin classes (IgG, IgM and IgE) (Chandrashekar *et al.*, 1984; Philipp *et al.*, 1984a). Patients and animals with chronic microfilaraemia do not possess circulating antibodies capable of mediating ADCA to mf (Subrahmanyam *et al.*, 1978; Storey, 1985; Ponnudarai *et al.*, 1974; Weiss, 1978a), show specific cellular unresponsiveness (Ottesen *et al.*, 1977; Ottesen, 1984; Piessens *et al.*, 1980a, 1982) and their sera may contain blocking or immunomodulatory factors the identity and function of which have not been fully elucidated (Ottesen *et al.*, 1981; Lammie *et al.*, 1984; Sim *et al.*, 1984).

Ottesen *et al.* (1981) described an IgG blocking antibody directed against *B. malayi* antigen, which inhibited histamine release following antigenic stimulation of human basophils *in vitro*. It was suggested that these antibodies modulated allergic responsiveness to parasite antigens in patients with high serum IgE.

Karavodin and Ash (1980) demonstrated circulating immune complexes (CIC) in jirds chronically infected with *B. pahangi* and showed that polythene glycol precipitated CIC inhibited ADCA of mf (Karavodin and Ash, 1982). CIC have been reported in other filarial infections and it is well established that CIC have powerful immunomodulatory effects on cell mediated immunity (WHO, 1977). Inhibition of ADCC by CIC may prevent the sequestration of mf in organs where they may be subsequently destroyed (Karavodin and Ash, 1982); alternatively, CIC may cause the generation of specific suppressor cells and thus specific cellular unresponsiveness (WHO, 1977; Theofilopoulos, 1980). However, Lammie *et al.* (1984), who also studied *B. pahangi* in chronically infected jirds, found suppressor activity in the sera 20 weeks post infection, which was not associated with CIC. Chronic *B. pahangi* jird serum suppressed the proliferation of lymph node cells in response to stimulation by parasite antigens but had a less consistent effect on lymphocyte reactivity to mitogens. Fractionation on Sephadex G-200 revealed that the factors involved were of high molecular weight and were present in the void volume and the IgG peak. Suppressive activity was not eliminated by protein A, anti-jird Ig, nor was it absorbed on *B. pahangi*–sepharose affinity columns. Polyethylene glycol-precipatated material did not exhibit the suppressive effect. Nevertheless, as the authors point out, jird immunoglobulins are not yet fully characterized and the possibility that antibodies are involved cannot be excluded.

Circulating factors promoting microfilaraemia and with inhibitory effects on the proliferation of antigen-sensitized lymphocytes have been reported in *D. viteae* infection (Haque *et al.*, 1978; Weiss, 1978b), but have not been further defined. More recently, Sim *et al.* (1984), found blocking factors which prevented ADCA to infective larvae in *B. malayi* microfilaraemic patients, whose sera rendered normal peripheral leukocytes incapable of adherence when incubated together, prior to use in the ADCA assay. Cells from patients with tropical pulmonary eosinophilia were unaffected by pre-incubation in microfilaraemic serum. It is possible that FC receptors on cells from tropical pulmonary eosinophilia patients were already occupied by parasite-specific, ADCA-promoting antibody and hence could not be blocked. However, Narayanan *et al.* (1986), who studied patients affected by *W. bancrofti*, found that sera from microfilaraemic and amicrofilaraemic individuals did not impair the mitogenic responsiveness of peripheral blood lymphocytes from normal controls. The authors concluded that humoral factors were not responsible for immunosuppression in bancroftian filariasis.

Studies of serum blocking/suppressive activity in microfilaraemic patients and animals are still at an extremely early stage and judging by the volume of literature on this subject in tumour immunology, parasite immunologists still have a long way to go (Hellstrom *et al.*, 1977). Future studies will undoubtedly uncover alternative mechanisms but, as has been pointed out by Karavodin and Ash (1980) and Ottesen (1984), a central issue is whether circulating immune complexes and blocking/suppressive activity are epiphenomena resulting from the chronic presence of the adult worms and mf or whether these mechanisms are crucial in benefiting parasite survival. It is more than likely that blocking activity is only one manifestation of perturbed immunoregulation (Lammie *et al.*, 1984) which encompasses a variety of component mechanisms, operating in concert to enable parasites to evade immunity (Sim *et al.*, 1984). The biological significance of these processes in relation to parasite survival would be given greater credence if it were to be demonstrated that microfilaraemic serum has the capacity to transfer suppression/blocking to animals which would otherwise clear the infection. Perhaps mouse models of filariasis, e.g. *D. viteae*, incorporating strains of mice with opposite response phenotypes could be used to examine this point further.

2. *Specific and non-specific cellular hyporesponsiveness*

(a) Filarial infections. Non-specific (NSID) and antigen specific (ASID)

immunodepression have been described in *B. pahangi* (Portaro *et al.*, 1976; Lammie and Katz, 1982, 1983), *B. malayi* (Kwa and Mak, 1980; Piessens *et al.*, 1980a,b), *W. bancrofti* (Ottesen *et al.*, 1977; Grove and Forbes, 1979; Narayanan *et al.*, 1986), *D. viteae* (Weiss, 1978b; Haque and Capron, 1982) and *O. volvulus* (Piessens and MacKenzie, 1982; Ottesen, 1984). In general, non-specific effects show little consistency and cannot be correlated with parasite survival, whereas specific cellular unresponsiveness is associated with the onset and duration of microfilaraemia and is alleviated only when the infection becomes latent, at which time mf-specific antibodies may also appear in the circulation (Ponnudurai *et al.*, 1974; Ottesen *et al.*, 1977; Piessens *et al.*, 1980b; Haque *et al.*, 1981, 1983; Barriga, 1984). Microfilariae and/or mature worms have the capacity to induce depression of responses to homologous parasite antigens and although non-specific depression may provide an environment at critical stages of infection, in the context of which specific (ASID) mechanisms may be initiated, it is unlikely to be an important mechanism for parasite survival *per se*. Microfilaraemic hosts can respond quite normally to non-related antigens and their peripheral blood lymphocytes show unaltered reactivity to mitogens (Narayanan *et al.*, 1986), despite exhibiting severely suppressed antigen-specific cellular responsiveness (Ottesen *et al.*, 1977; Piessens *et al.*, 1980a,b; Lammie and Katz, 1983). Non-specific depression could be the consequence of perturbation in immunoregulatory/homeostatic control and therefore not directly responsible for parasite survival, although possibly a direct consequence of the chronic infection. As in the preceding section, credence for ASID as a mechanism for survival would be greatly improved if it were demonstrated that suppression could be adoptively transferred to animals which otherwise would have cleared the infection. This approach has already been initiated by Schrater and Piessens (as cited by Philipp, 1984) who have found that the transfer of splenic T-cells from prepatent jirds infected with *B. malayi* to naive recipients reduced the direct anti-trinitrophenyl-plaque forming cell (TNP-PFC) response in recipients immunized with TNP-microfilariae (Schrater and Piessens, 1982). Whether these cells have the capacity to interfere with host protective mechanisms, hence prolonging microfilaraemia, is not yet known.

(b) Gastrointestinal infections. Mice infected with *N. dubius* exhibit wide spectrum non-specific immunodepression to concurrently presented antigens such as sheep red blood cells, lipopolysaccharide and oxazolone (Shimp *et al.*, 1975; Ali and Behnke, 1983, 1984a,b). The mechanism of non-specific immunodepression to sheep red cells was analysed by Pritchard *et al.* (1984a) who found that immunodepression could be induced by injecting the saline soluble fraction of an adult worm homogenate. The mice were injected intravenously with 1 mg of homogenate from day − 2 to day + 3, on day 0

with sheep red cells and direct PFCs were determined on day + 4. Treated mice had severely depressed responses to red cells and suppression was transferable to naive mice by spleen cells from adult homogenate-treated red cell-sensitized donors. In mice infected with *N. dubius*, antigen processing by macrophages was shown to be defective and it is possible that inappropriate antigen presentation by parasite-affected macrophages may have generated suppressor cells. Thus, mice infected with *N. dubius* may provide an environment for the generation of suppressor cells to incoming heterologous antigens. The significance of these findings in relation to parasite survival is not clear, especially as the restoration of the full capacity to respond to sheep red cells by treatment of infected mice with 2 deoxyguanosine (a drug known to selectively impair the development of suppressor T-cells (Dosch *et al.*, 1980)) did not initiate the rejection of adult worms. Furthermore, non-specific immunodepression (NSID) at the intestinal level is rapidly reversed and normal reactivity restored when adult *N. dubius* are cleared by anthelmintic treatment (Behnke *et al.*, 1978).

Several features of non-specific immunodepression in mice infected with *N. dubius* are difficult to reconcile with the hypothesis of NSID as an important mechanism for parasite survival. Infection with 25 krad-irradiated larvae (Hagan *et al.*, 1981) and the 9 day anthelmintic abbreviated regime (Behnke and Robinson, 1985) both give rise to non-specific immunodepression 2 weeks following the onset of immunization (Ali and Behnke, 1984a). In the absence of adult worms, mice immunized by these two regimes show more than 90% protection against challenge infection, and hence the long-lasting immunodepression induced by larval parasites cannot extend to challenge with homologous larvae. Furthermore, NSID is often associated with heavy infections (Ali and Behnke, 1983) and with a period 14 days following primary infection, with gradual waning thereafter (Ali and Behnke, 1984b). However, even 50 worms caused chronic infections in the mice used for these experiments and hence if NSID was caused by parasite immunomodulatory factors, the effect must have been restricted to the intestine throughout all of the subsequent period of infection (Ali and Behnke, 1985).

Experiments seeking evidence for the involvement of parasite-specific suppressor cells in *N. dubius*, have been carried out in my laboratory. Primary infection mesenteric lymph node cells in various quantities have been adoptively transferred to recipient mice being immunized by different protocols; thus far we have been unable to demonstrate that primary infection mesenteric lymph node cells impair the development of immunity in recipient mice (J. M. Behnke and D. I. Pritchard, unpublished observations). Our experiments have not exhausted all the possibilities and it may be that we have not yet arrived at the optimum formula for such experiments. However, if suppressor cells located in the mesenteric lymph nodes are a major barrier preventing mice from expelling primary infection worms, a hint that we were on the correct track ought to have become apparent by now.

Ascaris suum, a parasite of pigs, has also been studied for evidence of non-specific immunodepression, but unfortunately in mice and guinea-pigs, host species which do not support adult worms in the intestine. Khoury and Soulsby (1977) found evidence for suppressor T-cell involvement in guinea-pigs, whereas Crandall *et al.* (1978) were unable to demonstrate such cells in mice, although depressed responses to a T-cell mitogen were reported. Antibody responses are also affected by non-specific immunodepression in mice infected with *A. suum* (Crandall and Crandall, 1976) and the effect can be reproduced by parasite homogenates and by ES products of adult worms (Komatsu *et al.*, 1979).

3. *Local non-specific immunodepression*

One of the most dramatic consequences of the immunomodulatory activity of adult *N. dubius* is the effect which the parasite exerts on the course of infection with other intestinal helminths. All the widely used murine nematodes such as *T. spiralis* (Behnke *et al.*, 1978), *N. brasiliensis* (Jenkins, 1975) and *T. muris* (Jenkins and Behnke, 1977), and even the tapeworms *H. diminuta* and *H. citelli* (Hopkins, 1980; Alghali *et al.*, 1985) have greatly prolonged survival in mice concurrently harbouring *N. dubius*. The pattern of survival of *T. spiralis* in concurrently infected mice is for expulsion to be delayed by several days and for a residual worm burden to persist well beyond the normal time of expulsion (Behnke *et al.*, 1978). Therefore, some worms manage to avoid the acute expulsion phase and remain thereafter at a subthreshold level or possibly the worms capitalize on "safe" environments created in the vicinity of adult *N. dubius* (Pritchard and Behnke, 1985). This phenomenon is dependent on the presence of adult *N. dubius*, because their removal prior to challenge with *T. spiralis* enabled the normal expulsion of the latter species (Behnke *et al.*, 1978). Immunodepression is therefore rapidly reversible at the intestinal level. If *T. spiralis* takes advantage of "safe" sites the two species should be located in close proximity to each other. Experiments to study details of parasite distribution in concurrently infected mice have been initiated to resolve this question.

Analysis of the interaction between *N. dubius* and *T. spiralis* has revealed that the homing of lymphoblasts, capable of transferring adoptive immunity to *T. spiralis*, to the intestine is impaired (Hagan and Wakelin, 1982). It was speculated that the parasite exerts an anti-inflammatory influence on intestinal lymphoid tissue and this conclusion has received support from experiments which have confirmed that mastocytosis is delayed in the intestines of concurrently infected mice (S. Dehlawi, J. M. Behnke and D. Wakelin, unpublished observations). *N. dubius* by itself did not elicit mastocytosis in the small intestine.

Tissue dwelling nematodes are often located in sites where cellular infiltration is most marked and in which allografts of equal size would only have a transient period of survival. Nodules removed from individuals afflicted by onchocerciasis contain dying worms alongside fecund and prepatent parasites (Büttner, 1985), all living in an environment which is rich in lymphocytes; both suppressor and helper T-cell phenotypes were abundant in normal ratios (Parkhouse *et al.*, 1985). The tissue reaction around adult worms within nodules varies from extensive granulomatous lesions to no reaction at all (Piessens and Mackenzie, 1982), but it still remains to be determined whether the host response can kill mature parasites or whether the worms are invaded after dying of senility. The presence of live and dying worms alongside each other implies that protective immune responses, if involved, operate locally against specific worms within nodules. The key question is whether the parasites are actively involved in keeping local host defences at bay and relatively ineffective against the majority of worms. Evidence for active involvement is provided by the demonstration that another species, *O. gibsoni*, secretes <10 Kd immunomodulatory factors which inhibit mitogen-induced proliferation *in vitro* (Foo *et al.*, 1983).

4. *Remaining strategies*

A variety of additional mechanisms for the evasion of host immunity by parasitic organisms have been described, but the majority of these are irrelevant to chronic nematodes or have received little attention. The homeostatic control of the immune system is an extremely complex process involving both helper and suppressor systems, controlled by a variety of positive and negative feedback pathways. Immune responses in the intestine are particularly complex and their control is still poorly understood. Depending on the circumstances, antigens presented via the mucosa can induce systemic responses, systemic unresponsiveness or a localized reaction in the intestine. Peyer's patches are very sensitive to the dose and/or route of antigen presentation and may initiate tolerance or an active response. The lymphoid tissues associated with the intestine have several unusual properties, including the presence of specialized suppressor and contrasuppressor cells; the complexity of the interactions reflect the importance of distinguishing between pathogens and irrelevant immunogenic molecules in the intestinal contents (see the following reviews—Wade and Szewczuk, 1984; Green and Gershon, 1984). It is conceivable that parasites have evolved mechanisms for interfering with these regulatory pathways and that by secreting appropriate factors, perhaps resembling the host's own communication factors, they initiate inhibitory rather than sensitizing processes.

Hypothetically, it is also possible that parasites influence the control network involving idiotypic, anti-idiotypic and anti-anti-idiotypic antibody. Anti-idiotypic antibodies, which are specifically immunodepressive, may develop following a single injection of antigen, but usually repeated chronic antigenic stimulation is required in experimental systems and the latter may be particularly relevant to chronic nematode infections. Anti-idiotypic antibody has been reported in patients suffering from malignant tumours, but it is still not clear whether the antibodies were the cause or the consequence of uncontrolled tumour growth (for a review see Schreiber, 1984). In nematode infections a multiplicity of antigens would be presented to the host and if anti-idiotypic antibodies are to cause parasite survival, this would require the generation of anti-idiotypic antibodies to all the idiotypes of the different clonotypes involved in the response to each functional antigen. The experimental administration of anti-idiotypic antisera to adults induces only short-term suppression, while treatment of neonates may induce chronic life-long suppression. Chronic nematode infections are frequent in childhood and in some species, exposure to parasite antigens may be initiated *in utero* (Haque and Capron, 1982). Antigen–antibody reactions and chronic exposure to parasite antigens may initiate anti-idiotypic responses during this early period, resulting in clonal deletion and life-long tolerance (see Schreiber, 1984).

Another strategy which has generated some interest in recent years is the secretion of "Fab"ulating enzymes which cleave antibody bound by Fc receptors to the parasite surface, leaving bound, functionless, Fc portions camouflaging the surface antigens (Auriault *et al.*, 1981). Although such enzymes have been reported for various micro-organisms, including protozoa and schistosomes (Dessaint *et al.*, 1977; Auriault *et al.*, 1981), there have been no reports of Fabulating enzymes in nematodes. However, some species do have the ability to shed immunoglobulins bound to their surface. The live parasitic stages of *A. caninum* do not bind specific antibody on the surface, unless inhibited metabolically by azide or low temperature. When the inhibitory factors were removed, the active parasites shed the antibody (Klaver-Wesseling *et al.*, 1978; Vetter and Klaver-Wesseling, 1978). These results implied that *A. caninum* had the capacity to rapidly turn over surface cuticular antigens, thereby preventing permanent attachment of antibody. Recent studies on other species confirm that when maintained *in vitro* nematodes shed their surface antigens (Pritchard *et al.*, 1985; Philipp *et al.*, 1980), but equally, some of these organisms bind specific antibody to their surface in a more stable, longer-lasting union than *A. caninum* (Pritchard *et al.*, 1984b).

As we learn more about the components and pathways in immunoregulatory homeostasis, novel strategies for evasion of host immunity will become apparent. The mechanisms described in this section, although conceptually feasible and intellectually challenging, remain as yet unproven as important ingredients in chronic nematode infections. A fundamental obstacle is still our relative naivity about what actually constitutes a functional nematode antigen. Until relevant molecules are fully defined, it will not be possible to dissect the interaction of nematode immunostimulatory (protective antigens) and inhibitory factors with the various immunoregulatory pathways involved in resistance to infection.

IX. Concluding Remarks

The relative merits of NSID and ASID as survival strategies remain controversial. As has been pointed out by Barriga (1984), the former may be easier to achieve since the latter would have to identify and inhibit a particular response in a host which is continually generating diverse responses to the many antigens with which it comes into contact. NSID would also have a more permanent usefulness to the parasite as a species because it would not need to contend with antigenic variation (Barriga, 1984). However, it makes more sense for a long-lived parasite to deprive its host of the capacity to destroy it, whilst at the same time preserving its ability to contend with other pathogens. Otherwise the host's value to the parasite may be extremely short-lived. Nevertheless, as discussed earlier (Section VIII B), it is possible that general NSID is an inevitable/essential consequence of forms of local NSID or ASID aimed primarily at keeping the parasite safe within its niche in the host.

Gastrointestinal nematodes seldom distribute themselves evenly along the intestine (Lewis and Bryant, 1976). Worms aggregate in bundles which may contain many individuals. In partially immune animals aggregates of *N. dubius* may contain several hundred worms, all clumped within a few mm sections of the intestine (unpublished observations). If the survival of *N. dubius* is mediated through immunomodulatory factors with an extremely local effect, then under conditions of concerted attack by the host, the activities of a single worm may be insufficient to protect it from expulsion and a cumulative effort is required. Other intestinal nematodes also aggregate in a similar way, e.g. *N. brasiliensis*, *Ostertagia*, *Trichostrongylus* and *Nematodirus* spp. *T. vitrinus* which survives in lambs for some 12 weeks post infection (Coop *et al.*, 1979) accumulate in "finger print" lesions. These are patches of the intestine which have undergone villus atrophy (Jackson *et al.*, 1983; Angus and Coop, 1984). Similar changes have been observed in the intestines of mice infected with *N. dubius* (T. Jenkins and J. M. Behnke, unpublished observations). The mucosa below "finger print" lesions in lambs is deficient in intra-epithelial globule leukocytes and mast cells (Angus and Coop, 1984), even though both cell types abound in the surrounding tissue. Thus, *T. vitrinus*, like *N. dubius*, may resort to communal anti-inflammatory efforts, creating foci of relative safety from the host responses. Very little is known about the chemical nature of nematode immunomodulatory factors (IMF), but it is likely that the molecules involved will be found to be short-lived, small, lymphokine-like entities with potent local effects, as for example in *Oesophagostomum radiatum* which secretes factors with a molecular weight of 25–35 kd, capable of inhibiting mitogen induced proliferation of bovine lymphocytes (Gasbarre *et al.*, 1985).

In filarial infections immunomodulatory factors (IMF) have a more general effect, although systemic ASID must lie at the core of the survival strategies adopted. The infective stages of filarial parasites may be introduced by insect bites over large areas of the skin surface, but as in *N. dubius*, adult worms frequently aggregate in close proximity, e.g. *O. volvulus* in nodules, *W. bancrofti* and *B. pahangi* in lymphatics and *L. carinii* in the pleural cavity. Systemic ASID aided by general NSID at critical periods of infection and a more powerful local NSID may well prove to be the ultimate solution.

Whatever the nature of IMF, an understanding of their biochemistry, synthesis and mode of immunological activity are urgent priorities for research. The antigens in ES products and homogenates of chronic nematodes are not powerful immunogens (Day *et al.*, 1979) and it is likely that in addition to potentially protective antigens, these preparations are contaminated by IMF which hinder successful vaccination (Pritchard and Behnke, 1985). The complete characterization of IMF should enable ways of neutralizing their effects, to be devised, for example, by the synthesis of analogues with no immunodepressive activity, but sufficient similarity to parasite IMF to elicit cross reactive neutralizing antibody. Patients with neutralizing antibody may then develop effective immune responses without needing to be boosted by antigenic preparations. Alternatively, immunoprophylactic strategies consisting of treatment with anthelmintic alongside vaccination may need to be considered, in order to remove the established sources of IMF in indigenous populations.

In this review, I hope to have brought together information from four biological disciplines. Human parasite epidemiologists, veterinary parasitologists, parasite biologists and immunologists all have an interest in the strategies employed by parasites to evade host immune responses and presumably also in control measures aimed at breaking the transmission of these important pathogens. Clearly much remains to be accomplished in this challenging area of parasite immunology and I hope to have identified some of the outstanding problems here. Hopefully a closer liaison between all research groups interested in chronic nematode parasites will ensure rapid progress in the near future.

Acknowledgements

I would like to express my appreciation to all my colleagues and students in the department, past and present, who have, over the years, provided ideas and stimulating discussions. I am grateful to Professors R. M. Anderson, G. Schad and D. Wakelin and Dr. H. R. P. Miller, for making unpublished material available to me and to Drs B. Coop and F. Jackson for their assistance with relevant information. I would like to thank Ms W. Lister for typing this manuscript and the MRC, Wellcome Trust and the University of Nottingham for financial support. Finally I am particularly indebted to Professor P. N. R. Usherwood and Professor D. Wakelin for unfailing support and encouragement.

References

Adams, D. B. (1981). Changes in blood leukocytes, bone marrow and lymphoid organs in sheep infected with *Haemonchus contortus*. *International Journal for Parasitology* **11,** 309–317.

Adams, D. B. and Beh, K. J. (1981). Immunity acquired by sheep from an experimental infection with *Haemonchus contortus*. *International Journal for Parasitology* **11,** 381–386.

Alghali, S. T. O., Hagan, P. and Robinson, M. (1985). *Hymenolepis citelli* (Cestoda) and *Nematospiroides dubius* (Nematoda): interspecific interaction in mice. *Experimental Parasitology* **60,** 369–370.

Ali, N. M. H. and Behnke, J. M. (1983). *Nematospiroides dubius*: factors affecting the primary response to SRBC in infected mice. *Journal of Helminthology* **57,** 343–353.

Ali, N. M. H. and Behnke, J. M. (1984a). Non-specific immunodepression by larval and adult *Nematospiroides dubius*. *Parasitology* **88,** 153–162.

Ali, N. M. H. and Behnke, J. M. (1984b). Non-specific immunodepression by *Nematospiroides dubius* of concurrent responses to oxazolone and lipopolysaccharide. *Journal of Helminthology* **58,** 301–311.

Ali, N. M. H. and Behnke, J. M. (1985). Observations on the gross changes in the secondary lymphoid organs of mice infected with *Nematospiroides dubius*. *Journal of Helminthology* **59,** 167–174.

Ali, N. M. H., Behnke, J. M. and Manger, B. R. (1985). The pattern of peripheral blood leucocyte changes in mice infected with *Nematospiroides dubius*. *Journal of Helminthology* **59,** 83–93.

Allonby, E. W. and Urquhart, G. M. (1973). Self-cure of *Haemonchus contortus* infections under field conditions. *Parasitology* **66,** 43–53.

Amagai, T. and Cinader, B. (1981). Resistance against tolerance induction in SJL mice. *Immunological Communications* **10,** 349–358.

Anderson, R. M. (1980). The dynamics and control of direct life cycle helminth parasites. *Lecture Notes in Biomathematics* **39,** 278–322.

Anderson, R. M. (1982). Population dynamics and control of hookworm and roundworm infections. *In* "Population Dynamics of Infectious Diseases: Theory and Applications" (R. M. Anderson, ed.). pp. 67–108. Chapman and Hall, London.

Anderson, R. M. (1985). Mathematical models in the study of the epidemiology and control of ascariasis in man. *In* "Ascariasis and its Public Health Significance" (D. W. T. Crompton, M. C. Nesheim and Z. S. Pawlowski, eds.) pp. 39–67. Taylor & Francis, London and Philadelphia.

Anderson, R. M. and May, R. M. (1982). Population dynamics of human helminth infections: control by chemotherapy. *Nature (Lond.)* **297,** 557–563.

Anderson, R. M. and May, R. M. (1985). Herd immunity to helminth infection: implications for parasite control. *Nature (Lond.)* **315,** 493–496.

Anderson, R. M. and Medley, G. F. (1985). Community control of helminth infection of man by mass and selective chemotherapy. *Parasitology* **60,** 629–660.

Anderson, R. M. and Schad, G. A. (1985). Hookworm burdens and faecal egg counts: an analysis of the biological basis of variation. *Transactions of the Royal Society of Tropical Medicine and Hygiene* **79,** 812–825.

Andrew, D. K., Schellenburgh, R. R., Hogg, J. C., Hanna, C. J. and Pare, P. D. (1984). Physiological and immunological effects of chronic antigen exposure in immunized guinea-pigs. *International Archives of Allergy and Applied Immunology* **75,** 208–213.

Angus, K. W. and Coop, R. L. (1984). Chronic infections with *Trichostrongylus colubriformis* in lambs: influence of anthelmintic treatment on intestinal morphology and mucosal cell populations. *Journal of Comparative Pathology* **94,** 433–443.

Armour, J., Jarrett, W. F. H. and Jennings, F. W. (1966). Experimental *Ostertagia circumcincta* infections in sheep: development and pathogenesis of a single infection. *American Journal of Veterinary Research* **27,** 1267–1278.

Ash, L. R. (1973). Chronic *Brugia pahangi* and *Brugia malayi* infections in *Meriones unguiculatus*. *Journal of Parasitology* **59,** 442–447.

Auriault, C., Ouaissi, M. A., Torpier, G., Eisen, H. and Capron, A. (1981). Proteolytic cleavage of IgG bound to the Fc receptor of *S. mansoni* schistosomula. *Parasite Immunology* **3,** 33–44.

Ball, P. A. J. and Bartlett, A. (1969). Serological reactions to infection with *Necator americanus*. *Transactions of the Royal Society of Tropical Medicine and Hygiene* **63,** 362–369.

Barger, I. A., Le Jambre, L. F., Georgi, J. R. and Davies, H. I. (1985). Regulation of *Haemonchus contortus* populations in sheep exposed to continuous infection. *International Journal for Parasitology* **15,** 529–533.

Barriga, O. O. (1984). Immunomodulation by nematodes: a review. *Veterinary Parasitology* **14,** 299–320.

Bartlett, A. and Ball, P. A. J. (1974). The immune response of the mouse to larvae and adults of *Nematospiroides dubius*. *International Journal for Parasitology* **4,** 463–470.

Beaver, P. C. (1970). Filariasis without microfilaraemia. *American Journal of Tropical Medicine and Hygiene* **19,** 181–189.

Befus, A. D. and Bienenstock, J. (1982). Factors involved in symbiosis and host-resistance at the mucosa–parasite interface. *Progress in Allergy* **31,** 76–177.

Behnke, J. M. and Hannah, J. (1984). *Nematospiroides dubius* in the jird, *Meriones unguiculatus*: stimulation and expression of acquired immunity. *Journal of Helminthology* **58,** 221–229.

Behnke, J. M. and Parish, H. A. (1979a). Expulsion of *Nematospiroides dubius* from the intestine of mice treated with immune serum. *Parasite Immunology* **1,** 13–26.

Behnke, J. M. and Parish, H. A. (1979b). *Nematospiroides dubius*: arrested development of larvae in immune mice. *Experimental Parasitology* **47,** 116–127.

Behnke, J. M. and Parish, H. A. (1981). Transfer of immunity to *Nematospiroides dubius*: co-operation between lymphoid cells and antibodies in mediating worm expulsion. *Parasite Immunology* **3,** 249–259.

Behnke, J. M. and Robinson, M. (1985). Genetic control of immunity to *Nematospiroides dubius*; a 9 day anthelmintic abbreviated immunising regime which separates weak and strong responder strains of mice. *Parasite Immunology* **7,** 235–253.

Behnke, J. M. and Wakelin, D. (1973). The survival of *Trichuris muris* in wild populations of its natural host. *Parasitology* **67,** 157–164.

Behnke, J. M. and Wakelin, D. (1977). *Nematospiroides dubius*: stimulation of acquired immunity in inbred strains of mice. *Journal of Helminthology* **51,** 167–176.

Behnke, J. M., Wakelin, D. and Wilson, M. M. (1978). *Trichinella spiralis*: delayed rejection in mice concurrently infected with *Nematospiroides dubius*. *Experimental Parasitology* **46,** 121–130.

Behnke, J. M., Hannah, J. and Pritchard, D. I. (1983). *Nematospiroides dubius* in the mouse: evidence that adult worms depress the expression of homologous immunity. *Parasite Immunology* **5,** 397–408.

Behnke, J. M., Ali, N. M. H. and Jenkins, S. N. (1984). Survival to patency of low level infections with *Trichuris muris* in mice concurrently infected with *Nematospiroides dubius*. *Annals of Tropical Medicine and Parasitology* **78,** 509–517.

Behnke, J. M., Paul, V. and Rajasekariah, G. R. (1986). The growth and emigration of *Necator americanus* following infection of neonatal hamsters. *Transactions of the Royal Society of Tropical Medicine and Hygiene* **80,** 146–149.

Bell, R. G., McGregor, D. D., Woan, M. C. and Adams, L. S. (1983). *Trichinella spiralis*: selective intestinal immune deviation in the rat. *Experimental Parasitology* **56,** 129–142.

Bell, R. G., Adams, L. S. and Ogden, R. W. (1984). *Trichinella spiralis*: genetics of worm expulsion in inbred and F_1 mice infected with different worm doses. *Experimental Parasitology* **58,** 345–355.

Bertram, D. S. (1966). Dynamics of parasitic equilibrium in cotton rat filariasis. *Advances in Parasitology* **4,** 255–319.

Bird, A. F. (1971). "The Structure of Nematodes." Academic Press, London.

Bloom, B. R. (1979). Games parasites play: how parasites evade immune surveillance. *Nature (Lond.)* **279,** 21–26.

Boag, B. and Thomas, R. J. (1977). Epidemiological studies on gastrointestinal nematode parasites of sheep. The seasonal number of generations and succession of species. *Research in Veterinary Science* **22,** 62–67.

Boycott, A. E. (1911). Ankylostoma infections. *Lancet* **1,** 717–721.

Brindley, P. J. and Dobson, C. (1981). Genetic control of liability to infection with *Nematospiroides dubius* in mice: selection of refractory and liable populations of mice. *Parasitology* **83,** 51–65.

Brindley, P. J. and Dobson, C. (1982). *Nematospiroides dubius* in mice selected for liability to infection: modification of parasite biology through host selection. *International Journal for Parasitology* **12,** 573–578.
Brindley, P. J. and Dobson, C. (1983). Genetic control of liability to infection with *Nematospiroides dubius* in mice: direct and correlated responses to selection of mice for faecal parasite egg count. *Parasitology* **87,** 113–127.
Bundy, D. A. P., Thompson, D. E., Golden, M. H. N., Cooper, E. S., Anderson, R. M. and Harland, P. S. E. (1985). Population distribution of *Trichuris trichiura* in a community of Jamaican children. *Transactions of the Royal Society of Tropical Medicine and Hygiene* **79,** 232–237.
Butterworth, A. E. (1984). Cell-mediated damage to helminths. *Advances in Parasitology* **23,** 143–235.
Büttner, D. W. (1985). The significance of morphological studies on microfilariae from onchocerciasis in patients for the evaluation of control measures. *Tropical Medicine and Parasitology* **36,** Supplement 2–4.
Calkins, C. E. and Stutman, O. (1978). Changes in suppressor mechanisms during postnatal development in mice. *Journal of Experimental Medicine* **147,** 87–97.
Capron, A., Dessaint, J. P., Haque, A. and Capron, M. (1982). Antibody-dependent cell-mediated cytotoxicity against parasites. *Progress in Allergy* **31,** 234–267.
Carme, B. and Laigret, J. (1979). Longevity of *Wuchereria bancrofti* var. *pacifica* and mosquito infection acquired from a patient with low level parasitaemia. *American Journal of Tropical Medicine and Hygiene* **28,** 53–55.
Carroll, S. M. and Grove, D. I. (1984). Parasitological, hematologic and immunologic responses in acute and chronic infections of dogs with *Ancylostoma ceylanicum*: a model of human hookworm infection. *Journal of Infectious Diseases* **150,** 284–294.
Cayzer, C. J. R. and Dobson, C. (1983). Suppression of antibody production in mice given multiple concurrent infections with *Nematospiroides dubius. International Journal for Parasitology* **13,** 61–66.
Chaicumpa, V. and Jenkin, C. R. (1978). Studies *in vitro* on the reaction of peritoneal exudate cells from mice immune to infection with *Nematospiroides dubius* with the infective third stage larvae of this parasite. *Australian Journal of Experimental Biology and Medical Science* **56,** 61–68.
Chaicumpa, V., Jenkin, C. R. and Fischer, H. (1977). The effect *in vivo* of peritoneal exudate cells of immune and normal mice on the infectivity of the third stage larvae of *Nematospiroides dubius. Australian Journal of Experimental Biology and Medical Science* **55,** 561–570.
Chan, S. H., Mak, J. W. and Zaman, V. (1981). Immunogenetics of filariasis. *WHO Scientific Working Group on Lymphatic Filariasis Meeting.*
Chan, S. H., Dissanayake, S., Mak, J. W., Ismail, M. M., Wee, G. B., Srinivasan, N., Soo, B. H. and Zaman, V. (1984). HLA and filariasis in Sri Lankans and Indians. *South East Asian Journal of Tropical Medicine and Public Health* **15,** 281–286.
Chandler, A. C. (1926). The rate of loss of hookworms in the absence of reinfection. *Indian Journal of Medical Research* **13,** 625–634.
Chandler, A. C. (1935). A review of recent work on rate of acquisition and loss of hookworms. *American Journal of Tropical Medicine* **15,** 357–370.
Chandrashekar, R., Rao, U. R., Subrahmanyam, D., Hopper, K., Nelson, D. S. and King, M. (1984). *Brugia pahangi*: serum-dependent cell mediated reactions to sheathed and exsheathed microfilariae. *Immunology* **53,** 411–417.
Chandra, R. K. (1975). Reduced secretory antibody responses to live attenuated

measles and polio virus vaccines in malnourished children. *British Medical Journal* **2,** 583–585.

Chapman, C. B., Knopf, P. M., Anders, R. F. and Mitchell, G. F. (1979a). IgG_1 hypergammaglobulinaemia in chronic parasite infections in mice: evidence that the response reflects chronicity of antigen exposure. *Australian Journal of Experimental Biology and Medical Science* **57,** 389–400.

Chapman, C. B., Knopf, P. M., Douglas-Hicks, J. and Mitchell, G. F. (1979b). IgG_1 hypergammaglobulinaemia in chronic parasitic infections in mice: magnitude of the response in mice infected with various parasites. *Australian Journal of Experimental Biology and Medical Science* **57,** 369–387.

Cohen, S. (1982). Survival of parasites in the immunocompetent host. *In* "Immunology of Parasitic Infections" (S. Cohen and K. S. Warren, eds.). pp. 138–161. Blackwell Scientific Publications, Oxford, England.

Conn, H. C. and Greenslit, F. S. (1952). Filariasis residuals in veterans with report of a case of microfilaraemia. *American Journal of Tropical Medicine and Hygiene* **1,** 474–476.

Connan, R. M. (1973). The immune response of the lactating rat to *Nippostrongylus brasiliensis. Immunology* **25,** 261–267.

Cooke, A. and Hutchings, P. (1984). Defective regulation of erythrocyte autoantibodies in SJL mice. *Immunology* **51,** 489–492.

Coop, R. L., Angus, K. W. and Sykes, A. R. (1979). Chronic infection with *Trichostrongylus vitrinus* in sheep. Pathological changes in the small intestine. *Research in Veterinary Science* **26,** 363–371.

Courtney, C. H., Parker, C. F., McClure, K. E. and Herd, R. P. (1983). Population dynamics of *Haemonchus contortus* and *Trichostrongylus* spp. in sheep. *International Journal for Parasitology* **13,** 557–560.

Crandall, C. A. and Crandall, R. B. (1976). *Ascaris suum*: immunosuppression in mice during acute infection. *Experimental Parasitology* **40,** 363–372.

Crandall, R. B., Crandall, C. A. and Franco, J. A. (1974). *Heligmosomoides polygyrus* (= *Nematospiroides dubius*): humoral and intestinal immunological responses to infection in mice. *Experimental Parasitology* **35,** 275–287.

Crandall, R. B., Crandall, C. A. and Jones, J. F. (1978). Analysis of immunosuppression during early acute infection of mice with *Ascaris suum. Clinical and Experimental Immunology* **33,** 30–37.

Croll, N. A. and Ghadirian, E. (1981). Wormy persons: contributions to the nature and patterns of overdispersion with *Ascaris lumbricoides*, *Ancylostoma duodenale*, *Necator americanus* and *Trichuris trichiura. Tropical and Geographical Medicine* **33,** 241–248.

Croll, N. A. and Smith, J. M. (1977). The location of parasites within their hosts: the behaviour of *Nippostrongylus brasiliensis* in the anaesthetised rat. *International Journal for Parasitology* **7,** 195–200.

Croll, N. A., Anderson, R. M., Gyorkos, T. W. and Ghadirian, E. (1982). The population biology and control of *Ascaris lumbricoides* in a rural community in Iran. *Transactions of the Royal Society of Tropical Medicine and Hygiene* **76,** 187–197.

Crompton, D. W. T. (1984). "Parasites and People". MacMillan Publishers, London.

Cross, J. H. (1960). The natural resistance of the white rat to *Nematospiroides dubius* and the effect of cortisone on this resistance. *Journal of Parasitology* **46,** 175–185.

Cross, J. H. and Duffy, C. E. (1963). *Nematospiroides dubius* in the abnormal host. *Annals of the New York Academy of Science* **113,** 88–99.

Cypess, R. H., Lucia, H. L., Zidian, J. L. and Rivera-Ortiz, C. I. (1977). *Heligmosomoides polygyrus*: temporal, spatial and morphological population characteristics in LAF_1/J mice. *Experimental Parasitology* **42,** 34–43.

Dargie, J. D. and Allonby, E. W. (1975). Pathophysiology of single and challenge infections of *Haemonchus contortus* in Merino sheep: studies on red cell kinetics and the self-cure phenomenon. *International Journal for Parasitology* **5,** 147–157.

Day, K. P., Howard, R. J., Prowse, S. J., Chapman, C. B. and Mitchell, G. F. (1979). Studies on chronic versus transient intestinal nematode infections in mice. I. A comparison of responses to excretory/secretory (ES) products of *Nippostrongylus brasiliensis* and *Nematospiroides dubius* worms. *Parasite Immunology* **1,** 217–239.

Denham, D. A., Ponnudurai, T., Nelson, G. S., Guy, F. and Rogers, R. (1972). Studies with *Brugia pahangi*. I. Parasitological observations on primary infections of cats (*Felis catus*). *International Journal for Parasitology* **2,** 239–247.

Despommier, D. D. (1981). Partial purification and characterization of protection-induced antigens from the muscle larva of *Trichinella spiralis* by molecular sizing chromatography and preparative flatbed isoelectric focussing. *Parasite Immunology* **3,** 261–272.

Dessaint, J. P., Camus, D., Fischer, E. and Capron, A. (1977). Inhibition of lymphocyte proliferation by factors(s) produced by *Schistosoma mansoni*. *European Journal of Immunology* **7,** 524–629.

Dineen, J. K and Kelly, J. D. (1972). The suppression of rejection of *Nippostrongylus brasiliensis* in lactating rats: the nature of the immunological defect. *Immunology* **22,** 1–12.

Dineen, J. K and Kelly, J. D. (1973). Immunological unresponsiveness of neonatal rats to infection with *Nippostrongylus brasiliensis*. The competence of neonatal lymphoid cells in worm expulsion. Immunology **25,** 141–150.

Dobson, C. (1982). Passive transfer of immunity with serum in mice infected with *Nematospiroides dubius*: influence of quality and quantity of immune serum. *International Journal for Parasitology* **12,** 207–213.

Dobson, C. and Cayzer, C. J. R. (1982a). Immunosuppressive activity in serum from mice infected with *Nematospiroides dubius* following passive serum transfer. *International Journal for Parasitology* **12,** 561–566.

Dobson, C. and Cayzer, C. J. R. (1982b). Passive transfer of immunity with serum in mice infected with *Nematospiroides dubius*: *in vitro* effect of immune serum on larval infectivity. *International Journal for Parasitology* **12,** 413–421.

Dobson, C., Brindley, P. J. and Sitepu, P. (1982). Influence of serum donor and recipient mouse genotype on the passive transfer of protective immunity with serum against *Nematospiroides dubius*. *International Journal for Parasitology* **12,** 567–572.

Dobson, C., Sitepu, P. and Brindley, P. J. (1985). Influence of primary infection on the population dynamics of *Nematospiroides dubius* after challenge infections in mice. *International Journal for Parasitology* **15,** 353–359.

Donald, A. D. and Waller, P. J. (1982). Problems and prospects in the control of helminthiasis in sheep. *In* "Biology and Control of Endoparasites" (L. E. A. Symons, A. D. Donald and J. K. Dineen, eds). pp. 157–186. Academic Press, Sydney, Australia.

Dosch, H. M., Mansour, A., Cohen, A., Shore, A. and Gelfand, E. W. (1980). Inhibition of suppressor T-cell development following deoxyguanosine administration. *Nature (Lond.)* **285,** 494–496.

Duke, B. O. L. (1968). The effects of drugs on *Onchocerca volvulus*. I. Methods of assessment, population dynamics of the parasite and the effects of diethylcarbamazine. *Bulletin of the WHO* **39,** 137–146.

Ehrenford, F. A. (1954). The life cycle of *Nematospiroides dubius* Baylis (Nematoda; Heligmosomidae). *Journal of Parasitology* **40,** 480–481.

Elkins, D. B., Haswell-Elkins, M. and Anderson, R. M. (1986). The epidemiology and control of intestinal helminths in the Pulicat Lake region of Southern India. I. Study design and pre- and post treatment observations on *Ascaris lumbricoides* infection. *Transactions of the Royal Society of Tropical Medicine and Hygiene* **80,** 774–792.

Fanning, M. M. and Kazura, J. W. (1983). Genetic association of murine susceptibility to *Brugia malayi* microfilaraemia. *Parasite Immunology* **5,** 305–316.

Faubert, G. M. (1976). Depression of the plaque-forming cells to sheep red blood cells by the newborn larvae of *Trichinella spiralis. Immunology* **30,** 485–489.

Foo, D. Y., Nowak, M., Copeman, B. and McCabe, M. (1983). A low molecular weight immunosuppressive factor produced by *Onchocerca gibsoni. Veterinary Immunology and Immunopathology* **4,** 445–451.

Forsyth, K. P., Copeman, D. B. and Mitchell, G. F. (1984). Differences in the surface radioiodinated proteins of skin and uterine microfilariae of *Onchocerca gibsoni. Molecular and Biochemical Parasitology* **10,** 217–229.

Fujita, K. and Kobayashi, J. (1969). The development of antibodies in the cotton rat transplanted with adult cotton rat filaria, *Litomosoides carinii. Japanese Journal of Experimental Medicine* **39,** 585–592.

Gasbarre, L. C., Romanowski, R. D. and Douvres, F. W. (1985). Suppression of antigen and mitogen induced proliferation of bovine lymphocytes by excretory–secretory products of *Oesophagostomum radiatum. Infection and Immunity* **48,** 540–545.

Gould, S. E. (1945). "Trichinosis". Charles C. Thomas, U.S.A.

Green, D. R. and Gershon, R. K. (1984). Contrasuppression: the second law of thymodynamics, revisited. *Advances in Cancer Research* **42,** 277–335.

Grencis, R. K. and Wakelin, D. (1983). Immunity to *Trichinella spiralis* in mice. Factors involved in direct anti-worm effects. *Wiadomos'ci Parazytologiczne* **29,** 387–399.

Grencis, R. K., Crawford, C., Pritchard, D. I., Behnke, J. M. and Wakelin, D. (1986). Immunization of mice with surface antigens from the infective L_1 muscle larvae of *Trichinella spiralis. Parasite Immunology* **8,** 587–596.

Grove, D. I. and Forbes, I. J. (1979). Immunosuppression in bancroftian filariasis. *Transactions of the Royal Society of Tropical Medicine and Hygiene* **73,** 23–26.

Guptavanij, P. and Harinasuta, C. (1971). Spontaneous disappearance of microfilaria *Brugia malayi* and *Wuchereria bancrofti* in infected patients living in a non-endemic area. *Southeast Asian Journal of Tropical Medicine and Public Health* **2,** 578.

Gyorkos, T. W., Sukal, N. C. and Dasdal, A. (1983). Filariasis and ABO blood group status: a critical appraisal. *Transactions of the Royal Society of Tropical Medicine and Hygiene* **77,** 564–565.

Hagan, P. and Wakelin, D. (1982). *Nematospiroides dubius*: effect of infection on lymphocyte responses to *Trichinella spiralis* in mice. *Experimental Parasitology* **54,** 157–165.

Hagan, P., Behnke, J. M. and Parish, H. A. (1981). Stimulation of immunity to

Nematospiroides dubius in mice using larvae attenuated by cobalt 60 irradiation. *Parasite Immunology* **3,** 149–156.

Haig, D. M., Lima, G. C. and Mota, I. (1980). Antibody suppression in mice infected with *Nippostrongylus brasiliensis*. *Parasite Immunology* **2,** 175–187.

Hannah, J. and Behnke, J. M. (1982). *Nematospiroides dubius* in the jird, *Meriones unguiculatus*: factors affecting the course of a primary infection. *Journal of Helminthology* **56,** 329–338.

Haque, A. and Capron, A. (1982). Transplacental transfer of rodent microfilariae induces antigen-specific tolerance in rats. *Nature (Lond.)* **299,** 361–363.

Haque, A., Lefebvre, M. N., Ogilvie, B. M. and Capron, A. (1978). *Dipetalonema viteae* in hamsters: effect of antiserum on immunization with parasite extracts on production of microfilariae. *Parasitology* **76,** 61–75.

Haque, A., Worms, M. J., Ogilvie, B. M. and Capron, A. (1980a). *Dipetalonema viteae*: microfilariae production in various mouse strains and in nude mice. *Experimental Parasitology* **49,** 398–404.

Haque, A., Joseph, M., Ouaissi, M. A., Capron, M. and Capron, A. (1980b). IgE antibody-mediated cytotoxicity of rat macrophages against microfilariae of *Dipetalonema viteae in vitro*. *Clinical and Experimental Immunology* **40,** 487–496.

Haque, A., Ogilvie, B. M. and Capron, A. (1981). *Dipetalonema viteae*: response of spleen cells in experimental mouse filariasis to mitogens and antigens. *Experimental Parasitology* **52,** 25–34.

Haque, A., Capron, A., Ouaissi, A., Kouemeni, L., Lejeune, J. P., Bonnel, B. and Pierce, R. (1983). Immune unresponsiveness and its possible relation to filarial disease. *Contributions to Microbiology and Immunology* **7,** 9–21.

Harness, E., Sellwood, S. A. and Young, E. R. (1971). Experimental *Haemonchus placei* infection in calves: influence of anaemia and numbers of larvae on worm development. *Journal of Comparative Pathology* **81,** 129–136.

Hayashi, Y., Nogami, S., Nakamura, M., Shirasaka, A. and Noda, K. (1984). Passive transfer of protective immunity against *Brugia malayi* in BALB/c mice. *Japanese Journal of Experimental Medicine* **54,** 183–187.

Hellstrom, K. E., Hellstrom, I. and Nepom, J. T. (1977). Specific blocking factors—are they important? *Biochimica et Biophysica Acta* **473,** 121–148.

Hockley, D. J. (1973). Ultrastructure of the tegument of *Schistosoma*. *Advances in Parasitology* **11,** 233–305.

Hong, C., Michel, J. F. and Lancaster, M. B. (1986). Populations of *Ostertagia circumcincta* in lambs following a single infection. *International Journal for Parasitology* **16,** 63–67.

Hopkins, C. A. (1980). Immunity and *Hymenolepis diminuta*. *In* "Biology of the Tapeworm *Hymenolepis diminuta*" (H. P. Arai, ed.). pp. 551–614. Academic Press, New York.

Hotez, P. J. and Cerami, A. (1983). Secretion of a proteolytic anticoagulant by *Ancylostoma* hookworms. *Journal of Experimental Medicine* **157,** 1594–1603.

Hotez, P. J., Le Trang, N., McKerrow, J. H. and Cerami, A. (1985). Isolation and characterization of a proteolytic enzyme from the adult hookworm *Ancylostoma caninum*. *Journal of Biological Chemistry* **260,** 7343–7348.

Howells, R. E. and Chen, S. N. (1981). *Brugia pahangi*: feeding and nutrient uptake by the filarial worm *in vitro* and *in vivo*. *Experimental Parasitology* **51,** 42–58.

Howells, R. E., Mendis, A. M. and Bray, P. G. (1983). The mechanisms of amino acid uptake by *Brugia pahangi in vitro*. *Zeitschrift für Parasitenkunde* **69,** 247–253.

Hurley, J. C. and Vadas, M. A. (1983). Eosinophilia and acquisition of resistance to *Nematospiroides dubius* in mice sensitized with adult worms. *Australian Journal of Experimental Biology and Medical Science* **61,** 1–9.

Hurley, J. C., Day, K. P. and Mitchell, G. F. (1980). Accelerated rejection of *Nematospiroides dubius* intestinal worms in mice sensitized with adult worms. *Australian Journal of Experimental Biology and Medical Science* **58,** 231–240.

Inglis, W. G. (1983). The design of the nematode body wall: the ontogeny of the cuticle. *Australian Journal of Zoology* **31,** 705–716.

Immunological Reviews (1982). Vol. 61, Immunoparasitology.

Jackson, F., Angus, K. W. and Coop, R. L. (1983). Development of morphological changes in the small intestine of lambs continuously infected with *Trichostrongylus vitrinus*. *Research in Veterinary Science* **34,** 301–304.

Jacobson, R. H., Brooks, B. O. and Cypess, R. H. (1982). Immunity to *Nematospiroides dubius*: parasite stages responsible for and subject to resistance in high responder (LAF_1/J) mice. *Journal of Parasitology* **68,** 1053–1058.

Jenkins, D. C. (1972). *Nippostrongylus brasiliensis*: observations on the comparative immunogenicity of adult worms from primary and immune adapted infections. *Parasitology* **65,** 547–550.

Jenkins, D. C. (1974). *Nippostrongylus brasiliensis*: observations on factors affecting the establishment of secondary worm populations in rats. *Parasitology* **68,** 13–17.

Jenkins, D. C. (1975). The influence of *Nematospiroides dubius* on subsequent *Nippostrongylus brasiliensis* infections in mice. *Parasitology* **71,** 349–355.

Jenkins, D. C. (1977). *Nematospiroides dubius*: the course of primary and challenge infections in the jird, *Meriones unguiculatus*. *Experimental Parasitology* **41,** 335–340.

Jenkins, D. C. and Phillipson, R. F. (1971). The kinetics of repeated low-level infections of *Nippostrongylus brasiliensis* in the laboratory rat. *Parasitology* **62,** 457–465.

Jenkins, S. N. and Behnke, J. M. (1977). Impairment of primary expulsion of *Trichuris muris* in mice concurrently infected with *Nematospiroides dubius*. *Parasitology* **75,** 71–78.

Jenkins, S. N. and Wakelin, D. (1983). Functional antigens of *Trichuris muris* released during *in vitro* maintenance: their immunogenicity and partial purification. *Parasitology* **86,** 73–82.

Johnson, M. H., Orihel, T. C. and Beaver, P. C. (1974). *Dipetalonema viteae* in the experimentally infected jird, *Meriones unguiculatus*. I. Insemination, development from egg to microfilaria, reinsemination and longevity of mated and unmated worms. *Journal of Parasitology* **60,** 302–309.

Jones, C. E. and Rubin, R. (1974). *Nematospiroides dubius*: mechanisms of host immunity. I. Parasite counts, histopathology and serum transfer involving orally or subcutaneously sensitized mice. *Experimental Parasitology* **35,** 434–452.

Jones, J. F., Crandall, C. A. and Crandall, R. B. (1976). T-dependent suppression of the primary antibody response to sheep erythrocytes in mice infected with *Trichinella spiralis*. *Cellular Immunology* **2,** 102–110.

Jungery, M. and Ogilvie, B. M. (1982). Antibody response to stage-specific *Trichinella spiralis* surface antigens in strong and weak responder mouse strains. *Journal of Immunology* **129,** 839–843.

Kalkofen, U. P. (1970). Attachment and feeding behaviour of *Ancylostoma caninum*. *Zeitschrift für Parasitenkunde* **33,** 339–354.

Kalkofen, U. P. (1974). Intestinal trauma resulting from feeding activities of

Ancylostoma caninum. *American Journal of Tropical Medicine and Hygiene* **23,** 1046–1053.

Karavodin, L. M. and Ash, L. R. (1980). Circulating immune complexes in experimental filariasis. *Clinical and Experimental Immunology* **40,** 312–317.

Karavodin, L. M. and Ash, L. R. (1982). Inhibition of adherence and cytotoxicity by circulating immune complexes formed in experimental filariasis. *Parasite Immunology* **4,** 1–12.

Kelly, J. D. and Dineen, J. K. (1973). The suppression of rejection of *Nippostrongylus brasiliensis* in Lewis strain rats treated with ovine prolactin. The site of the immunological defect. *Immunology* **24,** 551–558.

Kendrick, J. F. (1934). The length of life and rate of loss of hookworms, *Ancylostoma duodenale* and *Necator americanus*. *American Journal of Tropical Medicine and Hygiene* **14,** 363–379.

Keymer, A. (1985). Experimental epidemiology: *Nematospiroides dubius* and the laboratory mouse. *In* "Ecology and Genetics of Host–Parasite Interactions" (R. M. Anderson and D. Rollinson, eds.). pp. 55–76. Academic Press, London, New York.

Khoury, P. B. and Soulsby, E. J. L. (1979). Isolation of a suppressor cell subpopulation in the spleen of guinea pigs immune to *Ascaris suum* infection. 52nd Meeting of the American Society for Parasitology. *Journal of Parasitology* **157,** Abstract 65.

King, S. J. and Miller, H. R. P. (1984). Anaphylactic release of mucosal mast cell protease and its relationship to gut permeability in *Nippostrongylus* primed rats. *Immunology* **51,** 653–660.

Kirkwood, B., Smith, P., Marshall, T. and Prost, A. (1983). Variations in the prevalence and intensity of microfilarial infections by age, sex, place and time in the area of the Onchocerciasis Control Programme. *Transactions of the Royal Society of Tropical Medicine and Hygiene* **77,** 857–861.

Klaver-Wesseling, J. C. M., Vetler, J. C. M. and Visser, W. K. (1978). A comparative *in vitro* study of antibody binding to different stages of the hookworm *Ancylostoma caninum*. *Zeitschrift für Parasitenkunde* **56,** 147–157.

Klei, T. R., McCall, J. W. and Malone, J. B. (1980). Evidence for increased susceptibility of *Brugia pahangi*-infected jirds (*Meriones unguiculatus*) to subsequent homologous infections. *Journal of Helminthology* **54,** 161–165.

Klei, T. R., Enright, F. M., Blanchard, D. P. and Uhl, S. A. (1981). Specific hyporesponsive granulomatous tissue reactions in *Brugia pahangi*-infected jirds. *Acta Tropica* **38,** 267–276.

Komatsu, T., Nishimura, T., Sano, R. and Shinka, S. (1979). *Ascaris suum*: suppression of reaginic and haemagglutinating antibody responses in the mouse by crude extract and maintenance fluid. *Experimental Parasitology* **47,** 158–168.

Koster, F. and Pierce, N. F. (1985). Effect of protein deprivation on immunoregulatory cells in the rat mucosal immune response. *Clinical and Experimental Immunology* **60,** 217–224.

Kwa, B. H. and Mak, J. W. (1980). Specific depression of cell-mediated immunity in Malayan filariasis. *Transactions of the Royal Society of Tropical Medicine and Hygiene* **74,** 522–527.

Lammie, P. J. and Katz, S. P. (1982). Antigen-specific suppression in jirds (*Meriones unguiculatus*) infected with *Brugia pahangi*. *Federal Proceedings* **41,** 371.

Lamie, P. J. and Katz, S. P. (1983). Immunoregulation in experimental filariasis. II.

Responses to parasite and nonparasite antigens in jirds with *Brugia pahangi*. *Journal of Immunology* **130,** 1386–1389.

Lamie, P. J., Katz, S. P. and Anderson, W. H. K. (1984). Serosuppression in experimental filariasis. *Clinical and Experimental Immunology* **55,** 602–610.

Lee, D. L. (1970). The fine structure of the excretory system in adult *Nippostrongylus brasiliensis* (Nematoda) and a suggested function for the "excretory glands". *Tissue and Cell* **2,** 225–231.

Lee, D. L. and Martin, J. (1976). Changes in *Nematodirus battus* associated with the development of immunity to this nematode in lambs. *In* "Biochemistry of Parasites and Host–Parasite Relationships" (H. van den Bossche, ed.). pp. 311–318. Elsevier/North Holland, Amsterdam.

Lee, G. B. and Ogilvie, B. M. (1982). The intestinal mucus barrier to parasites and bacteria. *In* "Mucus in Health and Disease II". *Advances in Experimental Medical Biology* **144,** pp. 247–248. Plenum Press, New York.

Lee, T. D. G. and Wakelin, D. (1982). Cortisone-induced immunotolerance to nematode infection in CBA/Ca mice. I. Investigation of the defect in the protective response. *Immunology* **47,** 227–232.

Lee, T. D. G. and Wright, K. A. (1978). The morphology of the attachment and probable feeding site of the nematode *Trichuris muris* (Schrank, 1788) Hall, 1916. *Canadian Journal of Zoology* **56,** 1889–1905.

Leeuwin, R. S. (1962). Microfilaraemia in Surinamese living in Amsterdam. *Tropical and Geographical Medicine* **14,** 355–360.

Lewis, J. W. and Bryant, V. (1976). The distribution of *Nematospiroides dubius* within the small intestine of laboratory mice. *Journal of Helmithology* **50,** 163–171.

Liu, S. K. (1966). Genetic influences on resistance of mice to *Nematospiroides dubius*. *Experimental Parasitology* **18,** 311–319.

Mahoney, L. E. and Aiu, R. (1970). Filariasis in Samoan immigrants to the United States. *American Journal of Tropical Medicine and Hygiene* **19,** 629–636.

Maizels, R. M., Philipp, M. and Ogilvie, B. M. (1982). Molecules on the surface of parasitic nematodes as probes of the immune responses in infection. *Immunological Reviews* **61,** 109–136.

Maizels, R. M., Philipp, M., Dasgupta, A. and Partono, F. (1984). Human serum albumin is a major component on the surface of microfilariae of *Wuchereria bancrofti*. *Parasite Immunology* **6,** 185–190.

Manson-Bahr, P. (1959). The story of *Filaria bancrofti*. *Journal of Tropical Medicine and Hygiene* **62,** 160–173.

Mapes, C. J., Coop, R. L. and Angus, K. W. (1973). The fate of large infective doses of *Nematodirus battus* in young lambs. *International Journal for Parasitology* **3,** 339–347.

Martin, J., Keymer, A., Isherwood, R. J. and Wainwright, S. M. (1983). The prevalence and intensity of *Ascaris lumbricoides* infections in Moslem children from northern Bangladesh. *Transactions of the Royal Society of Tropical Medicine and Hygiene* **77,** 702–706.

McElroy, P. J., Szewczak, M. R. and Befus, A. D. (1983). Regulation of heterologous IgM, IgG and IgA antibody responses in mucosal-associated lymphoid tissues of *Nippostrongylus brasiliensis*-infected mice. *Journal of Immunology* **130,** 435–441.

McGreevy, P. B., Ismail, M. M., Phillips, T. M. and Denham, D. A. (1975). Studies with *Brugia pahangi*. 10. An attempt to demonstrate the sharing of antigenic determinants between the worm and its hosts. *Journal of Helminthology* **49,** 107–113.

McLaren, D. J. (1976). Nematode sense organs. *Advances in Parasitology* **14,** 195–265.

McLaren, D. J. (1984). Disguise as an evasive strategem of parasitic organisms. *In* "Parasite Evasion of the Immune Response" (Symposia of the British Society for Parasitology 21). *Parasitology* **88,** 597–611.

McLaren, D. J., Burt, J. S. and Ogilvie, B. M. (1974). The anterior glands of adult *Necator americanus* (Nematoda: Strongyloidea). II. Cytochemical and functional studies. *International Journal for Parasitology* **4,** 39–46.

Michel, J. F. (1970). The regulation of populations of *Ostertagia ostertagi* in calves. *Parasitology* **61,** 435–447.

Michel, J. F. (1976). The epidemiology and control of some nematode infections in grazing animals. *Advances in Parasitology* **14,** 355–397.

Michel, J. F. (1982). Some thoughts on the control of parasitic gastroenteritis. *In* "Biology and Control of Endoparasites" (L. E. A. Symons, A. D. Donald and J. K. Dineen, eds.). pp. 113–131. Academic Press, Sydney.

Michel, J. F. (1985). Strategies for the use of anthelmintics in livestock and their implications for the development of drug resistance. *Parasitology* **90,** 621–628.

Michel, J. F., Lancaster, M. B. and Hong, C. (1978). The length of *Ostertagia ostertagi* in populations of uniform age. *International Journal for Parasitology* **8,** 437–441.

Miller, H. R. P. (1984). The protective mucosal response against gastrointestinal nematodes in ruminants and laboratory animals. *Veterinary Immunology and Immunopathology* **6,** 167–259.

Miller, H. R. P., Huntley, J. F. and Wallace, G. R. (1981). Immune exclusion and mucus trapping during the rapid expulsion of *Nippostrongylus brasiliensis* from primed rats. *Immunology* **44,** 419–429.

Mims, C. A. (1982). Innate immunity to parasitic infections. *In* "Immunology of Parasitic Infections" (S. Cohen and K. S. Warren, eds.). pp. 3–27. Blackwell Scientific Publications, Oxford, England.

Mitchell, G. F. (1979a). Response to infection with metazoan and protozoan parasites in mice. *Advances in Parasitology* **28,** 451–511.

Mitchell, G. F. (1979b). Effector cells, molecules and mechanisms in host-protective immunity to parasites. *Immunology* **38,** 209–223.

Mitchell, G. F. and Anders, R. F. (1982). Parasite antigens and their immunogenicity in infected hosts. *In* "The Antigens" (M. Sela, ed.). pp. 69–149. Academic Press, New York.

Mitchell, G. F. and Cruise, K. M. (1984). Immunization with *Nematospiroides dubius* adult worms plus pertussigen has different consequences in mice of various genotypes. *Australian Journal of Experimental Biology and Medical Science* **62,** 523–530.

Mitchell, G. F. and Munoz, J. J. (1983). Vaccination of genetically susceptible mice against chronic infection with *Nematospiroides dubius* using pertussigen as adjuvant. *Australian Journal of Experimental Biology and Medical Science* **61,** 425–434.

Mitchell, G. F. and Prowse, S. J. (1979). Three consequences of infection with *Nematospiroides dubius* in three inbred strains of mice. *Journal of Parasitology* **65,** 820–822.

Mitchell, G. F., Hogarth-Scott, R. S., Lewers, H. M., Edwards, R. D., Cousins, G. and Moore, T. (1976). Studies on immune responses to parasite antigens in mice. I. *Ascaris suum* larvae numbers and anti phosphorylcholine responses in infected mice of various strains and in hypothymic nu/nu mice. *International Archives of Allergy and Applied Immunology* **52,** 64–78.

Mitchell, G. F., Anders, R. F., Brown, G. V., Handman, E., Roberts-Thomson, I. C., Chapman, C. B., Forsyth, K. P., Kahl, L. P. and Cruise, K. M. (1982). Analysis of infection characteristics and antiparasite immune responses in resistant compared with susceptible hosts. *Immunological Reviews* **61,** 137–188.

Molinari, J. A., Ebersole, J. L. and Cypess, R. H. (1978). Specific antibody levels in the serum of *Heligmosomoides polygyrus*-infected mice. *Journal of Parasitology* **64,** 233–238.

Morgan, D. O., Parnell, I. W. and Rayski, C. (1951). The seasonal variations in the worm burden of Scottish hill sheep. *Journal of Helminthology* **25,** 177–212.

Murray, M., Jarrett, W. F. H. and Jennings, F. W. (1971). Mast cells and macromolecular leak in intestinal immunological reactions. The influence of sex of rats infected with *Nippostrongylus brasiliensis*. *Immunology* **21,** 17–31.

Murray, M., Jennings, F. W. and Armour, J. (1970). *Bovine ostertagiasis*: structure, function and mode of differentiation of the bovine gastric mucosa and kinetics of the worm loss. *Research in Veterinary Science* **11,** 417–427.

Narayanan, P. R., Vanamala, C. R., Alamelu, R., Kumaraswamy, V., Tripathy, S. P. and Prabhakar, R. (1986). Reduced lymphocyte responses to mitogens in patients with bancroftian filariasis. *Transactions of the Royal Society of Tropical Medicine and Hygiene* **80,** 78–84.

Nawa, Y. (1979). Increased permeability of gut mucosa in rats infected with *Nippostrongylus brasiliensis*. *International Journal for Parasitology* **9,** 251–256.

Nawalinski, T. A. and Schad, G. A. (1974). Arrested development in *Ancylostoma duodenale*: course of self-induced infection in man. *American Journal of Tropical Medicine and Hygiene* **23,** 895–898.

Nawalinski, T., Schad, G. A. and Chowdhury, A. B. (1978). Population biology of hookworms in children in rural West Bengal. I. General parasitological observations. *American Journal of Tropical Medicine and Hygiene* **24,** 1152–1161.

Neilson, J. T. M. (1978a). Primary infections of *Dipetalonema viteae* in an outbred and five inbred strains of golden hamsters. *Journal of Parasitology* **64,** 378–380.

Neilson, J. T. M. (1978b). Alteration of amicrofilaremia in *Dipetalonema viteae* infected hamsters with immunosuppressive drugs. *Acta Tropica* **35,** 57–61.

Neilson, J. T. M. and Forrester, D. J. (1975). Primary, secondary and tertiary infections of *Dipetalonema viteae* in hamsters. *Experimental Parasitology* **37,** 367–372.

Neilson, J. T. M., Crandall, C. A. and Crandall, R. B. (1981). Serum immunoglobulin and antibody levels and the passive transfer of resistance in hamsters infected with *Dipetalonema viteae*. *Acta Tropica* **38,** 309–318.

Nelson, G. S. (1966). The pathology of filarial infections. *Helminthological Abstracts* **35,** 311–336.

Nelson, G. S. (1970). Onchocerciasis. *Advances in Parasitology* **8,** 173–224.

Ngwenya, B. Z. (1976). Effects of lactation on cell-mediated immunity of Swiss mice to *Trichinella spiralis*. *Cellular Immunology* **24,** 116–122.

Ogilvie, B. M. (1974). Antigenic variation in the nematode *Nippostrongulus brasiliensis*. *In* "Parasites in the Immunized Host: Mechanisms of Survival". Ciba Foundation Symposium 25, pp. 81–100. Elsevier, Holland.

Ogilvie, B. M. and Jones, V. E. (1971). *Nippostrongylus brasiliensis*: a review of immunity and the host–parasite relationship in the rat. *Experimental Parasitology* **29,** 138–177.

Ogilvie, B. M. and Love, R. J. (1974). Co-operation between antibodies and cells in immunity to a nematode parasite. *Transplantation Reviews* **19,** 147–168.

Ogilvie, B. M. and MacKenzie, C. D. (1981). Immunology and immunopathology of infections caused by filarial nematodes. *In* "Parasitic Diseases. The Immunology" (J. Mansfield, ed.). pp. 227–289. Marcel Dekker, New York.

Ogilvie, B. M. and Wilson, R. J. M. (1977). Evasion of the immune response by parasites. *British Medical Journal* **32,** 177–181.

Ogilvie, B. M., Rothwell, T. L. W., Bremner, K. C., Schnitzerling, H. J., Nolan, J. and Keith, R. K. (1973). Acetylcholinesterase secretion by parasitic nematodes. I Evidence for secretion of the enzyme by a number of species. *International Journal for Parasitology* **3,** 589–597.

Ogilvie, B. M., Bartlett, A., Godfrey, R. C., Turton, J. A., Worms, M. J. and Yeates, R. A. (1978). Antibody responses in self-infections with *Necator americanus*. *Transactions of the Royal Society of Tropical Medicine and Hygiene* **72,** 66–71.

Oliver-Gonzalez, J. and Torregrosa, M. V. (1944). A substance in animal parasites related to the human isoagglutinogens. *Journal of Infectious Diseases* **74,** 173–177.

Ottesen, E. A. (1980). Immunopathology of lymphatic filariasis in man. *Springer Seminars in Immunopathology* **2,** 373–385.

Ottesen, E. A. (1984). Immunological aspects of lymphatic filariasis and onchocerciasis in man. *Transactions of the Royal Society of Tropical Medicine and Hygiene* **78** (Suppl.), 9–18.

Ottesen, E. A., Weller, P. F. and Heck, L. (1977). Specific cellular immune unresponsiveness in human filariasis. *Immunology* **33,** 413–421.

Ottesen, E. A., Kumaraswami, V., Paranjape, R., Poindexter, R. W. and Tripathy, S. P. (1981). Naturally occurring blocking antibodies modulate immediate hypersensitivity responses in human filariasis. *Journal of Immunology* **127,** 2014–2020.

Palmer, E. D. (1955). Course of egg output over a 15 year period in a case of experimentally induced nectoriasis americanus, in the absence of hyperinfection. *American Journal of Tropical Medicine and Hygiene* **4,** 756–757.

Pappas, P. W. and Read, C. P. (1975). Membrane transport in helminth parasites: a review. *Experimental Parasitology* **37,** 469–530.

Parkhouse, R. M. E. (1984). Editor: Parasite evasion of the immune response (Symposia of the British Society for Parasitology, *21*). *Parasitology* **88,** 571–682.

Parkhouse, R. M. E., Bofill, M., Gomez-Priego, A. and Janossy, G. (1985). Human macrophages and T-lymphocyte subsets infiltrating nodules of *Onchocerca volvulus*. *Clinical and Experimental Immunology* **62,** 13–18.

Pawlowski, Z S. (1983). Clinical aspects in man. *In* "Trichinella and Trichinosis" (W. C. Campbell, ed.). pp. 367–401. Plenum Press, New York.

Penttila, I. A., Ey, P. L. and Jenkin, C. R. (1983). Adherence of murine peripheral blood eosinophils and neutrophils to the different parasitic stages of *Nematospiroides dubius*. *Australian Journal of Experimental Biology and Medical Science* **61,** 617–627.

Penttila, I. A., Ey, P. L. and Jenkin, C. R. (1984a). Reduced infectivity of *Nematospiroides dubius* larvae after incubation *in vitro* with neutrophils or eosinophils from infected mice and a lack of effect by neutrophils from normal mice. *Parasite Immunology* **6,** 295–308.

Penttila, I. A., Ey, P. L. and Jenkin, C. R. (1984b). Infection of mice with

Nematospiroides dubius: demonstration of neutrophil-mediated immunity *in vivo* in the presence of antibodies. *Immunology* **53,** 147–154.

Penttila, I. A., Ey, P. L., Lopez, A. F. and Jenkin, C. R. (1985). Suppression of early immunity to *Nematospiroides dubius* in mice by selective depletion of neutrophils with monoclonal antibody. *Australian Journal of Experimental Biology and Medical Science* **63,** 531–543.

Philipp, M. (1984). Acetylcholinesterase secreted by intestinal nematodes: a reinterpretation of its putative role of "biochemical holdfast'. *Transactions of the Royal Society of Tropical Medicine and Hygiene* **78,** 138–139.

Philipp, M., Parkhouse, R. M. E. and Ogilvie, B. M. (1980). Changing proteins on the surface of a parasitic nematode. *Nature (Lond.)* **287,** 538–540.

Philipp, M., Worms, M. J., Maizels, R. M. and Ogilvie, B. M. (1984a). Rodent models of filariasis. *Contemporary Topics in Immunobiology* **12,** 275–321.

Philipp, M., Worms, M. J., McLaren, D. J., Ogilvie, B. M., Parkhouse, R. M. E. and Taylor, P. M. (1984b). Surface proteins of a filarial nematode: a major soluble antigen and a host component on the cuticle of *Litomosoides carinii*. *Parasite Immunology* **6,** 63–82.

Piessens, W. F. and Mackenzie, C. D. (1982). Lymphatic filariasis and onchocerciasis. *In* "Immunology of Parasitic Infections" (S. Cohen and K. S. Warren, eds). pp. 622–653. Blackwell Scientific Publications, Oxford, England.

Piessens, W. F., McGreevy, P. B., Piessens, P. W., McGreevy, M., Koiman, I., Saroso, J. S. and Dennis, D. T. (1980a). Immune responses in human infections with *Brugia malayi*. Specific cellular unresponsiveness to filarial antigens. *Journal of Clinical Investigation* **65,** 172–179.

Piessens, W. F., Ratiwayanto, S., Tuti, S., Palmieri, J. H., Piessens, P. W., Koiman, I. and Dennis, D. T. (1980b). Antigen-specific suppressor cells and suppressor factors in human filariasis with *Brugia malayi*. *New England Journal of Medicine* **302,** 833–837.

Piessens, W. F., Partono, F., Hoffman, S. L., Ratiwayanto, S., Piessens, P. W., Qiessens, P. W., Palmieri, J. R., Koiman, I., Dennis, D. T. and Carney, W. P. (1982). Antigen-specific suppressor T lymphocytes in human lymphatic filariasis. *New England Journal of Medicine* **307,** 144–148.

Ponnudurai, T., Denham, D. A., Nelson, G. S. and Rogers, R. (1974). Studies with *Brugia pahangi*. 4. Antibodies against adult and microfilarial stages. *Journal of Helminthology* **48,** 107–111.

Portaro, J. K., Britton, S. and Ash, L. R. (1976). *Brugia pahangi*: depressed mitogen reactivity in filarial infections in the jird, *Meriones unguiculatus*. *Experimental Parasitology* **40,** 438–446.

Pritchard, D. I. and Behnke, J. M. (1985). The suppression of homologous immunity by soluble adult antigens of *Nemospiroides dubius*. *Journal of Helminthology* **59,** 251–256.

Pritchard, D. I., Williams, D. J. L., Behnke, J. M. and Lee, T. D. G. (1983). The role of IgG_1 hypergammaglobulinaemia in immunity to the gastrointestinal nematode *Nematospiroides dubius*. The immunochemical purification, antigen-specificity and *in vivo* anti-parasite effect of IgG_1 from immune serum. *Immunology* **49,** 353–365.

Pritchard, D. I., Ali, N. M. H. and Behnke, J. M. (1984a). Analysis of the mechanism of immunodepression following heterologous antigenic stimulation during concurrent infection with *Nematospiroides dubius*. *Immunology* **51,** 633–642.

Pritchard, D. I., Behnke, J. M. and Williams, D. J. L. (1984b). Primary infection sera and IgG_1 do not block host-protective immunity to *Nematospiroides dubius*. *Immunology* **51,** 73–81.

Pritchard, D. I., Maizels, R. M., Behnke, J. M. and Appleby, P. (1984c). Stage-specific antigens of *Nematospiroides dubius*. *Immunology* **53,** 325–335.

Pritchard, D. I., Crawford, C. R., Duce, I. R. and Behnke, J. M. (1985). Antigen stripping from the nematode epicuticle using the cationic detergent cetyl trimethylammonium bromide (CTAB). *Parasite Immunology* **7,** 575–585.

Prowse, S. J. and Mitchell, G. F. (1980). On the choice of mice for dissection of strain variations in the development of resistance to infection with *Nematospiroides dubius*. *Australian Journal of Experimental Biology and Medical Science* **58,** 603–605.

Prowse, S. J., Mitchell, G. F., Ey, P. L. and Jenkin, C. R. (1979). The development of resistance in different inbred strains of mice to infection with *Nematospiroides dubius*. *Parasite Immunology* **1,** 277–288.

Ramalho-Pinto, F. J., Rossi, R. and Smithers, S. R. (1979). Murine *Schistosomiasis mansoni*: anti-schistosomula complement- and eosinophil-mediated killing of schistosomula *in vitro*. *Parasite Immunology* **1,** 295–308.

Reid, J. F. S. and Armour, J. (1975). Seasonal variations in the gastrointestinal nematode populations of Scottish hill sheep. *Research in Veterinary Science* **18,** 307–313.

Ridley, D. S. and Hedge, E. C. (1977). Immunofluorescent reactions with microfilariae. 2. Bearing on host–parasite relations. *Transactions of the Royal Society of Tropical Medicine and Hygiene* **71,** 522–525.

Ritchie, J. D. S., Anderson, N., Armour, J., Jarrett, W. F. H., Jennings, F. W. and Urquhart, G. M. (1966). Experimental *Ostertagia ostertagi* infections in calves: parasitology and pathogenesis of a single infection. *American Journal of Veterinary Research* **27,** 659–667.

Roberts, J. M. D., Neumann, E., Gockel, C. W. and Highton, R. B. (1967). Onchocerciasis in Kenya, 9, 11 and 18 years after elimination of the vector. *Bulletin of the World Health Organisation* **37,** 195–212.

Rosenstreich, D. L., Weinblatt, A. C. and O'Brien, A. D. (1982). Genetic control of resistance to infection in mice. CRC *Critical Reviews in Immunology* **3,** 263–330.

Rudin, W., Tanner, M., Bauer, P. and Weiss, N. (1980). Studies on *Dipetalonema viteae* (Filarioidea). 5. Ultrastructural aspects of the antibody-dependent cell-mediated destruction of microfilariae. *Tropenmedizin Parasitologie* **31,** 194–200.

Saint-Martin, M. and Dussault, R. (1957). A severe case of anaemia due to *Ankylostoma duodenale*. *Canadian Medical Association Journal* **77,** 34–37.

Saklayen, M. G., Pesco, A. J., Pollak, V. E. and Gabriel-Michael, J. (1984). Kinetics of oral tolerance: study of variables affecting tolerance induced by oral administration of antigen. *International Archives of Allergy and Applied Immunology* **73,** 5–9.

Sanger, I., Lämmler, G. and Kimmig, P. (1981). Filarial infections of *Mastomys natalensis* and their relevance for experimental chemotherapy. *Acta Tropica* **38,** 277–288.

Schad, G. A. (1979). *Ancylostoma duodenale*: maintenance through 6 generations in helminth naive pups. *Experimental Parasitology* **47,** 246–253.

Schad, G. A. and Anderson, R. M. (1985). Predisposition to hookworm infections in man. *Science* **228,** 1537–1540.

Schad, G. A., Nawalinski, T. A. and Kochar, V. (1983). Human ecology and the distribution and abundance of hookworm populations. *In* "Human Ecology and Infectious Diseases". pp. 187–223. Academic Press, New York.

Schrater, A. F. and Piessens, W. F. (1982). Antigens present on early larval stages induce carrier-specific suppression in *Brugia malayi* infected jirds. *Federal Proceedings* **41,** 371.

Schreiber, H. (1984). Idiotype network interactions in tumour immunity. *Advances in Cancer Research* **41,** 291–321.

Scott, J. A., MacDonald, E. M. and Olson, L. J. (1958). The early induction in cotton rats of immunity to their filarial worm. *Journal of Parasitology* **44,** 507–511.

Sen, H. G. (1972). *Necator americanus*; behaviour in hamsters. *Experimental Parasitology* **32,** 26–32.

Seo, B. S., Cho, S. Y. and Chai, J. Y. (1979). Frequency distribution of *Ascaris lumbricoides* in rural Koreans with special reference to the effect of changing endemicity. *Korean Journal of Parasitology* **17,** 105–113.

Seo, B. S., Cho, S. Y., Chai, J. Y. and Hong, S. T. (1980). Comparative efficacy of various internal mass treatment on *Ascaris lumbricoides* infection in Korea. *Korean Journal of Parasitology* **18,** 145–151.

Sher, A., McIntyre, S. and Van Lichtenberg, F. (1977). *Schistosoma mansoni*: kinetics and class specificity of hypergammaglobulinaemia induced during murine infection. *Experimental Parasitology* **41,** 415–422.

Shimp, R. G., Crandall, R. B. and Crandall, C. A. (1975). *Heligmosomoides polygyrus* (= *Nematospiroides dubius*) suppression of antibody response to orally administered sheep erythrocytes in infected mice. *Experimental Parasitology* **38,** 257–269.

Silberstein, D. S. and Despommier, D. D. (1984). Antigens from *Trichinella spiralis* that induce a protective response in the mouse. *Journal of Immunology* **132,** 898–904.

Sim, B. K. L., Kwa, B. H. and Mak, J. W. (1984). The presence of blocking factors in *Brugia malayi* microfilaraemic patients. *Immunology* **52,** 411–416.

Sitepu, P., Dobson, C. and Brindley, P. J. (1985). Immunization and immunosuppression in mice reared for high or low immune responsiveness against *Nematospiroides dubius*. *International Journal for Parasitology* **15,** 277–281.

Smith, H. V., Kusel, J. R. and Girdwood, R. W. A. (1983). The production of human A and B blood group like substances by *in vitro* maintained second stage *Toxocara canis* larvae: their presence on the outer larval surface and in their excretions/secretions. *Clinical and Experimental Immunology* **54,** 625–633.

Smithers, S. R. and Doenhoff, M. J. (1982). Schistosomiasis. *In* "Immunology of Parasitic Infections" (S. Cohen and K. S. Warren, eds.). pp. 527–507. Blackwell Scientific Publications, Oxford, England.

Smithers, S. R. and Terry, R. J. (1969). Immunity in schistosomiasis. *Annals of the New York Academy of Science* **160,** 826–840.

Smyth, J. D. (1972). Changes in the digestive–absorptive surface of cestodes during larval/adult differentiation. *In* "Functional Aspects of Parasite Surfaces", Symposia of the British Society for Parasitology *10* (A. E. R. Taylor and R. Muller, eds.). pp. 41–70. Blackwell Scientific Publications, Oxford, England.

Soulsby, E. J. L. and Coombs, R. R. A. (1959). Studies on blood group substances associated with *Ascaris lumbricoides*. *Parasitology* **49,** 505–510.

Sprent, J. F. A. (1959). Parasitism, immunity and evolution. *In* "The Evolution of Living Organisms". pp. 149. Melbourne University Press, Victoria, Australia.

Storey, D. M. and Al-Mukhtar, A. S. (1983). The survival of adult *Litomosoides*

carinii transplanted into cotton rats previously injected with irradiated stage 3 larvae. *Tropenmedizin Parasitologie* **34,** 24–26.
Storey, N., Wakelin, D. and Behnke, J. M. (1985). The genetic control of host responses to *Dipetalonema viteae* (Filarioidea) infections in mice. *Parasite Immunology* **7,** 349–358.
Strober, S. (1984). Natural suppressor (NS) cells, neonatal tolerance and total lymphoid irradiation. *Annual Reviews in Immunology* **2,** 219–237.
Subrahmanyam, D., Mehta, K., Nelson, D. S., Rao, Y. V. G. B. and Rao, C. K. (1978). Immune reactions in human filariasis. *Journal of Clinical Microbiology* **8,** 228–232.
Sugane, K. and Oshima, T. (1985). Induction of a marked eosinophilia by cyclophosphamide in *Toxocara canis* infected SJL mice. *Parasite Immunology* **7,** 255–263.
Sukhdeo, M. V. K., O'Grady, R. T. and Hsu, S. C. (1984). The site selected by the larvae of *Heligmosomoides polygyrus. Journal of Helminthology* **58,** 19–23.
Taylor, S. M. and Cawthorne, R. J. G. (1972). Species of gastrointestinal helminths of lambs in Northern Ireland. *Journal of Helminthology* **46,** 285–290.
Thein-Hliang (1985). Epidemiology of ascariasis in Burma. *In* "Ascariasis and its Public Health Significance" (D. W. T. Crompton, M. C. Nesheim and Z. S. Pawlowski, eds.). pp. 83–112. Taylor and Francis, London and Philadelphia.
Thein-Hliang, Than-Saw, Htay-Htay-Aye, Myint-Lwin and Thein-Maung-Myint (1984). Epidemiology and transmission dynamics of *Ascaris lumbricoides* in Okpo village, rural Burma. *Transactions of the Royal Society of Tropical Medicine and Hygiene* **78,** 497–504.
Theofilopoulos, A. N. (1980). Immune complexes in humoral responses: suppressive and enhancing effects. *Immunology Today* **1,** 1–2.
Thomas, R. J. (1974). The role of climate in the epidemiology of nematode parasitism in ruminants. *In* "The Effects of Meteriological Factors upon Parasites", Symposia of the British Society for Parasitology 12 (A. E. R. Taylor and R. Muller, eds.). pp. 13–32. Blackwell Scientific Publications, Oxford, England.
Thomas, R. J. and Boag, B. (1972). Epidemiological studies on gastrointestinal nematode parasites of sheep. Infection patterns on clean and summer-contaminated pasture. *Research in Veterinary Science* **13,** 61–69.
Thomas, R. J. and Waller, P. J. (1979). Field observations on the epidemiology of abomasal parasites in young sheep during winter and spring. *Research in Veterinary Science* **26,** 209–212.
Thompson, J. P., Crandall, R. B., Crandall, C. A. and Neilson, J. T. (1979). Clearance of microfilariae of *Dipetalonema viteae* in CBA/N and CBA/H mice. *Journal of Parasitology* **65,** 966–969.
Thompson, J. P., Crandall, R. B. and Crandall, C. A. (1985). *Brugia malayi*: intravenous injection of microfilariae in ferrets as an experimental method for occult filariasis. *Experimental Parasitology* **60,** 181–194.
Thorson, R. E. (1956). Proteolytic activity in extracts of the esophagus of adult *Ancylostoma caninum* and the effect of immune serum on this activity. *Journal of Parasitology* **42,** 21–30.
Trent, S. C. (1963). Re-evaluation of World War II veterans with filariasis acquired in the South Pacific. *American Journal of Tropical Medicine and Hygiene* **12,** 877–887.
Turner, M. J. (1984). Antigen variation in parasites. *In* "Parasite Evasion of the Immune Response", Symposia of the British Society for Parasitology. *Parasitology* **88,** 613–621.

Vetter, J. C. M. and Klaver-Wesseling, J. C. M. (1978). IgG antibody binding to the outer surface of infective larvae of *Ancylostoma caninum*. *Zeitschrift für Parasitenkunde* **58,** 91–96.

Wade. A. W. and Szewczuk, M. R. (1984). Aging, idiotype repertoire shifts and compartmentalization of the mucosal-associated lymphoid system. *Advances in Immunology* **36,** 143–188.

Wakelin, D. (1973). The stimulation of immunity to *Trichuris muris* in mice exposed to low-level infections. *Parasitology* **66,** 181–189.

Wakelin, D. (1978a). Genetic control of susceptibility and resistance to parasitic infection. *Advances in Parasitology* **16,** 219–308.

Wakelin, D. (1978b). Immunity to intestinal parasites. *Nature (Lond.)* **273,** 617–620.

Wakelin, D. (1984). "Immunity to Parasites. How Animals Control Parasitic Infection". Edward Arnold, U.K.

Wakelin, D. (1985). Genetic control of immunity to helminths. *Parasitology Today* **1,** 17–23.

Wakelin, D. and Denham, D. A. (1983). The immune response. *In* "Trichinella and Trichinosis" (W. C. Campbell, ed.), pp. 265–308. Plenum Press, New York.

Wakelin, D. and Lloyd, M. (1976). Immunity to primary and challenge infections of *Trichinella spiralis* in mice: a re-examination of conventional parameters. *Parasitology* **72,** 173–182.

Wakelin, D. and Selby, G. R. (1974). The induction of immunological tolerance to the parasitic nematode *Trichuris muris* in cortisone-treated mice. *Immunology* **26,** 1–10.

Wakelin, D., Donachie, A. M. and Grencis, R. K. (1985). Genetic control of immunity to *Trichinella spiralis* in mice. Capacity of cells from slow responder mice to transfer immunity in syngeneic and F_1 hybrid recipients. *Immunology* **56,** 203–211.

Wartman, W. B. (1947). Filariases in American Armed Forces in World War II. *Medicine* **26,** 333–394.

Wassom, D. L., Dougherty, D. A., Krco, C. J. and David, C. S. (1984). H-2 controlled, dose-dependent suppression of the response that expels adult *Trichinella spiralis* from the small intestine of mice. *Immunology* **53,** 811–818.

Watkins, A. R. J. and Fernando, M. A. (1986). Arrested development of the rabbit stomach worm *Obeliscoides cuniculi*: resumption of development of arrested larvae throughout the course of a single infection. *International Journal for Parasitology* **16,** 47–54.

Weiner, D. J. and Soulsby, E. J. L. (1976). Fate of *Litomosoides carinii* adults transplanted into the pleural cavity or peritoneal cavity of infected and naive multimammate rats (*Mastomys natalensis*). *Journal of Parasitology* **62,** 886–893.

Weiss, N. (1970). Parasitologische und immunobiologisches Untersuchungen über die durch *Dipetalonema viteae* erzeugte Nagertierfilariose. *Acta Tropica* **27,** 219–259.

Weiss, N. (1978a). Studies on *Dipetalonema viteae* (Filarioidea). 1. Microfilaraemia in hamsters in relation to worm burden and humoral immune response. *Acta Tropica* **35,** 137–150.

Weiss, N. (1978b). *Dipetalonema viteae*: *In vitro* blastogenesis of hamster spleen and lymph node cells to phytohaemagglutinin and filarial antigens. *Experimental Parasitology* **46,** 283–299.

Weiss, N. & Tanner, M. (1979). Studies on *Dipetalonema viteae* (Filarioidea). 3.

Antibody dependent cell-mediated destruction of microfilariae *in vitro*. *Tropenmedizin Parasitologie* **30,** 73–80.
WHO (1977). The role of immune complexes in disease. *World Health Organization Technical Report Series* 606.
WHO (1984). Onchocerciasis control programme in the Volta River Basin. Long-term strategy: information document (ref. OCP/84.4a). World Health Organization, Geneva, Switzerland.
Williams, D. J. L. & Behnke, J. M. (1983). Host protective antibodies and serum immunoglobulin isotypes in mice chronically infected or repeatedly immunized with the nematode parasite *Nematospiroides dubius*. *Immunology* **348,** 34–47.
Williams, R. W. (1948). Studies on the life cycle of *Litomosoides carinii*, filarial parasite of the cotton rat, *Sigmodon hispidus litoralis*. *Journal of Parasitology* **34,** 24–43.
Wilson, T. & Ramachandran, C. P. (1971). *Brugia* infections in man and animals: long term observations on microfilaraemia and estimates of the efficiency of transmission from mosquito vector to definitive host. *Annals of Tropical Medicine and Parasitology* **65,** 525–546.
Worley, D. E., Meisenhelder, J. E., Sheffield, H. A. & Thompson, P. E. (1962). Experimental studies on *Trichuris muris* in mice with an appraisal of its use for evaluating anthelmintics. *Journal of Parasitology* **48,** 433–437.
Worms, M. J., Terry, R. J. & Terry, A. (1961). *Dipetalonema witei*, filarial parasite of the jird, *Meriones libycus*. 1. Maintenance in the laboratory. *Journal of Parasitology* **47,** 963–970.

Parasite Behaviour: Understanding Platyhelminth Responses

M. V. K. SUKHDEO AND D. F. METTRICK
Department of Zoology, University of Toronto, Toronto, Ontario, Canada M5S 1A1

I. Introduction

The underlying thesis of this review is that parasitic organisms are similar to free-living organisms in that they respond to changes in their environment. These responses can take the form of measurable behavioural changes, underlying which there obviously has to be mechanisms involving the biochemistry and physiology of the parasitic organism. Over the last 10–15 years there has been an increasing tendency towards specialization in the field of parasitology. Evidence of this trend is seen in the recent birth of new journals such as *Molecular and Biochemical Parasitology*, *Parasite Systematics*, *Parasite Immunology* and a proposed journal for parasite ecology. In contrast to this speciation of journals, advances in parasite biochemistry, physiology, neurobiology, etc., suggest that a full understanding of any aspect of the host–parasite relationship can only be achieved by integrating the components of that relationship, a difficult and formidable task. Attention has already been drawn to the lack of collaboration between parasitolo-

ADVANCES IN PARASITOLOGY VOL. 26
ISBN 0-12-031726-5
Copyright © 1987 Academic Press Inc. (London) Ltd.
All rights of reproduction in any form reserved.

gists in various fields and the resulting errant conclusions (Sherman, 1981). Our approach in this review is to examine the essential nature of the behavioural responses of parasites and, where possible, to explain the underlying mechanisms involved. Despite the limited knowledge of parasite behaviour, sufficient information exists on both the stimuli and the responses of parasites for the formation of reasonable hypotheses on the types of information processing systems being used by parasites.

The study of parasite behavioural responses has had a relatively late start, as most of the early reports on parasite behaviour were footnotes to what were primarily life cycle and taxonomic studies. Papers are still being written on the behaviour of parasites in which the term "behaviour" refers to physiological interactions of the host–parasite relationship, e.g. expulsion from immune hosts. Precise laboratory experiments, based on a systems approach, describing the specific behaviours of parasites, were not initiated until the 1960s. It is only now accepted that a specific stimulus can be perceived by the parasite, which can, in turn, generate a specific response; the neurophysiological implications of this are far-reaching. This approach has been well developed in the study of bacterial chemoresponses, where simple orientation responses have provided the basis of a complete genetic description of the "chemotactic" system (Adler, 1983; Fig. 1). Helminths use a system that is similar to that of bacteria; information flow moves from receptor > integrating and transmitting centre > effector organs, and differs only in the complexity of the systems. In helminths, the components of this system are contained within well defined nervous systems.

Although the nervous systems of helminths have long been recognized and described, experimental proof of function have been rare or nonexistent. Technical difficulties in isolating neurophysiological preparations from parasite tissues are the major reason for the paucity of information in this area. However, there has recently been a wealth of new information generated on the behaviour, nervous system and neurophysiology of nematodes, primarily based on studies of the free-living nematode *Caenorhabditis elegans* (Ward, 1973, 1978; Ward *et al.*, 1975; Ware *et al.*, 1975; Dusenbery, 1976). The insights resulting from this work have generated considerable interest and they are now being applied to the study of parasitic nematodes and platyhelminths.

II. Behaviour of Parasites

A. Taxes and Kineses

In 1940, Fraenkel and Gunn summarized the current knowledge of the

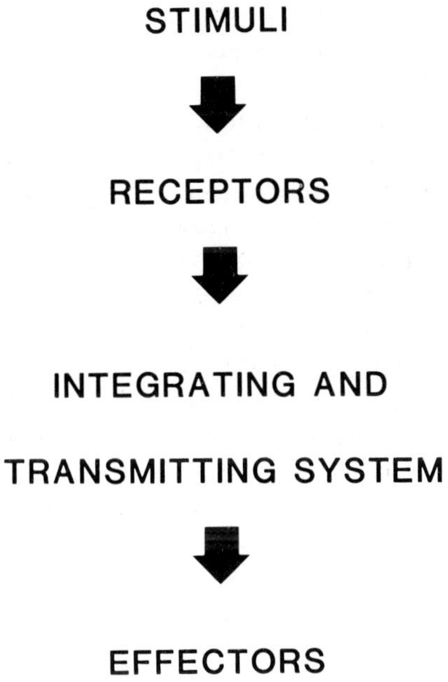

FIG. 1. The requirements of a bacterium that is capable of moving in response to stimuli (Adler, 1983).

behavioural responses of small organisms and classified the types of movement responses to specific stimuli on the basis of mechanical interpretations of these responses. Small organisms can respond to specific stimuli by moving towards (positive) or away from (negative) the stimulus. These orientation responses have been further divided into directed (taxis) or undirected (kinesis) movements (Fraenkel and Gunn, 1961). With very minor variations in the details of the underlying mechanisms, these classifications have withstood the test of several decades of behavioural research. Parasites show true orientation responses (Croll, 1970; MacInnis, 1974; Ward, 1978; Green, 1980; Zuckerman, 1981). Because of the rapidly growing interest in the neurophysiological correlates of behaviour, the accuracy of behavioural studies of parasites have become of crucial importance. Experimental designs have frequently been flawed because of the investigators' ignorance of the differences between tactic and kinetic orientation, and the subsequent failure to measure behavioural responses precisely.

1. *Definitions*

A kinesis is an undirected movement response to a stimulus, with no orientation of the longitudinal axis of the body of the organism in relation to the source of the stimulus. There are two major types of kineses, orthokinesis and klinokinesis.

A taxis is a directed movement to the source of the stimulus with the longitudinal axis of the body of the organism orientated in line with the source; locomotion may be towards (positive) or away from (negative) the source. Two major types of taxis, tropotaxis and klinotaxis, are recognized.

In orthokinesis, the speed or frequency of locomotion is dependent on the intensity of stimulation. Gradients of stimuli, temporal or spatial variations in stimulus intensity, and a minimum of one intensity receptor (specific for the stimulus) are required (Fig. 2b). One possible example of an orthokinesis in parasites involves the host finding response of the infective larvae of the hookworm *Ancylostoma duodenale*. The thermopositive response of this parasite, first described by Khalil (1922) is primarily a klinotactic orientation response but, in addition, there is a change in the rate of movement in relation to temperature. As the temperature increases, so does the speed of the worm (Croll and Smith, 1972). Several other nematodes, cestodes and

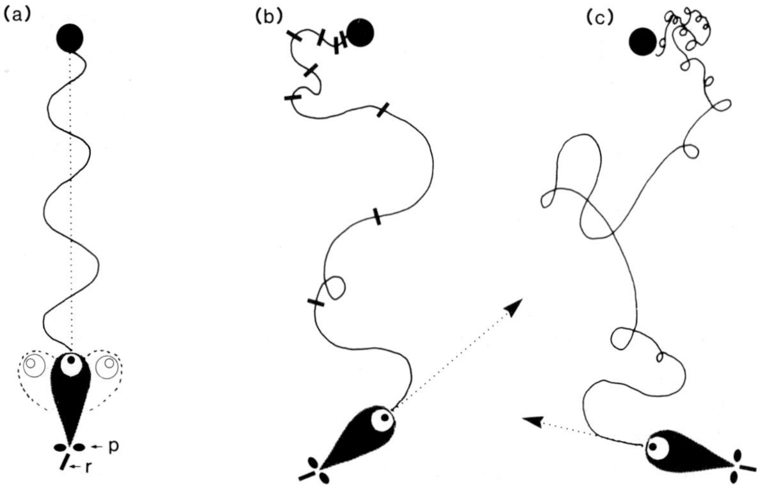

FIG. 2. Diagrammatic representations of the orientation mechanisms that can be used by an imaginary organism with a single receptor for the stimulus. Propulsion in this organism occurs by the turning of a propeller (p) and direction changes are effected by a rudder (r). The black dot represents the source of the stimulus. (a) Klinotaxis, an undulatory path is followed. (b) Orthokinesis, as the organism approaches the source of the stimulus, the intensity of stimulation increases and the speed of the propeller decreases, the bars on the path represent 1 second marks and (c) Klinokinesis, as the organism approaches the source of stimulation, the rate of turning the rudder increases.

acanthocephalans show thermopositive responses in temperature gradients (McCue and Thornson, 1964; Thornson *et al.*, 1964; El-Sherif and Mai, 1968, 1969; Croll, 1970), but the physiological mechanisms of the responses have not been well studied.

In klinokinesis, the frequency of turning is dependent on the intensity of stimulation. Gradients of stimuli, temporal or spatial variations in stimulus intensity, and a minimum of one intensity receptor is required (Fig. 2c). An example of klinokinesis is seen in the orientation response of the miracidium of *Schistosoma mansoni* to its snail host. As miracidia approach the snail host, the attractant concentration increases and the rate of turning (change in direction) of the miracidia increases, without a concomitant increase in speed (MacInnis, 1965; Samuelson *et al.*, 1984). The kinetic result of this behaviour is that the miracidia congregate in the host space and this increases the probability of contact with the host.

Kineses result in the aggregation of organisms at the source of the stimulus, but the mechanisms involved are inefficient and indirect. Although experimental evidence for the kinetic mechanisms of orientation for most parasites are not available, the response may be appropriate to organisms with narrow limits on perceptive ability and a large reproductive potential (large numbers of progeny make up for the inefficiency of the system). A major stumbling block in the investigation of the orientation responses of parasites is the design of appropriate experiments. This is further complicated by various uncontrollable factors, such as sensory adaptation to the stimulus. Both types of kinesis can be further divided into those in which sensory adaptation occurs, and those without sensory adaptation; each resulting in a different type of orientation (Ewer and Bursell, 1950).

A taxis is a more efficient mechanism of orientation and requires a higher level of information integration than does kinetic orientation. A taxis is not a tropism; a tropism is a botanical term describing growth movements in plants. In tropotaxis, the attainment of orientation is direct and occurs by the simultaneous comparison of stimulation on both sides of the body using at least two widely spaced receptors. A steep gradient of stimulus, and a minimum of two paired receptors which are arranged so that they are not always equally stimulated, are required. There has been no unequivocal demonstration of tropotactic orientation in parasites. Tropotactic orientation can be further divided into that resulting from bilaterally placed receptors and that from antero-posterior receptors (Ewer and Bursell, 1950). These authors have demonstrated tropotactic orientation from antero-posteriorly placed receptors in the free-living onychophore *Peripatopsis moseleyi* (Bursell and Ewer, 1950) and suggested that this type of orientation may be common in vermiform animals. The cestode *Hymenolepis diminuta* exhibits a circadian migration in the small intestine of the rat host (Read and

Kilejian, 1969). Experiments involving surgical shortening of the parasite have shown that the length of the worm determined its site in the gut; it was suggested that the location specificity was accomplished by balancing the information from the head and tail ends (Hopkins and Allen, 1979). This would be a tropotaxis.

In klinotaxis, the attainment of orientation is indirect and occurs by the temporal comparison of stimulus intensities (this implies a primitive memory comparing the intensities of stimulation at successive intervals in time) by regular lateral deviations of part or the whole of the body (Fig. 2a). A steep gradient of stimulus and a minimum of one shielded intensity receptor is required. Kinetic orientation can be performed with the simplest kind of receptor—a single, purely intensity-receptive ending. Klinotaxis requires a more complex arrangement, in that the receptor must not be equally accessible to stimulation from all directions; this shielding can be effected by the body, or, if light receptors are involved, by a special pigment. The chemoresponses of nematodes are klinotactic (Croll, 1976a; Ward, 1978; Green, 1980). Although the sense organs on nematodes are bilaterally symmetrical, suggesting possible tropotactic mechanisms, nematodes swim on their sides, so that the sense organs act as a single sensory input. Ward (1973), using the free-living nematode *C. elegans*, determined that speed was not a factor in orientation, since slow-moving (degenerate muscles) mutants oriented as well as the wild type and mutants without functional receptors in the tail (tail blistered) oriented normally. However, mutants with defects in head mobility (bent head, shortened head and defective head muscles) did not orient well. In a klinotaxis, the length of the head and its mobility is of critical importance in the response since it provides the regular lateral deviation necessary.

Knowledge of the orientation response can provide a tool that allows the accurate identification of biologically important stimuli, the location and identification of the receptors involved and the levels of complexity of the information processing systems (neural physiology). So far, the greatest advances have been based on studies of *C. elegans*. The fine structure of the head and the details of the axonal connections are known (Ward *et al*., 1975; Ware *et al*., 1975) and mutants can be compared to the wild type in order to correlate behavioural changes with morphological and anatomical defects.

The Fraenkel and Gunn mechanistic classifications of orientation have proven inadequate in the characterization of the complex chemo-orientation behaviour of insects (Bell and Tobin, 1982; Bell, 1984). These authors have suggested that, in addition to the Fraenkel and Gunn classification, researchers should describe factors such as the information available to the organism, the types of information processing involved and the types of motor output, e.g. search patterns elicited by the stimulus and the nature of the guidance systems (Bell, 1984). There is a justified concern for more exhaustive behavioural characterization when the differences between genetically-based information flow versus environmentally-derived information, or genetically-fixed motor patterns versus learned motor patterns become critical to the understanding of the behaviour. Nevertheless, we suggest that these are not the primary concerns in the study of parasite behaviour at the present time.

B. BEHAVIOUR OF FREE-LIVING STAGES

Parasite behaviours can be divided into those that occur in the free-living stages and those that occur in the parasitic stages. In free-living stages, the biological imperative is to find and infect the next host; behavioural activities may increase the success rate of the free-living stages. In the parasitic stages, the priorities lie in finding the optimum habitat (site finding), remaining in this site (site maintenance) and performing functions related to growth and reproduction. It would be incorrect to suggest that all parasite behaviours fit into either a taxis or a kinesis, since behaviour may also be related to any of several functions where movement from one place to another is not required, e.g. feeding.

There are several stimuli to which parasites may respond. In this review we are only concerned with those that are important in the life cycle; these stimuli are referred to as "cues". Several discussions of cues have appeared in the literature, but there has been a general lack of adequate definition. In parasite behaviour the criteria used to define cues are as follows: (1) Cues are normal host metabolites or other environmental factors with which the infective stage or the final stage of the parasite comes into contact during its life cycle; (2) Cues must effect a measurable behavioural change in the parasite; (3) The recognition of the cues by the parasite must be mediated through sensory receptors. A corollary of this is that the reception is highly specific. This parameter is often very difficult to establish.

The concept of trigger cues (Bullock, 1957) is now accepted in modern biological thought. Trigger cues are implicit in the activation of semi-dormant infective stages when they enter the host environment (Lackie, 1975). Trigger cues have also been associated with releaser reactions, which are defined as preprogrammed, stereotyped, behavioural patterns in response to a short period of specific stimulation (Wilson, 1965). Orientation is not involved and only a short temporal exposure to the cue is required to initiate the sequence. Examples of releaser reactions include eclosion behaviour in parasites that require active participation during emergence from the cyst or egg of the infective stage (Croll, 1972; Sukhdeo and Mettrick, 1986).

Adaptive behaviour for host-finding is not seen in acanthocephalans and cestodes because no free-living stages could occur in their life cycles. The infective stages are ingested, usually by an intermediate host, in what appears to be a random process. There may be some behavioural changes in the intermediate host, resulting from the infection, that predisposes them to ingestion by the definitive host (Mueller, 1968). Qualitative investigations of this aspect of acanthocephalan and cestode biology are rare.

Trematodes and nematodes often have a free-living stage in their life cycles, which provides a selective advantage by increasing the efficiency of transmission. The host-finding behaviours of several parasites have now been recognized and described. Saladin (1979) argued for the creation of a new interdiscipline, "Behavioural Parasitology", based on the need to integrate the diverse aspects of research in this field; similar arguments are implicit in the reports of several earlier investigators (Davenport, 1955; Read, 1958; Thornson, 1969; Ulmer, 1971; MacInnis, 1976). Nevertheless, as indicated in the Introduction of this review, fragmentation of parasitology merely hides the overall understanding of parasite biology.

1 *Miracidial host-finding behaviour*

The first published reports of host attraction in trematodes were studies of the response of the miracidia of *Fasciola hepatica* to lymnaeid snails (Thomas, 1883; Leuckart, 1894; Ulmer, 1971; Saladin, 1979). Over the next half century, the field was evenly divided between those who favoured chemo-attraction of miracidia to the snail host and those who felt that finding a host was a random event. Part of the problem was the difficulties some investigators experienced in believing that the excited behaviour of miracidia near the snail host (kineses) represented a form of orientation (Saladin, 1979).

The majority of the studies on miracidial host-finding behaviour have been based on a few medically or economically important parasites. After decades of intensive effort, the complexity of the problem is indicated by the numerous controversies that currently exist on the mechanisms of the response (kinesis versus taxis), the diversity of the attractants (more than 50 different attractants reported), and the relevance of laboratory simulation of field conditions. This situation may have resulted from nonstandardized techniques used in different laboratories (MacInnis, 1976), or a lack of rigorous experimental designs (Chernin, 1970; Ulmer, 1971; Roberts *et al.*, 1979; Plorin and Gilbertson, 1981). We are inclined to the view, based on our own studies, that there are often at least two factors influencing behavioural responses. Synergism may also be involved, so that the details of the overall mechanisms are complex and interactive.

Early interpretation of host finding behaviour in parasitoids (parasitic insects) suggested two sequential steps: host habitat selection and host selection (Salt, 1935; Laing, 1937). Using these studies as a basis for interpreting his primarily hypothetical insights, Wright (1959) separated host finding by trematode miracidia into three sequential steps:

(1) Host habitat selection—the newly emerged miracidia make their way to the environment of their specific snail hosts;

(2) A period of random movement in the host habitat;

(3) Host finding—the miracidia orient towards the host using tactic or kinetic mechanisms.

This sequence of miracidial host finding behaviour is widely accepted (Ulmer, 1971; Saladin, 1979; Christensen, 1980). Entomologists have now separated parasitoid host selection into five basic sequential steps (Doutt, 1959; Vinson, 1975; Lewis *et al.*, 1976), of which two, host acceptance and host suitability, may also have counterparts in miracidial host finding behaviour.

(a) Location of the host habitat. Location of the host habitat occurs just after miracidial hatching, at a time when the miracidia are not responsive to the snail attractants that are important later in their life cycles. The young miracidium of *Megalodiscus temperatus* displays maximum efficiency in finding its snail host *Helisoma trivolis* within a period 3–5 hours after hatching (Ulmer, 1971). However, the snail finding ability of the miracidium, when freshly hatched, is significantly diminished (Ulmer, 1971). Similarly, the freshly hatched miracidia of *Fascioloides magna* do not have fully developed sensitivity to the stimulus provided by the snail host (Campbell and Todd, 1955), and it appears that the miracidia cannot sense the snail attractants until they mature (Ulmer, 1971; Saladin, 1979). The divergent opinions of many of the early workers concerning miracidial host finding behaviour may have resulted from their failure to consider the age of the miracidia in their experiments (Ulmer, 1971).

There are also measureable, qualitative differences in miracidial behaviour during this first phase. Using a dark ground photographic technique that allows an accurate tracing of the movements of individual miracidia, newly hatched miracidia of *S. mansoni* were shown to swim rapidly and linearly for the first hour following hatching, after which they slow down (12% drop in speed) and increase their rate of turning (Mason and Fripp, 1976). This initial swimming pattern is conducive to rapid dispersion in the environment, and is controlled primarily by responses to light and gravity, although responses to other environmental factors have also been implicated (MacInnis, 1976).

Miracidia respond to light and gravity in a manner that is similar to their respective snail host and thus induce a distribution of miracidia in the aquatic environment which parallels the distribution of the snail host (Chernin and Dunavan, 1962; Upatham, 1972a,b). Using an outdoor pond, snails were suspended in cages from the surface to a depth of 46 cm and miracidia of *Schistosoma haematobium* were released at the surface, equidistant from the cages. The vast majority of the snails that became infected were confined to the bottom in the shade (Shiff, 1969). *In vitro*, these miracidia preferentially infected snails in the shade (88 lux) over snails in the light (2400 lux) (Shiff, 1969). The miracidia of *S. mansoni* react to light in an opposite manner. Using choice chambers (light versus dark) and "two light" experiments (light stimuli from two separate sources), it was demonstrated that the miracidia of *S. mansoni* respond positively to directed illumination, although they did not congregate in the light (Mason and Fripp, 1977). Chernin and Dunavan (1962) also reported a positive photoresponse by the miracidia of *S. mansoni* and they found that the miracidia aggregated in the lighted sides of sealed choice chambers. The mechanism for light reception by the schistosome miracidia is unclear since they do not possess macroscopic photoreceptors. The miracidia of *Schistosoma douthitti* also respond positively to light, particularly in the blue green region of the spectrum (500–525 nm) (Wright *et al.*, 1972). Light in this region of the spectrum penetrates deepest in clear water (Luria and Kinney, 1970). Interestingly, this response is similar to most other invertebrates that have a dermal light sense, where maximum sensitivity occurs to wavelengths between 470–530 nm (Steven, 1963).

The miracidia of *Schistosoma japonicum* are also positively photoresponsive at light levels of 100 lux and below, and at temperatures of 20–28°C; at temperatures of 20°C and light levels of 5000 lux, the photoresponse changes to negative (Takahashi *et al.*, 1961). The photic responses of *S. mansoni, S. japonicum* and *S. haematobium* have all been shown to be dependent on temperature; changes in temperature either reverse the response or the miracidia may lose their ability to orient (Takahashi *et al.*, 1961; Shiff, 1974; Mason and Fripp, 1977). Despite the absence of macroscopic photoreceptors on the miracidia of schistosomes, a photographic technique tracing the paths of miracidia of *S. mansoni* in two light experiments demonstrated that the light-orienting response was an orthokinesis, i.e. the rate of locomotion increased as the miracidia neared the source of stimulation (Mason and Fripp, 1977). The miracidia of *F. hepatica* also orient positively to light and a similar photographic technique demonstrated that these miracidia used a klinokinetic mechanism to orient to light; light stimulated an increase in the rate of turning (Wilson and Denison, 1970a). Miracidia of *F. hepatica* possess well-defined eyespots. The photic response of these miracidia is also reversed by temperature changes, but these effects are believed to be mediated through changes in metabolism and not through changes in sensory physiology (Wilson and Denison, 1970a).

Some miracidia also display strong responses to gravity. *Schistosoma mansoni* miracidia respond positively to light but are indifferent to gravity, while the miracidia of *S. haematobium* are negatively photoresponsive and strongly positive to gravity (Prah and James, 1978). *Biomphalaria glabrata*, the intermediate host of *S. mansoni*, are commonly seen on the surface of ponds, attached to leaves and branches. *Bulinus globusus*, intermediate host to *S. haematobium*, prefers sluggish streams with muddy bottoms and shaded banks (Gerber, 1952). Experiments under semi-field conditions show that the miracidia of *S. mansoni* are negative in their response to gravity, and that in shallow ponds, the miracidia gravitate to the edges where the snails congregate (Upatham, 1972a,b,c). Temperature changes are also believed to alter the distribution of the snails in the ponds and the photo- and georesponses of the miracidia are similarly altered to result in parallel distributions (Takahashi *et al.*, 1961; Shiff, 1969; 1974). Prah and James (1978) provided evidence that the photo- and georesponses may not be as important as described above; despite the positive photo- and negative georesponses of the miracidia of *S. mansoni*, miracidia released on the surface of a pond can infect snails two metres below the surface. Miracidia of *S. douthitti* respond to both light and unknown chemicals in the mucus of its host. When tested in four-armed choice chambers *in vitro*, the response to a combination of light and chemicals was significantly greater than the response to either stimulus alone (Wright and Ronald, 1972). This synergistic effect suggests an interaction between sensory modalities where success in host finding determines precedence. An alternative explanation is that there may be a hierarchy in the sensory modalities. The miracidia of *Philopthalmus gralli* shows a positive response to both light and gravity in horizontal test chambers. In vertical test chambers the georesponse becomes dominant and the miracidia no longer respond to light (Keshavarz-Valian and Nollen, 1980). The snail host of this parasite is a bottom dweller, found in shallow streams.

Light and temperature are less important to the survival and infectivity of the miracidia of either *S. mansoni* or *S. haematobium* in field conditions (Prah and James, 1977). Water flow is of crucial importance; water flow greater than 15 cm/second prevents location of *B. globosus* by the miracidia of *S. haematobium* (Schiff, 1968), while the miracidia of *S. mansoni* can locate *Biomphalaria* spp. when the water flow is as high as 105 cm/seconds (Webbe, 1966). There are a number of other factors including predation, turbidity and the presence of various natural obstacles, that affect host finding under normal conditions (Christensen, 1980). Therefore, extreme caution is advised in the interpretation of laboratory data and the relevance of such data to field conditions.

(b) Activity in the host habitat. Having arrived at the host habitat, the miracidia wander at random. This behaviour has incorrectly been labelled as a klinokinesis (Saladin, 1979), but it is generally believed that, during this phase, the miracidia are not orienting to a specific stimulus. In the first hour after hatching (dispersal phase) the linear speed of the miracidia of *S. mansoni* was measured as 2.27 mm/second, falling to 2.00 mm/second in step 2, at which time the angular velocity (rate of change of direction) increased from 55°/second to 110°/second (Mason and Fripp, 1976). This study was criticized because the method of measuring angular velocity was copied from a system to determine net directional changes in slowly gliding turbellarians (Ullyot, 1936), rather than swimming miracidia (Plorin and Gilbertson, 1981). In a new study, descriptive statistics were applied to helical swimming amplitude and wavelength, linear speed, turning frequency and turning angles of *S. mansoni*. The results of this study showed no correlation between amplitude and wavelength, but turning frequency was completely random (Plorin and Gilbertson, 1981). Thus, in the second step of host finding, the miracidia appear to move at random in the environment; the miracidia used in this study were 30–90 minutes old.

(c) Host finding. A miracidium is informed of the snail host's proximity by chemical cues. It is now no longer argued that the snail host elaborates chemical signals that the miracidia use as cues in orientation. This controversy was interesting, and for historical details the reader is referred to Ulmer (1971) and Saladin (1979). Saladin claims that in published trials of over 176 miracidium–snail combinations and 28 combinations of miracidia with other targets, which together involved 30 trematode species, 75% of the reports indicated responsiveness of the miracidia to their hosts.

Early studies of miracidial chemoresponses were subjective. Experimental devices to test miracidial responses have been of several types (Neuhaus, 1953; Campbell and Todd, 1955; Kloetzel, 1958; Kawashima *et al.*, 1961; Campbell, 1961; Davenport *et al.*, 1962; Plempel, 1964; Plempel *et al.*, 1966; Cheng, 1968; Shiff, 1969; Wilson and Denison, 1970a). These devices can be placed into four major categories; representative examples of these devices are summarized below.

In 1963, Etges and Decker developed an objective assay of miracidial chemoresponse. They used a choice chamber, i.e. an apparatus containing a central chamber connected to four terminal chambers. Snails or sham snails were placed in the terminal chambers and miracidia introduced into the central chamber. At the end of the test period, the terminal chambers could be stoppered and the numbers of miracidia in each counted. The miracidia of *S. mansoni* were preferentially attracted to their natural intermediate host *Australorbis glabratus* (now called *Biomphalaria glabrata*) over sham snails

(569:406) but preferred the sham snails over two other pulmonate snails, *Bulinus* or *Helisoma* spp. (Etges and Decker, 1963). Nevertheless, the authors concluded that, despite the significant attraction of the miracidia to the snail host, the miracidial responses to light and gravity were much more important in host finding. This experimental design is popular, and there have been several studies using the choice chamber, or various modifications of it, to demonstrate miracidial chemoresponses. A drawback of this technique is that no information was provided on the mechanisms of the response.

A new system was developed (MacInnis, 1965) to test the chemical stimulation and attraction of free-swimming trematode miracidia using agar or starch gel pyramids impregnated with various chemicals. This was a major breakthrough in the study of miracidial behaviour. Whereas previous workers measured aggregation of miracidia to snails or chemical cues, in MacInnis' system the behaviour of individual miracidia could be examined under the dissecting microscope as they responded to the chemical stimuli. MacInnis demonstrated unequivocally that the miracidia of *S. mansoni*, *S. douthitti* and *F. hepatica* could orient positively to snails and chemical attractants. More importantly, using the classification of Fraenkel and Gunn (1961), MacInnis described taxes and kineses in the behavioural repertoire of the miracidia based on the observation of 5000 miracidia. He identified orthokinetic, klinokinetic, tropotactic and klinotactic responses by the miracidia. His system of objective assay, based on the behavioural study, classified miracidial responses to stimulation into one of two broad categories, contact with return (CR), a positive response involving eight easily observed responses, and contact without return, a negative or indifferent response. This assay gave consistent and accurate results and is now the most popular method of assaying miracidial responses to chemical cues.

An experimental system based on the mass reaction of miracidia to a "point inoculation" of test material demonstrated that the miracidia of *S. mansoni* responded positively to substances emitted by *B. glabrata* (Chernin, 1970). Although this measure of aggregation response was a return to a more primitive type of assay, the results were consistent and these authors introduced the concept of snail conditioned water (SCW). This work, to a great extent, started the race to identify the attractant substances in SCW. The point inoculation method was popular because of the simple apparatus required and it magnified the changes in miracidial behaviour by converting it into easily observed mass phenomena.

Chernin (1970) confirmed that the miracidial response to snail attractants was a chemokinesis. However, analysis of behaviour in the point inoculation system that he used was entirely subjective and the activity of the miracidia in the presence of attractants could only be described as "excited". A further breakthrough in the study of miracidial behaviour came from the development of a photographic technique by Wilson and Denison (1970a), which was developed from methods used to measure swimming by *Paramecium* spp. If the miracidia are photographed against a dark background with horizontal lighting, the miracidia appear as moving white spots, and exposures of half a second or more record the movements of the miracidia as continuous tracks on film; this results in an objective record of individual behaviour. All of the subsequent work to determine the nature of the miracidial response have used this, or some variation of this method.

Normal tracks of the unstimulated miracidia of *F. hepatica* are practically linear, showing a tendency to regular undulations; the frequency of the undulations is approximately 2/second, with a wavelength of 0.6 mm, an amplitude of 0.08 mm, and a linear speed of 1.3–1.4 mm/second (Wilson and Denison, 1970a). The unstimulated miracidia of *S. mansoni* show behaviour with a wavelength of 0.8 mm, amplitude of 0.02 mm and a linear speed of 2.10 mm/second (Plorin and Gilbertson, 1981). In the presence of attractants there is a significant increase in the rate of turning (+660%) by the miracidia of *F. hepatica*, which was interpreted as a klinokinesis (Wilson and Denison, 1970a). Klinokinetic mechanisms of miracidial responses to various snail attractants have also been implicated (some more rigorously than others) in several species of trematodes including *M. temperatus* (Prechel and Nollen, 1979), *S. haematobium* (Shiff and Kriel, 1970), *Schistosoma mattheei* (Kinoti, 1968), *S. douthitti* (Wright and Ronald, 1972) and *P. gralli* (Keshavarz-Valian *et al.*, 1981). The rate of turning of the miracidia of *S. mansoni* also increases after stimulation (+1000%), but the response returns to normal after 30–40 minutes, suggesting "klinokinesis with adaptation" as the mechanism of orientation (Mason and Fripp, 1976). This kind of orientation response is believed to produce behaviour patterns that result in aggregation at the highest stimulus density (Ewer and Bursell, 1950; Patlack, 1953). Other investigators believed the kinetic response to be a boundary type of response. Miracidia of *S. mansoni* moving uphill in a concentration gradient did not alter their swimming speed or their angular velocity, nor did they orient to the gradient. However, when they encountered a sufficiently abrupt decrease in stimulation, there was a sharp increase in angular velocity (Roberts *et al.*, 1979). This response has been defined as a boundary reaction and it acts to keep the miracidia from leaving the area of high concentrations of stimulus (Fraenkel and Gunn, 1961). Using a similar experimental design (photographic technique) with the same parasite, Samuelson *et al.* (1984) reported that the increase in the rate of turning was initiated when the miracidia entered the zone of high stimulus concentration, and not when they leave the zone, as was reported by Roberts *et al.* (1979). This suggests that the boundary reaction is not operative and that the miracidia home in on the source of the stimulus. Mason and Fripp (1976) reported an increase in the speed of locomotion (orthokinesis) upon contact with the attractant; this was not substantiated in other studies (Roberts *et al.*, 1979; Samuelson *et al.*, 1984). These authors also reported that the rate of turning was concentration-dependent (Mason and Fripp, 1976; 1977), while others reported that the rate of turning in response to uniform concentrations of stimulant, was unaltered (Roberts *et al.*, 1979; Plorin and Gilbertson, 1985). In summary, it appears that the miracidial responses to snail attractants involve kinetic orientations. Although most investigators now agree that the response is a klinokinesis, there is still some controversy on the mechanics of the response; this may be related to the experimental designs used by different investigators.

(d) Nature of the attractants. Clearly there is not yet enough information on the nature of the receptors involved in the host-finding response. Most of the work on receptor physiology of miracidia remains theoretical (Wright, 1959; MacInnis, 1965, 1976; Saladin, 1979), and technology imposes a practical limitation. There is also a great deal of confusion on the identification of the components of the snail secretions that serve as the attractant. The nature of the attractant poses an evolutionary problem; if it increases the chances of a snail becoming infected it must have low value in the gene pool of the species since infected snails show a decline in fecundity (Shiff and Kriel, 1970). These authors felt that the attractant was either the end product of an essential physiological process or was allied to the snail population control factor described by Berrie (1968).

Several investigators have reported an organic basis for the attractant substance, usually small thermostable carboxylic molecules such as amino acids, fatty acids or sugars (MacInnis, 1965, 1976; Shiff and Kriel, 1970; Wilson and Denison, 1970a,b; Chernin, 1970; Wright and Ronald, 1972; MacInnis, 1974; Etges *et al.*, 1975; Prechel *et al.*, 1976; Plorin and Gilbertson, 1985). Most of these studies involved identification of the organic components of snail conditioned water (SCW) and the assay of the miracidial response to these chemicals by one or more of the assay methods previously described. However, the responses of the miracidia of *S. mansoni* to ashed-, unashed- and reconstituted SCW were similar (Sponholtz and Short, 1976), clearly indicating that the attractant was inorganic. These investigators demonstrated a positive response to Ca/Mg ratios using a CR method of assay, and it was suggested that the increased Ca/Mg ratios are effected by depletion of calcium in the immediate vicinity of the snails by snail uptake (MacInnis, 1976). These conclusions were confirmed by Stibbs *et al.* (1976), who extracted the attractant in SCW to a high level of purity and identified it as $MgCl_2$. The addition of $MgCl_2$ to wells used in the point inoculation assay cancelled normal miracidial attraction to known attractants, through blockage or sensory adaptation of the receptors (Stibbs *et al.*, 1976). However, the miracidia of *M. temperatus* are indifferent or only slightly responsive to Mg^{++} (Prechel and Nollen, 1979). The miracidia of *S. mansoni* respond better and more consistently to SCW than to Mg^{++} (Roberts *et al.*, 1979); part of the problem may be in the preparation of SCW (MacInnis, 1976). Various investigators differ significantly in their preparations of SCW (MacInnis, 1974; Wright and Ronald, 1972; Sponholtz and Short, 1976; Stibbs *et al.*, 1976; Roberts *et al.*, 1979; Samuelson *et al.*, 1984). The basis of SCW may range from 125 snail hours/ml to 12 800 snail hours/ml depending on the investigator (Saladin, 1979). At present it is believed that the inorganic and organic components interact in some undetermined way at the level of the receptor sites.

C. BEHAVIOUR OF PARASITIC STAGES

It has long been recognized that parasites are restricted to specific sites within their hosts. Details on the sites occupied by various parasites have been reviewed (Thornson, 1969; Ulmer, 1971; Holmes, 1973, 1976; Crompton, 1973, 1976). Some parasites can be characterized by the restricted sites they occupy while others have complex migrations during and after maturation (Crompton, 1973). The reasons for organ specificity and/or tissue specificity of parasites are still unknown, but the consistency of these phenomena suggests that the process is not random. It has been experimentally demonstrated with several species of parasites that there is a return to the normal sites after surgical implantation into abnormal locations (Goodchild, 1958; Roche, 1966; Alphey, 1970; Bräten and Hopkins, 1969; Bailey, 1972; Mettrick and Podesta, 1974; Croll, 1976b; Sukhdeo and Mettrick, 1983). These experiments strongly argue for the parasites' capacity to migrate and to recognize the conditions necessary for their survival.

In a summary of site finding by helminths, Ulmer (1971) pointed out that the manner in which "helminths recognize and respond to those essential sites which are prerequisite to their establishment and survival constitutes an almost virgin field for parasitologists". Fifteen years later, this statement is still true. Very little is known of the causal factors of the sometimes elaborate *in vivo* migrations of many parasites, and while this state of affairs has not hindered descriptions of these behaviours and the categorization of the ecological and philosophical components (Crompton, 1973, 1976; Holmes, 1973, 1976), the specific cues and the parasites' behavioural responses that contribute to site finding remain largely unknown. A primary reason lies in the extreme difficulties encountered while studying parasite behaviour *in vivo* and the lack of sufficient knowledge of the physiology and other aspects of the host–parasite relationship that would allow *in vitro* experimentation. Nevertheless, there has been some progress and most of the significant work on the site finding behaviour of parasites has been done with gastrointestinal parasites. A major impetus has been provided by the significant advances in gastrointestinal physiology (see Mettrick and Podesta, 1974).

1. *Site finding by gastrointestinal parasites*

Acanthocephalans and cestodes are usually restricted to the small intestine, where digestion and absorption of nutrients by the host occurs. The trematodes and nematodes that inhabit the gut are much more mobile and varied in their distribution. Trematodes and nematodes generally have a high degree of site specificity as demonstrated by some of the unusual site locations in the liver, lungs, bladder and mesenteries. Most investigators suggest that sites are determined by labile factors resulting from the temporary fluctuating environmental conditions, e.g. the effects of food or the physicochemical gradients created by the digestion process (Read, 1950, 1971; Bawden, 1969; Alphey, 1971; Mettrick, 1971,a,b,c). Site selection may also be determined by critical architectural factors and there are several examples of host and site finding by cestodes based on the architecture of the gut (Williams *et al.*, 1970; Carvajal and Dailey, 1975; McVicar, 1977, 1979). The evidence of site finding based on gut architecture by other parasitic groups is scanty, but it could be argued that the epithelial cells of the small intestine are essential for the site finding of *Trichinella spiralis* and *Trichuris muris* (Despommier *et al.*, 1978; Lee and Wright, 1978; Wright, 1979) or that the size and topography of the duodenal villi are directly related to the site finding of *Heligmosomoides polygyrus* (= *Nematospiroides dubius*) (Kleinschuster *et al.*, 1978). In studies of site finding, the notions of labile (changing) and constant (architectural) factors, the interactions between these factors and the critical thresholds that may be involved in site finding, have not been well developed. A review of the literature indicates that several factors, including the rate of intestinal flow, diet, bile and pancreatic secretions, various physicochemical gradients, microbial flora, biogenic amines, hormones, etc., have been implicated in site finding. Clearly these labile components of the parasite's environment are superimposed on the more constant architectural substrate of cells, tissues and organs that make up the gastrointestinal system. These factors are interdependent and the interactions are complex. Nevertheless, in several reviews it has been implied that the conditions in the alimentary tract are homeostatic (Read, 1971; Ulmer, 1971; Crompton, 1973; Holmes, 1973). This concept of a site as a constant topographic region with chemical homeostasis is questionable in view of the many physical and chemical gradients in the intestine; these gradients are largely determined by the composition, volume and nutrient complexity of the food ingested by the host animal (Mettrick and Podesta, 1974; Croll, 1976a). It has been argued that sites cannot be measured in linear units along the gut, since site specificity is really a causal relationship between the parasite and its surroundings; measuring the linear site does not automatically describe the physicochemical conditions of the gut (Croll, 1976a). As the labile factors in the gut are in constant motion, the concept of sites and habitats must be considered more as dynamic environmental interactions between hosts and their parasites, and all play important parts in site finding, whether that selection is developmental, permanent or circadian. Historically, the identification and descriptions of the preferred sites of parasites have been based on purely physical measurements. In only a few instances has it been recognized that site finding is dynamic and varies with the fluctuations of physicochemical conditions in the gut. An example is the cestode *H. diminuta*, which displays a circadian migration pattern that is believed to be based on maintaining its strobila in the region of the gut where its nutrient uptake is optimal (this will be discussed in a later section). Although there are several other examples where many or all of the gradients have been implicated in site finding (Read, 1950, 1971; Dobson, 1961; Smyth and Haslewood, 1963; Mettrick, 1970, 1971c; Alphey, 1971, 1972) there has been little experimental substantiation and the assertions of these investigators have not been rigorously tested.

2. *Activation*

Entry of the infective stages of gastrointestinal parasites usually occurs through ingestion. The infective stages are protected from adverse environmental conditions or the immune response of the intermediate hosts through encystment, ensheathment or in eggshells. Within the eggs or cysts the parasites are limited in their movements and the infection process is passive; these stages are usually semi-dormant or resting stages with low metabolic rates. Sheaths (incompletely moulted L_2 cuticles in nematodes) protect against environmental factors, yet allow freedom of movement to increase the probability of host finding; these stages are non-feeding and development only continues in the definitive host.

The activation stimuli are the specific factors within the host that induce the continuation of development. Usually the activation stimulus is part of the physicochemical conditions associated with the regions of the gut just anterior to the preferred sites and are sufficiently specific to prevent premature activation. There is a great deal of information now available on the stimuli, mostly derived from *in vitro* simulation of conditions in the host gut, that activate the infective stages of several parasites (Lackie, 1975).

The activation stimuli for the infective stages of helminths vary greatly; cestodes require proteases and bile salts (Silverman, 1954; Schiller, 1965; Smyth and Haslewood, 1963), nematodes require CO_2 or carbonic acid and sometimes bile salts (Hwang, 1960; Rogers, 1960; Chapman and Undeen, 1968; Mapes, 1972), trematodes require CO_2, proteases and bile (Dawes and Hughes, 1964; Erasmus and Bennett, 1965; Dixon, 1966) and acanthocephalans require CO_2, proteases and bile salts (Graff and Kitzmann, 1965; Lackie, 1974). A frequent common denominator is bile. Bile is composed of water, mucin, protein, bile pigments, bile salts (conjugated and unconjugated), phospholipids, neutral fats and various organic ions (Haslewood, 1978). These constituents vary with the diet, pH, presence of parasites, microflora and with host different species (Smyth and Haslewood, 1963; Mettrick and Podesta, 1974; Haslewood, 1978). Smyth and Haslewood (1963) proposed that the composition of bile is a factor in the determination of host specificity. Although these authors support their hypothesis with *in vitro* studies on *Echinococcus granulosus*, there has been little substantiation from other parasites in the 23 years since their hypothesis was formulated.

A component of the activation process which appears to have received little attention is the alteration or initiation of behavioural patterns of the parasite. The activation stimulus for *T. spiralis* (37°C, HCl, pepsin) (Gursch, 1948) initiates a specific behaviour pattern (type 1) that allows the parasite to break out of the cyst (Sukhdeo, 1981). Specific patterns of behaviour associated with the activation, and subsequent emergence from the protective coat of the infective stage, have been reported in several cestodes and trematodes. However, the descriptions of these behaviour patterns have been cursory and were often described as simple increases in movement and activity. Recent studies on the activation and emergence behaviour of *F. hepatica* show well-defined patterns of behaviour during activation and emergence (Sukhdeo and Mettrick, 1986). The remainder of this section will deal with activity related to infection and site finding in cestodes and trematodes, the possible importance of these behaviour patterns, the contributions of these behaviour patterns to site finding, and the cues that initiate these behaviours.

3. *Platyhelminth site finding behaviour*

(a) Cestode activation. One of the problems that is obvious from a review of the literature of cestode activation is that the requirement of hatching and activation are subject to variations in accordance with their taxonomic groupings. Thus, while infection usually follows ingestions of cysticercoid, cysticercus, coenurus, hydatid cyst or egg, comparisons on the behavioural activity are difficult. In general, behaviour of the cestode larval

stages may contribute to hatching of the oncospheres or evagination of the scolex.

Hatching usually occurs in the gut of the intermediate host and, with the exception of the cyclophillidean cestodes, the process has been little studied. The eggshells or embryophores of the cyclophillideans are extremely resistant to digestive enzymes and infection necessitates mechanical disruption by the mouthparts of the insect intermediate host (Reid *et al.*, 1951; Berntzen and Voge, 1965; Lethbridge, 1971). Larval activity (hook movements) may be initiated while the larvae are still within the embryophore, as in *Dipylidium caninum* (Chen, 1934; Venard, 1938) or just after the embryophore has been disrupted and while the larvae are still within the oncospheral membranes, as demonstrated in *H. diminuta* (Berntzen and Voge, 1962, 1965). Thus it is believed that this activity is part of the hatching process. Nevertheless, this behaviour continues long after the hatching process is terminated and the pattern of hook movements are believed to be admirably suited to attachment to the intestinal epithelium and to the cutting and tearing of host tissue. Presumably the same behaviour pattern may have two functions. These movements of the hooks are cyclical in nature and have been described in a number of cestode species, including *Cittotaenia* spp. (Stunkard, 1934), *D. caninum* (Venard, 1938) and *Ariotaenia procyonis* (Gallati, 1959); the best behavioural analyses have come from the studies of oncospheres of *H. diminuta* (Ogren *et al.*, 1969; Lethbridge, 1971). The first movements are the symmetrical extension of the two pairs of lateral hooks, pushing outwards and downwards to anchor the oncosphere, this is followed by a forward and downward thrusting of the median hooks that serves to lever the migrating oncospheres deeper into the tissue. Freshly hatched oncospheres of *H. diminuta* perform at approximately 20 cycles/minute, but this rate is significantly affected by temperature and the age of the oncosphere (Ogren *et al.*, 1969; Anderson and Lethbridge, 1975). Typically, there are enough energy reserves to continue movement for 2–4 hours and this is consistent with the time required to penetrate the insect gut (Lethbridge, 1980). The specific activation stimuli for this behaviour are still unclear.

In the taeniid species *Taenia taeniaeformis* and *T. pisiformis* that infect vertebrate hosts, the specific stimulus for the activation of the hexacanth larva is bile (Silverman, 1954). The majority of the hymenolepid species have insect intermediate hosts and bile tends to have an inhibitory effect. Bile salts inhibit hatching in *Hymenolepis microstoma* and *Hymenolepis citelli* but not in *Hymenolepis nana* and *H. diminuta* (Berntzen and Voge, 1965). The lack of inhibitory effects of bile salts on the hatching of *H. nana* (bile salts actually stimulate hatching in this species) is thought to be an adaptation that allows its direct life cycle. In most hymenolepids studied, the sustained oncospheral activity begins immediately after the eggshell has been cracked, and it is argued that the stimulus is dependent on the chemical and physical nature of the environment (Berntzen and Voge, 1962, 1965). The oncospheres of *H. diminuta* in 0.3% NaCl showed a delayed initiation of activity when compared to oncospheres in distilled water, suggesting a salt–water balance sensitivity (Ogren *et al.*, 1969), but sudden changes in temperature could also initiate activity in this and other species (Reid *et al.*, 1949; Collins and Hutchins, 1965). An extensive study by Berntzen and Voge (1965) concluded that the primary stimulus to activation in the four species of hymenolepids studied was the presence of dissociated sodium carbonate and free CO_2, while additional factors such as temperature, pH and proteolytic enzymes inhibit or potentiate this stimulating effect.

Infection of vertebrates usually follows the ingestion of a cysticercoid, cysticercus, coenurus or hydatid cyst. In general, there are two phases to this infection process. First is excystment, a mechanical phase where the cystic envelope is removed; this usually occurs in the stomach. The second phase involves evagination of the scolex, a distinct behavioural activity that appears to be a response to specific stimuli. Again, the requirements for excystment and evagination is species-specific and is presumed to be dependent on host factors.

Evagination of the cysticercus of *T. pisiformis* is due to the initiation of powerful peristaltic contractions of the body, which force the scolex out (de Waele, 1934). The evagination of hymenolepid cysticercoids is similar; upon appropriate stimulation the scolex initially explores the inner wall of the cyst, then opposing suckers grasp and pull on the cyst wall; this eventually leads to its rupture and results in the emergence of the scolex (Rothman, 1959; Goodchild and Davis, 1972). Clearly, in many species, evagination is a result of larval behaviour; these observations cast doubts on the assertion that evagination is primarily a result of increased osmotic pressure which forces the scolex out (Wardle and McLeod, 1952). Interestingly, the retraction of the scolex during development of the cysticercoid is also an active muscular process. Retraction starts about 6 days after infection of the intermediate host with *H. microstoma.* It consists of four sequential patterns of behaviour which produce rhythmical waves of muscle contractions; these force the inner part of the scolex through the neck and into the midbody, where a circular constriction prevents the return to the protracted state (Caley, 1974). Evagination is not a reversal of the retraction movements. The powerful muscles involved in retraction regress, and evagination is explained as the unrolling of reflexed neck tissue (stored energy) from around the scolex by muscular wriggling (Caley, 1974). In addition, the muscular mechanisms for retraction and evagination differ widely between species; in *Tatria* spp. the scolex is retracted with special muscles (Rees, 1973).

Early work on the evagination behaviour of cysticerci of *Taenia pisiformis* and *Taenia solium* recognized that conditions simulating those of the host small intestine (pH > 6, temperature 37–38°C and the presence of bile) were required (Buntning, 1927; de Waele, 1934). Bile salts are the primary requirement and the parasites are indifferent to various proteases, bile pigments, lecithin, cholesterol, fatty acids and detergents (de Waele, 1934). Bile is also required for the initiation of evagination of cysticercoids of several taeniid species including *Hymenolepis nana. H. diminuta, H. citelli, Oochoristica symmetrica, Taeinia hydatigena* and *T. taeniaeformis* (Rothman, 1959; Featherston, 1971). The presence of bile greatly accelerates evagination in the protoscoleces of *Echinococcus granulosus*, but the same degree of evagination (at a slower rate) is reached without bile (Smyth, 1969). The nature of the action of bile salts remains unclear. The effects of bile are not limited to activation since bile also aids in the digestion of the cyst through its effects on protein denaturing and by the enhancement of proteolysis (Rothman, 1959). Some investigators have reported that ordinary detergents were just as effective as bile in initiating evagination (Campbell and Richardson, 1960; Campbell, 1963), while others have argued that evagination is not a function of the surfactant properties of the molecule (de Waele, 1934; Edgar, 1940, 1941; Fuentes *et al.*, 1960). De Waele (1940) suggested that the bile salts stimulated smooth muscle contraction via a cholic radical strengthened with an −OH group. Substitution of the −OH group by other groups, e.g. as in sodium dehydrocholate, removes the stimulatory activity. However, the cysticerci of *T. pisiformis* evaginate in ordinary detergents and a surface tension of 54.0 dynes/cm^2 was reported as optimal (Campbell, 1963). Both hypotheses on the mode of action of bile on evagination of *T. pisiformis* cystericerci have been supported in a single study (de Rycke and van Grembergen, 1966) and the matter is still unresolved.

(b) Cestode site finding. The story of the circadian migration of *H. diminuta* is now well known and it has been reviewed in great detail (Arai, 1980). Since this last review there have been numerous significant advances in our understanding of the behaviour of this cestode and these more recent results will be the primary concern of this section. Nevertheless, it will be instructive to examine some of the highlights of this story to illustrate the evolution of concepts of the cestode–host relationship and the problems involved with inferences of behaviour based on the manipulation of the *in vivo* situation.

Initially, the cestode–host relationship was viewed as that of a lethargic worm hanging within a homeostatic gut. The cestode was presumed a "degenerate" worm that had lost most of its ancestral sensory, locomotory and digestive functions. This view was severely compromised by the discovery that the worms migrated anteriorly within a week of their initial medial establishment in the small intestine (ontogenetic migration) (Chandler, 1939; Mettrick and Dunkely, 1969; Bräten and Hopkins, 1969; Turton, 1971) and the observation that worms surgically transplanted into the ileum would quickly make their way back to their normal anteriad sites (Goodchild, 1958; Goodchild and Harrison, 1961; Bräten and Hopkins, 1969). The most tenable hypothesis to account for these observations was based on the assumption that the worms were attempting to keep the greater parts of their bodies within the region of the intestine most favourable to their survival (Holmes, 1961, 1962; Crompton and Whitfield, 1968; Bräten and Hopkins, 1969; Mettrick and Dunkely, 1969). Thus, the lethargic worm could move, but of even greater consequence was the realization that the cestode must be capable of recognizing its own environment, is able to distinguish between optimal and suboptimal sites, can interpret directional stimuli, and must possess a neuromuscular system that is complex enough to coordinate the presumed sensory input with the muscular effort of a long segmented worm. Obviously, the concept of a degenerate worm was no longer valid!

The second major observation on the behaviour of *H. diminuta* was described by Read and Kilejian (1969), who found that the adult exhibited a consistent circadian pattern of migration in the small intestine; this observation was confirmed by several subsequent studies (Chappell *et al.*, 1970; Bailey, 1971; Evans and Wickham, 1971; Tanaka and MacInnis, 1975). The stimulus for migration was related to feeding; the worms migrated anteriorly after host feeding and short periods of starvation delayed migration (Read and Kilejian, 1969; Hopkins, 1969; Bailey, 1971; Evans and Wickham, 1971). It was a perfect model to study the stimuli by which a dynamic cestode responded, because the worm was changing its position in response to its perception of the environment on a daily basis. The subsequent search for the environmental cues that controlled the behaviour was based on this concept of the worm.

It was thought that there was some factor in the host diet that provided the stimulus for anteriad migration. Despite intensive efforts, it was concluded that neither the quantity nor quality of the host diet had any effect on migration (Chappell *et al.*, 1970; Mettrick, 1971a,b,c, 1972, 1973, 1975; Mettrick and Podesta, 1974; Dunkely and Mettrick, 1977). It was felt that the worms were responding to the indirect effects of feeding. One gram of glucose given to rats that were fasted for 24 hours would stimulate anteriad migration (Mettrick, 1971a,c, 1972). When the normal gradients of glucose were experimentally altered, the worms would migrate anteriorly despite the presence of higher concentrations of glucose distally (Mead and Roberts, 1972; Mead, 1976). In addition, changing the host to total parenteral nutrition resulted in an initial destrobilization followed by normal subsequent development in the absence of luminal food (Castro *et al.*, 1976). Even in those animals with no food in the gut, the worms were located in the anterior small intestine. It was suggested that the worms responded to biliary, pancreatic or duodenal secretions, based on the assumption that gastrointestinal secretions occurred at basal low levels in the absence of feeding. Two important implications of these results were not recognized until years later. First, the worms appeared to respond to the gastrointestinal secretions in the absence of luminal food and second, the worms' anteriad migration was apparently not dependent on the recognition of an optimal environment since the worms would move anteriorly even when the optimal environment was posterior (Mead, 1976).

The search for other hymenolepid species that showed a circadian type migration proved unsuccessful. *Hymenolepis microstoma* has an ontogenetic migration during its development (Cooreman and de Rycke, 1972; Pappas and Mayer, 1976), but no evidence for a circadian migration was found in this or any other hymenolepid species (Arai, 1980). This adaptation of *H. diminuta* may be significant in our understanding of its behaviour. In the search for the cues that triggered the anteriad migration of *H. diminuta*, a narrower focus was required to overcome the complexity of the environment. Stimulation of the left afferent vagal nerve (2 mseconds, 5V, 10Hz) of the host rat for up to 60 minutes induced significant anteriad migration of the scolex and biomass of *H. diminuta* (Mettrick and Cho, 1981a). Vagal stimulation is known to release endogenous cholecystokinin (CCK), serotonin (5-HT), secretin and pancreatic secretions (Konturek *et al.*, 1974; Ahlman *et al.*, 1976; Schwartz *et al.*, 1978). In addition, the effects of oral and/or intravenous administration of a number of gastrointestinal hormones and amines could alter the migrational patterns of the worms. Secretin, CCK and 5-HT treatment resulted in anteriad migration, while histamine treatment resulted in posteriad migration of the worms (Podesta and Mettrick, 1981; Mettrick and Podesta, 1982). These authors concluded that parasite relocation in the intestine was a reaction to a complex of changes in the pre- and postprandial intestinal lumen, which occur as part of the host's normal response to the physiological stimulation of a meal. Nevertheless, it was erroneously believed that because of the major importance of 5-HT on the biology of the cestode, 5-HT was a good candidate for the specific cue in migration.

There is pharmacological evidence of 5-HT receptors in a large number of platyhelminths (Mansour, 1957, 1964; Beernink *et al.*, 1963; Barker *et al.*, 1966; Hillman and Senft, 1973) and 5-HT was reported from *H. diminuta* (Lee *et al.*, 1978). 5-HT stimulates glucose uptake, affects the regulation of carbohydrate metabolism in *H. diminuta* (Mettrick *et al.*, 1981; Rahman *et al.*, 1983), and is actively transported into the worm (Cyr *et al.*, 1983). 5-HT was also thought to be a neurotransmitter that increases worm motility (Lee *et al.*, 1978; Mettrick *et al.*, 1981). However, despite the multiplicity of functions of this molecule in the biology of the worm, *H. diminuta* is able to synthesize only negligible amounts of 5-HT from tryptophan or 5-HTP (Ribiero and Webb, 1983), and the 5-HT levels in worm tissues are primarily, if not exclusively, of host origin (Mansour, 1979; Cho and Mettrick, 1982).

5-HT is secreted into the intestinal lumen by enterochromaffin cells in the mucosa of the proximal small intestine of all mammals and accounts for over 60% of total body 5-HT content (Thompson, 1971; Pettersson, 1979). The physiological role of 5-HT in the intestine is complex and includes the inhibition of gastric secretion (Black *et al.*, 1958; Jaffee *et al.*, 1977); it is a requirement for the vasodilatory effects of CCK and secretin (Dolani *et al.*, 1970); it inhibits protein synthesis in the intestine (Majumdar and Nakla, 1979), and it influences insulin release (Lechin *et al.*, 1975; Lebowitz and Feldman, 1983).

Intraperitoneal, intramuscular, subcutaneous and oral administration of 5-HT results in significant anteriad migration by *H. diminuta* (Mettrick and Cho, 1981b). A relationship also exists between the intestinal levels of 5-HT and the extent of the migrating response; the higher the luminal 5-HT concentrations, the more marked the worm's migratory response. The addition of the specific 5-HT antagonist methysergide resulted in over 90% inhibition in the worm migratory response to oral administration of 5-HT (Mettrick and Cho, 1982). Some of the most convincing evidence for the presumed direct relationship between migration and 5-HT levels came from a study that correlated the pattern of circadian migration with a similar variation in the levels of 5-HT in worm tissues, the intestinal lumen, the intestinal mucosa, intestinal food content and the time in the feeding cycle (Fig. 3, Cho and Mettrick, 1982). Host feeding begins at 1600 hours and this is followed by steadily increasing 5-HT levels in both the intestinal lumen and the worm tissues. The higher the worm 5-HT levels, the more marked the migratory response. Fasting reduces luminal and worm 5-HT levels and eliminates the migrational response (Cho and Mettrick, 1982).

In a study to determine the relative effects of gastric, biliary and pancreatic secretions on worm migrations it was demonstrated that pancreatic secretions provided the most potent stimulus for migration (Sukhdeo and Mettrick, 1984) (Table 1). These results were based on the effects of a known migrational stimulus (1 g glucose in rats fasted for 24 hours) in infected animals that had the gastrointestinal secretions surgically restricted or rerouted to the distal ileum. Inhibition of the migrational response always followed the restriction or rerouting of the pancreatic secretions. In addition, a cue that was inhibitory to migration was also found. Greatest anteriad migrations occurred only when the pylorus was ligatured to prevent entry of the gastric secretions into the intestinal lumen. When gastric secretions were

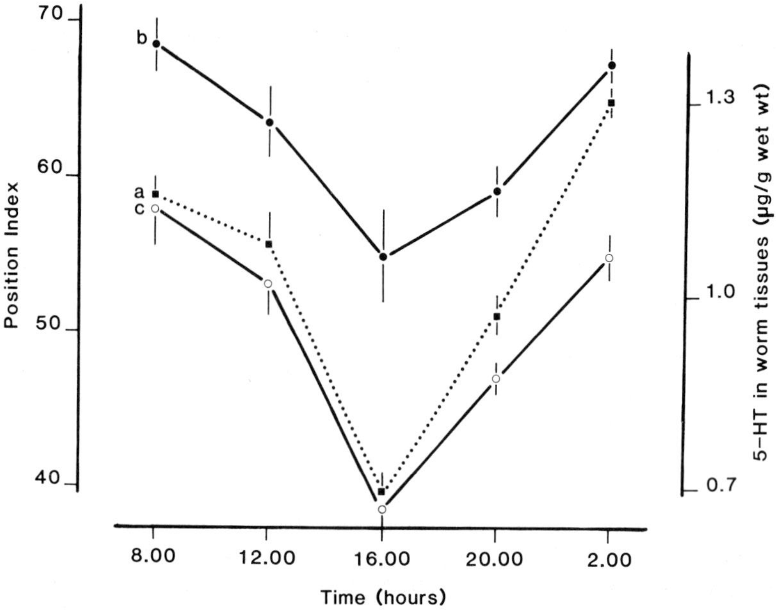

FIG. 3. Changes in (a) 5-HT levels of 16-day-old *Hymenolepis diminuta* and worm migratory responses, expressed as Position Indices in *ad libitum* fed rats, of (b) scoleces and (c) biomass (Cho and Mettrick, 1982).

relocated to more distal regions that were anteriad of the scolex, the worms did not migrate past the site of entry of the gastric secretions. The biological importance of preventing or inhibiting the worm from entering the stomach is obvious.

The present hypothesis on the migration of the "dynamic" cestode stresses that the worm has the ability to recognize its environment. It was reported that when the strobila of an adult worm was cut below the scolex, the scolex moved back to a position in the small intestine where a young worm of the new size would normally be found (Hopkins and Allen, 1979). This very important result was interpreted to mean that the tail controlled site location and that the tail contained sensory receptors that could recognize the environment and modify the scolex's selection of site. This hypothesis was based on an assumption that was only partially true, which was that the scolex's selection of holdfast site determined the position of the strobila. While scolex position may indeed determine the strobila position of a young worm, the scolex is too small and weak to provide purchase for the biomass of an adult worm. The adult worms do not align themselves posteriorly from the holdfast, but tend to be folded into flattened loops in the area of the

TABLE 1

The effects of a standard glucose meal (1g), following rerouting or ligation of bile and pancreatic secretions, on the migration behaviour of Hymenolepsis diminuta (*Sukhdeo and Mettrick, 1984*)

Treatment	Cannula to segments	*n*	BPI*	SPI*
Sham operation	—	3	107.8 ± 0.7^{a}	116.9 ± 1.6^{d}
Bile duct rerouted	6–7	3	103.2 ± 3.7^{a}	107.9 ± 1.3^{d}
Common bile duct rerouted	6–8	4	86.2 ± 2.9^{b}	105.7 ± 3.6^{d}
Bile duct ligature	—	4	85.7 ± 8.1^{b}	106.7 ± 5.6^{d}
Common bile duct ligature	—	4	79.7 ± 5.8^{b}	100.3 ± 6.3^{d}
Sham operation (no glucose)	—	3	63.8 ± 3.2^{c}	67.8 ± 15.9^{e}

*Biomass and Scolex Position Index; larger indices result from more anteriad positions; mean ± SEM with different superscripts are statistically different ($P < 0.05$).

scolex, clearly not relying on the holdfast abilities of the scolex (Sukhdeo, personal observation). Rerouting the pancreatic secretions (stimulatory) and the gastric secretions (inhibitory) posteriad of the scolex so that the secretions bathed in the mid- and posterior regions of the strobila eliminated the stimulatory/inhibitory effect (Sukhdeo and Mettrick, 1984). Thus, the cues that control migration seem to be mediated by receptors that are situated in the anterior regions of the worm, presumably in the scolex.

One of the limiting factors in our understanding of the migrational response of *H. diminuta* has been the total lack of information on the behaviour of the worm itself. This has occurred despite the development of *in vitro* culture systems that allow growth to egg producing adults (Evans, 1980). The scolex exhibits several types of behavioural movement, including contraction and elongation of the rostellum, expansion and contraction of the suckers, antero-posteriad oscillations of the suckers and waving movements of the entire scolex (Sukhdeo *et al.*, 1984). The behaviour patterns with the most consistent rhythms are the sucker oscillations (Fig. 4a), the contralateral suckers move anteriad and open while the second pair of suckers move posteriad and close. These movements are responsible for scolex migrations in the gut. In the strobila, two separate patterns of movement were recorded (Sukhdeo *et al.*, 1984). Sinusoidal type movements occur over large regions of the strobila and are generated predominantly by contraction of the longitudinal musculature (Fig. 4b). Backward-moving, peristaltic-like waveforms appeared to be spontaneously generated over short regions of the strobila and were due to contractions of the circular musculature (Fig. 4c). Experiments on worm movements in liquid and semi-solid media suggest that the major propulsive forces of the worm are

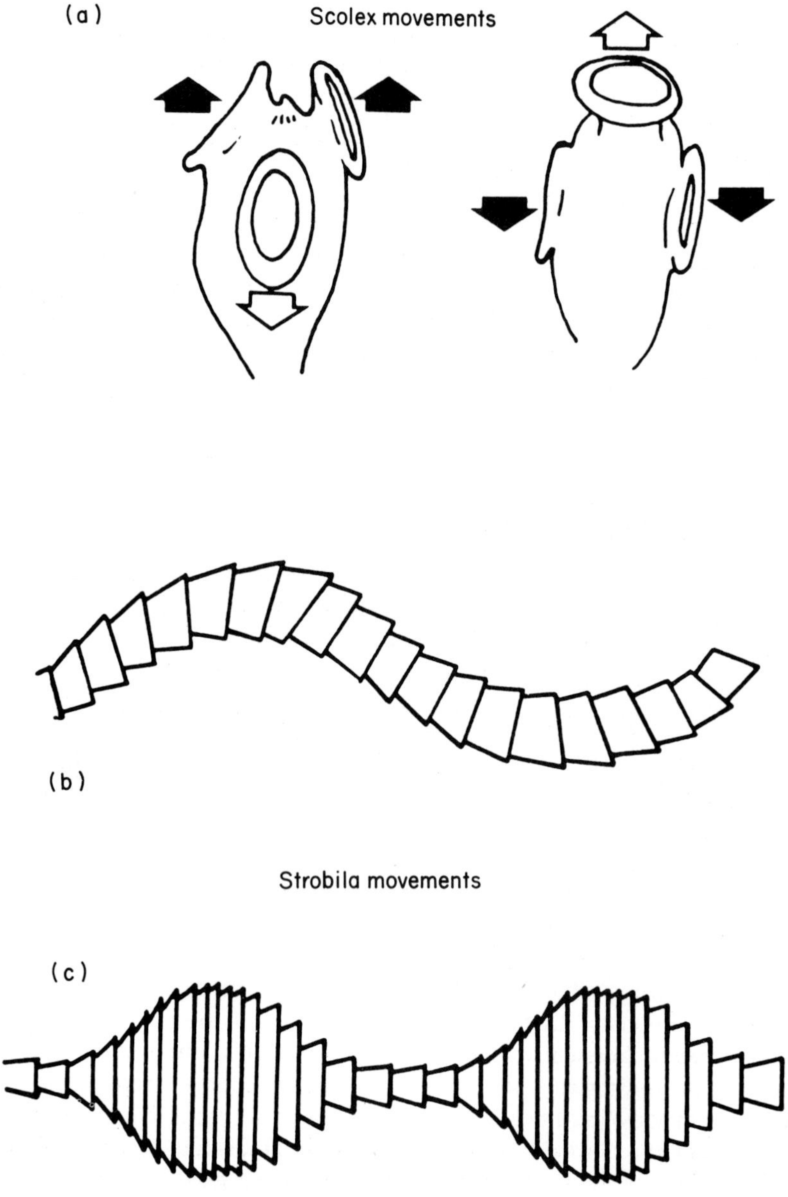

FIG. 4. Diagrammatic representations of the movements of *Hymenolepis diminuta*. (a) The rhythmic oscillations of the suckers on the scolex; black and white arrows show the movement of the contralateral suckers. (b) The sinusoidal-type motility in the strobila generated predominantly by the longitudinal muscles. (c) The peristaltic-like motility in the strobila generated predominantly by the circular muscles (Sukhdeo *et al*., 1984).

generated by the peristaltic-like waveforms. In addition, since the force exerted by these waves are related to size, the major propulsive force in the cestode comes from the tail region.

Thus, *in vitro* behaviour can be used to test the effects of presumptive migrational cues. 5-HT decreases the rate of sucker oscillations at all concentrations tested (10^{-9}–10^{-3}M) and increases the generation rate of the peristaltic-like waveforms only at high concentrations (10^{-3}M) (Sukhdeo *et al.*, 1984). Lower concentrations gave equivocal results on strobila motility and would even inhibit the motility (Table 2). 5-HT does not have the effects expected of a cue that had direct control of migration. The *in vivo* role of 5-HT on worm migration was re-evaluated and it was clearly demonstrated that the effects of 5-HT were mediated via the pancreatic secretions (Table 3) (Sukhdeo and Mettrick, 1985).

TABLE 2
The effects of 5-HT and ACh on the rate of scolex sucker oscillations of Hymenolepsis diminuta (*Sukhdeo* et al., 1984)

T		Mean number of oscillations per minute ± SEM		
Treatment	*n*	Pretreatment	Post-treatment	mean ± SEM
10^{-3}M 5-HT	5	57.3 ± 0.9	48.6 ± 1.4	−15.1 ± 2.1*
10^{-6}M 5-HT	5	48.7 ± 0.7	28.7 ± 3.7	−41.1 ± 7.9*
10^{-9}M 5-HT	5	64.0 ± 2.1	56.7 ± 0.3	−17.5 ± 3.1*
10^{-3}M Ach	5	60.0 ± 2.8	49.3 ± 0.8	−17.4 ± 3.6*
10^{-6}M Ach	5	57.7 ± 0.7	45.0 ± 1.5	−21.9 ± 2.2*
10^{-9}M Ach	5	54.3 ± 2.7	54.7 ± 1.5	4.6 ± 2.4*

*Using Student's paired *t*-test, the change in activity following treatment was significantly different from the activity in the paired controls ($P < 0.05$); mean ± SEM measures the mean percentage change in activity.

The hypotheses on migrational control of *H. diminuta* require revision. First, it is no longer necessary to postulate a complex sensory approach in the strobila that monitors the environment for "optimal" conditions. The results of Mead (1976) show that the worm migrates away from optimal conditions and Sukhdeo and Mettrick (1984) have demonstrated that migration results from secretions of the pancreas, even in the absence of luminal food. Despite the assertions by Hopkins and Allen (1979) that sensory feedback from the tail is important, it appears that mediation of migration behaviour occurs at the level of the scolex (Sukhdeo and Mettrick, 1984). The scolex is the seat of a rather complex nervous system that sends neural connections throughout

TABLE 3

The effects of intra-duodenal inoculation of 10 mg 5-HT on the anteriad migration of 15-day-old Hymenolepis diminuta *following surgical restriction of gastrointestinal secretions (Sukhdeo and Mettrick, 1985)*

Surgery	Treatment	BPI	SPI	No. of worms per infection
Cannula only	Control	85.8±2.1	109.3± 3.8	4.8±0.8
	5-HT	96.8±3.6*	117.7± 2.9	5.0±1.2
Bile restriction	Control	78.9±2.3	93.3±10.7	5.8±1.1
	5-HT	96.5±3.8*	105.9± 3.9	5.4±0.5
Bile and pancreatic restriction	Control	90.2±4.8	102.7± 2.0	5.8±2.0
	5-HT	93.0±3.4	99.4± 1.9	8.4±0.8
Gastric restriction	Control	73.4±6.8	96.3± 4.6	6.6±0.8
	5-HT	94.3±6.0*	107.1± 4.8	10.0±0.6

*Significantly different from corresponding control ($P<0.05$). BPI, SPI; Biomass, Scolex Position Index, large indices result from more anteriad positions.

the strobila (see Section III A for details); sensory perikarya are frequently encountered in the rostellar and cerebral ganglia and to a much lesser extent within the lateral nerve cord (Lumsden and Specian, 1980). This supports a scolex-mediated sensory function. Our hypothesis is that the migration of the adult *H. diminuta* is dependent on the simple modulation of basal activity. From observations of worms in laparotomized rats and *in vitro* culture systems, we find that the worms are continuously moving. A primary assumption is that it is this activity and not the scolex holdfast that counteracts the expulsive effects of intestinal propulsion. Thus, a general increase in this basal activity would kinetically drive the worm forward, while reduction in activity would lead to a posteriad migration. Since the major propulsive forces are generated by the largest parts of the worm, it is reasonable to assume that severing the strobila would lead to a posteriad relocation, as was observed by Hopkins and Allen (1979). The determination of cues that controlled the behaviour modulation would depend on stable host conditions (e.g. postprandial gastrointestinal secretions) and would be naturally selected to optimize the cestode's survival. When compared to other armed species of hymenolepids, the scolex of *H. diminuta* has a great reduction in its holdfast abilities; a behavioural compensation may have led to the evolution of the migration pattern. This may explain the absence of similar migration patterns in related species.

(c) Trematode activation. In the digenea, there are only a few forms that infect orally and these include the free or encysted metacercariae or tetracotyle in the intermediate host. Most of the studies on the activation of trematodes have been done on metacercariae. In the metacercariae, excystation may be either passive or active; passive excystment refers to the digestion of the cyst by host enzymes and the release of the metacercariae, while active excystment implies that the metacercariae respond to cues from their environment and actively break out of the cyst. It was generally assumed that trematode excystation was a passive process and that the active movements that were sometimes observed during excystment were not correlated with the process (Faust and Khaw, 1927; Hsu and Wang, 1938). It was also generally accepted and well demonstrated that the conditions that contributed to excystment were those encountered within the specific definitive host. Thus *Clonorchis sinensis* and *Apatemon pellucidis*, two vertebrate parasites, both required pretreatment in gastric juice before excystment occurred in intestinal juice (Faust and Khaw, 1925, 1927; Hoffman, 1959), *Cryptocotyle lingua*, a parasite of fish-eating birds, showed optimal excystment in gull intestinal juice (Stunkard, 1930; McDaniel, 1966), species parasitic in birds, e.g. *Parorchis acanthus* and *Posthodiplostomum minimum*, excyst more readily at 42°C than 37°C (Fried, 1970; Fried and Roth, 1974) and the only excystation stimulus for *Philopthalmus gralli* is an increase in temperature with an optimum at 39–54°C (Cheng and Thakur, 1967). In addition, since the nature of the cyst wall enclosing the metacercaria is extremely variable between species, the environmental conditions that contribute to excystation may also be expected to differ accordingly. Thus, although the cyst walls of *Holostephanus luehei* and *Cyathocotyle bushiensis* are morphologically identical (Erasmus, 1962, 1967), the extra layer of host tissue around the cyst of *H. luehei* necessitates longer HCl/pepsin treatment for excystment (Erasmus and Bennet, 1965). The metacercaria of *F. hepatica* has a complex four-layered wall that is resistant to all enzymic digestion (Wikerhauser, 1960; Dixon, 1965, 1966) and the worm must escape through a ventral plug (Dawes, 1961; Dixon, 1966). The metacercaria of *Parvatrema timondaridi* is covered by only a thin layer of transparent material which the metacercaria effortlessly breaches after a simple temperature stimulus (Yasuroaka *et al.*, 1974).

The search for the absolute requirements for the excystment of several trematodes has been unsuccessful, although the relative conditions under which metacercariae activate are known (Lackie, 1975). The effects of temperature, pH, pepsin, trypsin and bile, when examined together and separately, contribute towards the excystment of *C. lingua*; it was concluded that none of these chemical or physical conditions was an absolute requirement, since the absence of any one of them did not completely abrogate excystment (McDaniel, 1966). Whereas the outer wall of *P. acanthus* is digested in the stomach and duodenum of its host (Asanji and Williams, 1974), *in vitro* studies demonstrate that acid pepsin digestion is unnecessary (Fried and Roth, 1974). Although optimal excystment of *F. hepatica* metacercariae results from a sequential passage through the stomach and small intestine (Schumaker, 1938; Dixon, 1966), juvenile *Fasciola* could be recovered after the cysts were placed in the peritoneal cavity of mice (Dawes, 1961). The lack of absolute requirement for excystment has also been demonstrated in several other trematodes (Oshima *et al.*, 1958; Ching 1963a,b; Erasmus and Bennett, 1965; McDaniel, 1966; Howell, 1970). The possible effects of the internal secretions and activity by the metacercariae during excystment have been ignored in most of these studies.

Empty cysts with openings were recovered from the large intestine of frogs infected with *Diplodiscus temperatus*, and it was concluded that the worms actively escaped (Krull and Price, 1932). The metacercariae of *C. sinensis* and *Sphaeridiotrema globulus* free themselves from the partially digested cyst wall by their active movements (Hsu and Wang, 1938; Macy *et al.*, 1968). The excystment of *Clinostomum* spp. was suggested to be the result of increased muscular activity (Hemenway, 1948); Dawes (1961) argued that excystation of *F. hepatica* was an active process because excystment could take place in the peritoneal cavity in the absence of digestive enzymes.

After a careful study of the metacercariae of *F. hepatica*, the excystment process was divided into two phases: first, a passive phase referred to as activation, which is stimulated by the presence of CO_2, reducing conditions and a temperature of 37°C; secondly, an active phase, emergence, stimulated by the presence of bile (Dixon, 1964, 1966). During activation, the metacercariae rotate vigorously for a while before the quiescent phase (Dixon, 1966), during which the predominant activity appears to be the emptying of the caecal contents (Sukhdeo and Mettrick, 1986; Fig. 5). At the end of activation, the clear space around the metacercariae described by Dixon (1966) is now believed to be caecal contents. The secretion of enzyme(s) by the metacercariae has previously been suggested as the means by which the larvae must digest the ventral plug (Dixon, 1965). In *Maritrema arenaria* the release of enzymes (but not the source of the enzymes) has been demonstrated in electron microscopy studies that show digestion of the inner cyst wall during excystment (Irwin, 1983). It would appear, therefore, that an important function of the activation phase is the production of caecal secretions that are generated by an intrinsic behavioural pattern. The changes that these secretions effect on the inner cyst wall are a prerequisite for emergence. Circumstantial evidence would support this point of view, since emergence does not occur in the absence of activation (Dixon, 1966). In addition, histological studies of the caeca at both the light and electron microscope level, suggest that they are secretory in nature (Dawes, 1963; Bennett, 1975a).

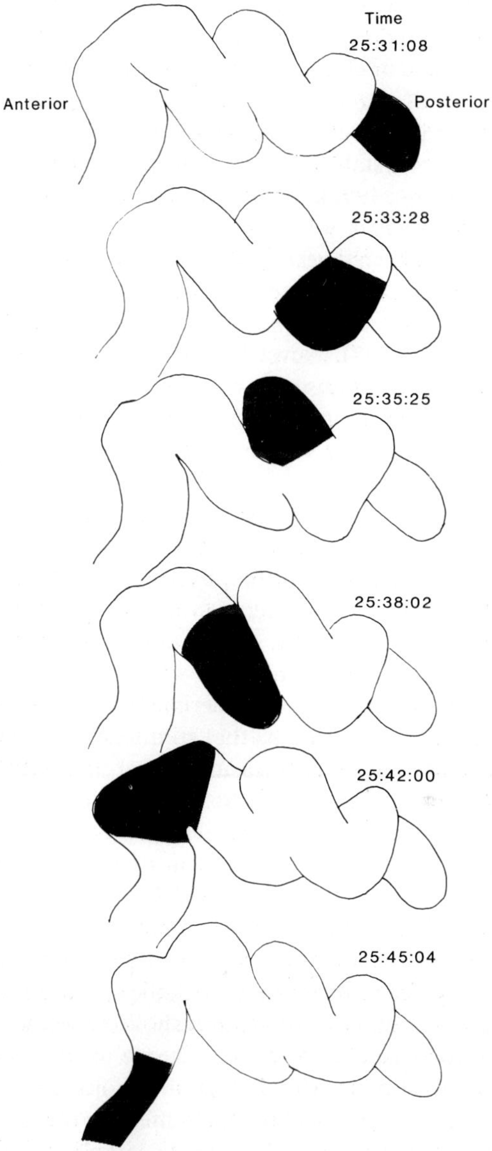

FIG. 5. The behaviour of the caeca during activation of the metacercariae of *Fasciola hepatica*. Tracings of one caecum from a video image show the progressive movements of the wave of contraction (filled in black) from the posterior to the anterior. The numbers in each sequence indicate the time (minutes : seconds : sec/30) after activation (Sukhdeo and Mettrick, 1986).

Emergence behaviour in *F. hepatica* is characterized by thrusting movements that are initiated by bile (Dixon, 1966). Bile or bile-plus-trypsin has been shown to initiate or enhance excystment in many species (Lackie, 1975). The metacercaria of *Paragonimus westermani* has an optimal range of temperature, pH and osmotic pressure within which it excysts, but the rate and percentage of excystation is enhanced when bile salts are added to the medium (Oshima *et al.*, 1958). Sodium cholate (0.05%) activates the metacercariae of *Echinoparyphium serratum* but the worm did not break out of the cyst wall until it had been digested by pepsin and trypsin (Howell, 1970). On the other hand, the metacercariae of *C. sinensis*, a liver fluke, do not require bile to excyst and will excyst *in vivo* in rabbits with ligatured bile ducts (Wykoff and Lepes, 1957). Nevertheless, bile has been shown to enhance excystation by increasing muscular activity in several trematodes, including *Zygocotyle lunata* (Fried *et al.*, 1978), *Himasthla quissetensis* (Kirschner and Bacha, 1980), *M. arenaria* (Irwin, 1983) and *Cloactrema michiganensis* (Leflore and Bass, 1983).

The mechanism by which bile initiates muscle activity is not known and various hypotheses have been proposed. It is generally believed that the mode of action is dependent on the physical or chemical properties of bile through either permeability effects on the cyst, potentiating effects on enzymes secreted by the worm, or a nonspecific stimulation of muscle (Dixon, 1966; Lackie, 1975). This view of the mode of action of bile has recently been challenged. In an experiment designed to investigate the physical characteristics of bile salts that stimulate emergence behaviour in *F. hepatica*, emergence rate was measured after treatment of pre-activated metacercariae with various bile salts. Bile salts that do not possess an aromatic structure identical to cholic acid (i.e. lithocholic, deoxycholic and chenodeoxycholic acids) were ineffective in stimulating emergence (Sukhdeo and Mettrick, 1986). Glycine conjugated bile salts were more effective at stimulating emergence behaviour than taurine conjugated bile salts, and optimal emergence occurred after treatment with cholic acid conjugated to glycine. The emergence response to glycocholic acid is dose-dependent and the log dose–effect curve shows a sharp threshold between 2×10^{-1}–2×10^{-2}M (Fig. 6). The conclusion is that emergence is the result of a specific recognition of the stimulus. Changing the molecular components of the aromatic structure of cholic acid has little effect on the biological, physical or chemical properties of the molecule, yet it completely abrogates the emergence response. In addition, the log dose–effect curve is sigmoidal and is characteristic of the binding of a ligand to a receptor, where a significant fraction of the receptors must be occupied before a noticeable response to the ligand occurs (Ross and Gilman, 1985). This type of response is characteristic of sensory receptors.

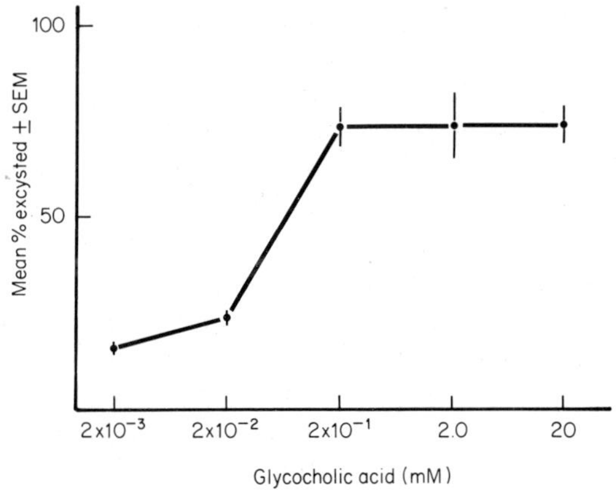

FIG. 6. The log dose–effect relationship between the emergence response of the metacercariae of *Fasciola hepatica* and glycocholic acid (Sukhdeo and Mettrick, 1986).

The suggestion of a receptor-mediated recognition of emergence cues is important and has several implications for the nature of host specificity. In addition, it suggests specific behavioural responses to specific stimuli. In general, most studies refer to the behavioural activities of the metacercariae in general terms such as "increased muscular activity" and the specific relationship between this increased activity and emergence is usually not clear. In *F. hepatica* the behaviour can be qualitatively differentiated (Dixon, 1966; Sukhdeo and Mettrick, 1986). The behaviour that leads to metacercarial emergence is not random, but involves a coordination between the vigorous sucker activity directed primarily towards the ventral plug and violent antero-posterior thrusting movements of the body which potentiate the disruptive effects of the suckers (Sukhdeo and Mettrick, 1986). This concentration of sucker activity on the ventral plug was also reported from *in vivo* studies (Dawes, 1961, 1963). If one assumes a spherical cyst, the ventral plug presents a surface area of only 2.0% of the total surface area of the inner cyst wall available for sucker attachment (Sukhdeo, personal observation). Thus, it is statistically improbable ($P > 0.02$) for the suckers to act on this ventral plug region by pure chance and it suggests that the worm must be able to specifically recognize this region and coordinate its activity to effect an escape. The complexity of the nervous system in this young trematode (see Section III A) is incompatible with previous concepts of simple worm behaviour. We believe that this complex nervous system is required for the specific recognition of and response to cues during excystation and in later stages of its life cycle.

Caution is advised before the results of experiments on *F. hepatica* are generalized to other species. While a similar two-phase excystation process has been reported for a number of other species (Kirschner and Bacha, 1980; Irwin, 1983; Leflore and Bass, 1983), it is reasonable to assume that the mechanisms which operate in *F. hepatica* are specific adaptations to escape from a thick walled cyst.

(d) Trematode site finding. Little information is available on the cues that contribute towards site finding in trematodes, probably because of the complexity of migratory routes. Studies on the site finding behaviour of schistosomes provide a good example of the trends in this area. The schistosome cercariae penetrate into the dermis across the basal lamellae of the epidermis, or via the hair follicles (Gordon and Griffiths, 1951; Stirewalt and Dorsey, 1974), and enter the venous system (Miller and Wilson, 1978), although some may go through the lymphatic system (Standen, 1953). The mechanism by which the schistosomula locate or recognize the blood vessels are unknown, but chemoreception along an oxygen gradient or along a gradient of humoral inflammatory factors has been postulated (Wheater and Wilson, 1979). The worms are passively carried to the lungs, where migration is blocked by the pulmonary capillaries and elongation of the body occurs to enhance the worm's ability to negotiate the capillary beds (Wilson *et al.*, 1978). Migration from the lungs to the liver may occur by three routes: (1) a direct migration through the diaphragm to the liver (Wilks, 1967; Bruce *et al.*, 1974); (2) a counter-current migration against the blood flow (Kruger *et al.*, 1969); (3) a migration with the blood flow (Yolles *et al.*, 1949). Recent studies strongly support a systemic migration (actually a passive transport) to the hepatic portal system and, after a period of maturation and mating in the liver, a migration to the mesenteries (Miller and Wilson, 1978; Van Marck and Gigasse, 1978; Wheater and Wilson, 1979).

The cues used for navigation during this complex migration are virtually unknown. Nevertheless, studies on pheromonal attraction indicate that the worms do have the ability to orient to specific stimuli. There is substantial *in vitro* evidence for mechanical (Armstrong, 1965) or chemical heterosexual attraction in adult schistosomes and other trematodes (Foreyt *et al.*, 1977; Fried *et al.*, 1980; Imperia and Fried, 1980; Fried and Robinson, 1981; Fried and Leiby, 1982) and, although some attempts have been made to characterize the attractants (Fried and Gioscia, 1976; Eveland *et al.*, 1983), the behavioural basis of these responses remain unclear. An attempt at answering the question of why schistosomes are attracted to the mesenteries has demonstrated that copulating worms are attracted to faecal extracts (Awwad and Bell, 1982), and it can be presumed that the highest concentrations of these extracts would be found in the mesenteries around the colon.

In *F. hepatica* infections, the newly excysted juvenile (NEJ) penetrates the small intestine and was believed to migrate at random within the abdominal cavity until it encountered the liver (Dawes, 1963). Recent evidence suggests that site finding may not be random and that the worms orient using an orthokinesis. Duodenal extracts (departure organs) increase the rate of locomotion, resulting in a tendency for the worms to disperse, while liver extracts (arrival organ) decrease the rate of locomotion, resulting in a tendency for the worms to aggregate (Sukhdeo and Mettrick, 1986; Table 4). In addition, in two-choice experiments, the NEJs demonstrated significant negative orientation responses to at least four stimuli, including organ extracts, high pCO_2 and acid pH (Sukhdeo and Mettrick, 1986).

TABLE 4
The effects of various in vitro *treatments on the locomotory response of newly excysted juveniles of* Fasciola hepatica (*Sukhdeo and Mettrick, 1986*)

Treatment	Number of locomotory waves in 10 minutes Mean ± S.E.*
Control	128.5 ± 19.5[a]
Bovine bile (10%)	175.0 ± 14.8[ac]
Duodenal contents	244.6 ± 20.9[b]
Duodenal organ supernatant	220.8 ± 18.8[bc]
Liver organ extract	20.2 ± 9.3[d]
ACh (10^{-3}M)	88.0 ± 28.9[d]
5-HT (10^{-3}	199.2 ± 22.2[cb]

*Values with different superscripts are significantly different ($P<0.05$).

III. The Nervous System of Platyhelminths

The control of all behavioural responses lies within the nervous system. In the nematode *Caenorhabditis elegans*, the entire worm has been sectioned and the nervous system described, the lineage of every one of the 302 nerve cells can be traced and the cell-to-cell interactions that lead to normal development have been assessed by mutation and cell ablation studies (Ward *et al.*, 1975; Ware *et al.*, 1975; Sulston, 1976; Krieg *et al.*, 1978). The behaviour and pharmacology of these worms have also been extensively characterized in mutation and ablation studies and, where *C. elegans* has been too small for electrophysiological studies, *Ascaris*, a very large nematode with homologous morphology has proved an excellent model (Stretton *et al.*, 1978; Ward, 1978; Johnson and Stretton, 1980). Recently, following extensive morphological, electrophysiological and biochemical analyses, a model of nematode locomotion has been developed, based on the interaction of the seven types of inhibitory and excitatory motor neuron (Stretton *et al.*, 1985). In contrast, the nervous system of the platyhelminths is poorly understood and the details of the neuroanatomy and neurocytology are only now emerging. There has been only one significant study on the neurophysiology of flatworms (Keenan and Koopowitz, 1982) and reports on the biochemistry and pharmacology are considered primitive by neurobiologists.

A. NEUROANATOMY

The platyhelminths are the lowest group of bilaterally symmetrical metazoans, yet they show significant centralization and cephalization of the nervous system. They possess a well-developed nervous system, consisting of a distinct brain and a set of longitudinal medullary cords, connected by commissures that form a typical orthogonal pattern. It has generally been argued in the older monographs that the nervous systems of platyhelminths are relatively simple, and that reduced nervous systems and sense organs reflected their simple parasitic existence. More recent investigators have strongly refuted this belief and argue that the high degree of complexity of the neuroanatomy of these worms does not suggest secondary simplification (Fairweather and Threadgold, 1983; Gustaffsson, 1984; Lumsden and Specian, 1980; Rohde, 1968a; Webb and Davey, 1974a).

1 *Trematodes*

The nervous system of trematodes is structurally very similar to that of the closely related turbellarians (Bullock and Horridge, 1965). Several classical studies using simple methylene blue and Gomori stains to elucidate the neuromorphology of the nervous systems of several trematodes, including *Cerceareum* spp., *Distomum hepaticum* (now *Fasciola hepatica*), *Haematoloechus variegatus*, *Polystoma integerrimum* and *Diplodiscus subclavatus* (Bettendorf, 1897; Havet, 1900; Zailer, 1914) have remained unchallenged. The more recent studies using modified gold and silver chloride impregnation techniques on the same and other species, confirm the older monographs and emphasize the invariant nature of the trematode nervous system, even among different genera (Ulmer, 1953; Reisenger and Graak, 1962; Rohde, 1968a,b).

The central nervous system consists of a brain connected to three pairs of longitudinal cords that run dorsally, laterally and ventrally. The ventral cord is dominant and is never reduced, while in some species the dorsal and lateral cords may be reduced or nonexistent (Ulmer, 1953; Williams, 1959). A number of transverse commissures connect the cords and these are most often found posterior to the ventral suckers (Bettendorf, 1897; Zailer, 1914).

The brain consists of a pair of cerebral ganglia joined by a dorsal transverse commisure; there is no equivalent of the circumoesophageal nerve ring found in higher groups, in which the nervous system has undergone more cephalization. It was originally believed that the nerve cells were scattered throughout the ganglia within a fibrous matrix (Havet, 1900; Zailer, 1914), but more recent evidence using transmission electron microscopy shows that the cerebral ganglia of *F. hepatica* consist of a rind of neural cells surrounding a meshwork of connectives called the neuropile (Dixon and Mercer, 1965). This neural organization of the cerebral ganglia is consistent with that found in other invertebrates (Bullock and Horridge, 1965).

Anteriorly from the cerebral ganglia, four pairs of nerves innervate the oral suckers, pharynx and some parts of the body wall musculature, while the ventral sucker is primarily innervated by the ventral nerve cord (Bettendorf, 1897; Zailer, 1914; Ulmer, 1953; Dixon and Mercer, 1965). The neurons possess axonal processes that are unmyelinated, as is typical of invertebrates (Bullock and Horridge, 1965). A number of vesicles and granules are conspicuous in these nerve processes when examined under transmission electron microscopy. On the basis of appearance and size of these inclusions, the neurons have been grouped into at least four distinct classes (Dixon and Mercer, 1965; Dei Cas *et al.*, 1980).

In the peripheral nervous system, the oral and ventral suckers are particularly well innervated, with numerous well-developed plexuses; those that are deep in the muscles are believed to be motor and those that are superficial are believed to be sensory (Bettendorf, 1897; Zailer, 1914; Ulmer, 1953; Bullock and Horridge, 1965; Dixon and Mercer, 1965). The sensory organs are nearly always superficial and at least three types of sensory endings have been identified in adult and cercarial forms (Bettendorf, 1897; Dixon and Mercer, 1965; Bennett, 1975). Scanning and transmission electron microscopy studies on *F. hepatica* show: (1) numerous receptors with characteristic bulbs and typical ciliary basal bodies, from which a single cilium (in the 9+2 arrangement) arises to protrude through the tegument and which are believed to be tangoreceptors; (2) receptors similar to (1), but which remain under a characteristic dome in the tegument and lack a cilium—these are believed to be contact receptors because of their location on the oral and ventral suckers; (3) a third type which has not been fully characterized, but which are believed to be chemoreceptors because of the pit-like openings and the position around the oral suckers (Bennett, 1975b). In *Cotylogaster occidentalis* the non-ciliated receptors could be separated into four distinct morphological types (Ip and Desser, 1984).

The axo-axoneural and neuromuscular synapses are similar to those found in vertebrates. Transmission electron microscopy of these contacts reveals that the membranes are closely apposed (200 Å) without the intervention of a basement membrane and that there is an asymmetric distribution of synaptic vesicles with the majority on the presynaptic side (Reisinger and Graak, 1962; Dixon and Mercer, 1965; Silk and Spence, 1969). Bettendorf (1897) described two kinds of muscle innervation; nerve endings on the myoblast cell body and those on the contractile fibres.

2. *Cestodes*

As with the trematodes, the early studies used methylene blue stains and golgi impregnations (Zernecke, 1895; Tower, 1900; Blochmann, 1911; Johnstone, 1812; Pintner, 1934). However, the texture and composition of the nervous tissue is similar to the surrounding parenchymatous tissue and prevents easy differentiation; golgi impregnations stained both nerve cells and myoblasts similarly and this was all compounded by the absence of a delimiting sheath or capsule around the nervous system. Later studies using reduced silver and gold chloride stains did not improve the resolution of these studies (Subramanian, 1940, 1941). The clearest pictures of the cestode nervous system, and so far the most accurate, utilized histochemical methods based on acetylcholinesterase localization combined with suitable fixation methods (Lee *et al.*, 1963; Hart, 1967; Shield, 1969; Lyons, 1972; Rees, 1973; Wilson and Schiller, 1969).

The central nervous system is biradially symmetrical, with a brain consisting of paired cerebral ganglia which elaborate into a series of longitudinal cords that run without interruption through the proglottids. The number of cords vary, ranging from a pair of lateral cords in the primitive Cestodaria to five or more in the Eucestoda (Watson, 1911; Johnston, 1912; Rees, 1951, 1959; Wardle and McLeod, 1952). The longitudinal cords are joined by commissures that vary in number, and although they are sometimes reported to be absent they were presumably not discerned by the staining methods used (Bullock and Horridge, 1965).

The arrangements of nervous structures within the scolex varies from simple to extremely intricate. Most cestodes have a unified mass (the brain) into which all the cords run, e.g. Cestodaria and Diphyllidia (Watson, 1911; Rees, 1951, 1956). Ring commissures, comparable to those in the proglottids, may occur close to the brain and in some groups become intimately associated with the brain (Rees, 1951). With the progressive muscularization of sucking organs, more nerves are diverted to the scolex structures and additional commissures develop (Rees, 1951; Shield, 1969; Webb and Davey, 1974a). These complex arrangements are characteristic of the Taeniodea and Tetrabothridea. Members of the genus *Hymenolepis* have developed attachment organs and the associated well developed nervous system in the scolex. *Hymenolepis diminuta* and *H. nana* have a two-tiered nervous system which includes an apical nerve ring that is associated with the reduced or nonfunctioning rostellar apparatus (Wilson and Schiller, 1969). In contrast, *H. microstoma* has a fully developed and functioning rostellum and presents a third tier of nervous tissue, the rostral ganglion and its associated nerves (Webb and Davey, 1974a).

Although various ganglionic cells have been identified in the brain, they appeared to be confined mainly to the transverse commissures and, in one cestode, *Acanthobothrium coronatum*, it was reported that the cerebral ganglion contained no ganglionic cells (Rees, 1966). Towers (1900) found that the cerebral ganglia of *Moniezia expansa* consisted of a core of cells and a cortex of fibres; this was confirmed in studies of *Grillotia erinaceus* (Johnstone, 1912). More recent studies on *H. microstoma* and *E. granulosus* using transmission electron microscopy have demonstrated that, like most invertebrate ganglia, the cerebral ganglia consist of a cell body rind and a nerve fibre core (Morseth, 1967; Webb and Davey, 1974a; Fairweather and Threadgold, 1983). Later investigators contend that electron microscopy is the only technique that allows differentiation of nervous elements from non-neural tissue. With this technique, nerve cell bodies can be identified by their characteristic vesicles and sensory neurons can be differentiated from other nerve cells by the types of vesicles (Webb and Davey, 1974a,b; Webb, 1976, 1977; Fairweather and Threadgold, 1983). On this basis, the parenchymatous cells described from the scolex of several cestodes (Rees, 1958, 1966; Goodchild and Harrison, 1961; Williams, 1966) may in fact have been nerve cells (Webb and Davey, 1974a).

The prominent nerve cell type in cestodes has been described as unipolar (Bullock and Horridge, 1965). However, in *H. microstoma*, multipolar neurons predominate although a few unipolar neurons were found (Webb and Davey, 1974a) and bipolar neurons are common (Rees, 1966). Webb and Davey (1974a,b) reported that the bipolar neurons were sensory. Sensory neurons are abundant and easily discerned with methylene blue or golgi stains (Blochmann, 1911; Zernecke, 1914). At least three types of sensory endings have been described in *Hymenolepis* (Cooper *et al.*, 1975; Fairweather and Threadgold, 1983; Webb and Davey, 1974b). Two contain cilia (characterized by a 9 + 6 + 1 microtubular arrangement) and one is unciliated (Blitz and Smith, 1973; Webb and Davey, 1974a; Cooper *et al.*, 1975; Lumsden and Specian, 1980; Fairweather and Threadgold, 1983). Axons are typically unmyelinated. Within the neuropile of *Hymenolepis*, cell junctions of three types have been described, based on morphological differences and the types of vesicles (Threadgold and Read, 1970; Webb, 1976; Lumsden and Specian, 1980). Ultrastructural evidence suggests that the three main vesicle types may relate to aminergic, peptidergic and cholinergic storage (Webb and Davey, 1976; Gustaffsson, 1984).

B. NEUROTRANSMITTERS IN PLATYHELMINTHS

The rationale behind investigating the effects of drugs on worm movement and physiology was to provide a basis for the development of anthelminthics (Chance and Mansour, 1949, 1953; Bueding, 1952; Barker *et al.*, 1966) and this is still so (Rew *et al.*, 1983; Pritchard *et al.*, 1982; Fairweather *et al.*, 1984; Hillman, 1983). One exciting offshoot of this work has been the interest generated in the neurophysiology of worms and in the identification of the neurotransmitter substances of these parasites. The identification of neurotransmitters is one of the very difficult problems in the study of neurobiology. A number of criteria have been developed over the years to identify neurotransmitters and each of these criteria involve a special methodology and "to a degree, indirect evidence, estimates and inferences" (Shepherd, 1983). The criteria required for the identification of a neurotransmitter have been summarized (Gainer and Brownstein, 1981; Shepherd, 1983):

(1) Biochemical evidence—the presence and functional operation of enzymes that synthesize the neurotransmitter in the presynaptic neuron and processes and enzymes that remove or inactivate the neurotransmitter at the synapse;

(2) Anatomical evidence—the presence of the neurotransmitter in appropriate amounts within the presynaptic process;

(3) Pharmacological evidence—the action of drugs that affect enzymatic or biophysical steps have their expected effects on synthesis, storage, release, action, inactivation and re-uptake of the neurotransmitter;

(4) Physiological evidence—the demonstration that physiological stimulation causes the presynaptic terminal to release the neurotransmitter and that ionophoretic application of the neurotransmitter in appropriate amounts at the postsynaptic site mimics the natural response.

Within the framework of these criteria, no neurotransmitters have been conclusively demonstrated in any parasite. However, many investigators feel that there is sufficient evidence to consider acetylcholine as an inhibitory neurotransmitter in trematodes and cestodes, 5-HT as an excitatory neurotransmitter in some trematodes, and glutamate as an excitatory neurotransmitter in some cestodes.

1. *Acetylcholine*

The biochemical identification of the enzymes associated with the metabolism of acetylcholine (ACh) has been reported from a number of trematodes and cestodes (Bacq and Oury, 1937; Pennoit de Cooman and van Grembergen, 1942; Schwabe *et al.* 1961; Read and Simmons, 1963), but these early reports were not primarily concerned with the relationship between these esterases and neurotransmission. Various suggestions for acetylcholinesterase function in platyhelminths include permeability control and osmoregulation (Schwabe *et al.*, 1961), lipid excretion (Lee *et al.*, 1963; Arme, 1966) and fat metabolism (Bacq and Oury, 1937; Probert and Durrani, 1977). The demonstration of the presence of ACh in the protozoan *Trypanosoma rhodesiense* and its association with the organism's motility (Bulbring *et al.*, 1949) led to interest in the role of ACh in the control of flatworm motility.

Cholinesterase, the enzyme that breaks down cholines, was present in homogenates of *S. mansoni* (Bueding, 1952). Differential hydrolysis between the ACh substrate and butyrylcholine substrate indicated that the cholinesterase in the worm consisted primarily of a specific acetylcholinesterase, similar in properties and concentration to that of central nervous tissues (Bueding, 1952). This basic work was repeated by a number of other investigators in this and other worm species. A similar assay looking at the evolution of CO_2 following hydrolysis of acetyl-β-methylcholine choride (for acetylcholinesterase) and benzoylcholine chloride (for nonspecific cholinesterase) demonstrated the presence of acetylcholinesterase, but no nonspecific cholinesterases in extracts of *F. hepatica* (Chance and Mansour, 1953). In addition, the presence of ACh or an ACh-like substance was reported from this parasite; ground up, eserinized (cholinesterase inhibitor) material assayed positively for ACh with the guinea pig ileum assay (0.19–1.7 μg/g wet weight); prolonged incubation of this material yielded increased levels of ACh, suggesting the presence of choline acetyltransferase, the enzyme that synthesizes ACh (Chance and Mansour, 1953). The spasmogenic activity of extracts of *S. mansoni* on guinea pig ileum could be abolished by cholinesterase treatment and blocked by low levels of atropine, an antagonistic that specifically blocks ACh receptors; the concentration of ACh in this worm was estimated at 5.3 μg/g wet weight (Barker *et al.*, 1966).

More sensitive assays using acetylthiocholine iodide and butyrylcholine iodide as substrates and the use of specific inhibitors show 74–79% of the cholinesterase activity to be due to acetylcholinesterase in *F. hepatica*, although the results were qualitative (Probert and Durrani, 1977). Radioenzymatic assays sensitive at the picogram level show that *F. hepatica* contains 3.14 pmol/mg wet weight ACh, 1.25 nmol/hour mg protein choline acetyltransferase; 238 nmol/hour mg protein acetylcholinesterase and 83 nmol/hour mg protein butyrylcholinesterase (Sukhdeo *et al.*, 1986).

In all studies, the biochemical analyses were done on extracts and homogenates of worm tissue and, at best, only regional estimates of the concentrations of ACh and its associated enzymes were determined. A number of investigators have used modifications of the Koelle or Gomori techniques to locate cholinesterases in the worm's nervous system. The histochemical techniques used are essentially similar and depend on colour changes resulting from the hydrolysis of acetyl or butyryl substrates to determine enzyme location in whole worm preparations or sections of the worms. In *F. hepatica* and *Fascioloides magna*, acetylcholinesterase activity was localized in the nervous tissues and also in the neuromuscular tissues (pharynx and suckers) and tegument, while nonspecific cholinesterases were found in the reproductive tissues (Halton, 1967; Panitz, 1970). In addition, Krvavica *et al.* (1967) found that acetylcholinesterase activity is primarily associated with the cerebral ganglia in the miracidia, rediae and cercariae of this parasite. In schistosomes, acetylcholinesterase was localized primarily in the cerebral ganglia and longitudinal nerve cords (Bueding *et al.*, 1966; Fripp, 1967). A kinetic analysis of this enzyme from the three human schistosomes suggest that isoenzymic differences exist between these species (Gear and Fripp, 1974).

A creative attempt to localize the ACh receptors of *S. mansoni* used fluorescence microscopy to detect the binding of fluorescent analogues of acetylcholine to the ACh receptors (Hillman *et al.*, 1976). Fluorescent labelling was seen in two large structures in the head (the cerebral ganglia) and in the gut, but the resolution was severely impaired by diffuse staining that may have been due to staining of nerve endings or synapses such as in muscle and secretory tissue (Hillman, 1983). Several modifications of this technique did not improve the localization of the ACh receptors, but were useful in studies of receptor kinetics (Hillman and Gibler, 1975; Hillman *et al.*, 1978). The histochemical localization of acetylcholinesterase has also been the most suitable method of outlining the gross neuroanatomy of cestodes, an indication of the relatively high concentration of this enzyme in neural tissues (Schardein and Waitz, 1965; Har, 1967; Ramisz, 1967). In *H. diminuta* and *H. nana* the enzyme associated with the nervous system was a specific acetylcholinesterase and not a nonspecific cholinesterase (Wilson and and Schiller, 1969). To date, neither the presynaptic location of ACh and its synthesizing enzymes, nor the postsynaptic location of the inactivating enzymes have been demonstrated in any platyhelminth.

Physiological and pharmacological studies on the effects of neurotransmitters in flatworms have been significantly hampered by the lack of a suitable neuromuscular preparation. The evidence for the biological activity of a neurotransmitter lies in effector responses, e.g. a muscle twitch or movement. In 1949, Chance and Mansour attached *F. hepatica* to a primitive recording device utilizing a kymograph and reported that cholinomimetic agents paralysed the preparation while amines stimulated it. Since then, there have been several attempts to develop more sensitive, objective and quantitative measurements of worm response to various treatments. Schistosomes were too small to adapt to the kymographic method and the early studies relied on visual observation to estimate changes in worm motility (Barker *et al.*, 1966; Tomosky-Sykes and Bueding, 1977). Although there has been some criticism of the subjectivity of this approach, results have been reliable (Mellin *et al.*, 1983); some investigators still prefer this direct and presumably more discriminating approach (Mellin *et al.*, 1983; Sukhdeo *et al.*, 1984).

Two "activity-type" cages were developed to measure schistosome behaviour. One measured ultrasonic doppler effects based on the frequency shift of megaherz sound caused by worm movement in the cage (Brown *et al.*, 1978; Chavasse *et al.*, 1979). The other used fibre optics leading to one or more photocells; the number of photocell crossings was used as a function of worm movements (Hillman and Senft, 1973; Jewsbury *et al.*, 1977; Hillman, 1979). Although these techniques appeared reliable they were criticized because they gave little information on the details; they were not sensitive to the wavelike activity on the surface of the worms, which may be important in locomotion, and the role of the large undulatory waves measured by the photoelectric and ultrasonic techniques were unclear (Hillman and Senft, 1975; Fetterer *et al.*, 1977). A more direct method was developed, whereby the worm was suspended by suction electrodes so that isotonic contractions and surface electrical activity could be recorded simultaneously (Fetterer *et al.*, 1977). This method detected responses to much lower doses of stimulants than the previous methods. Although there have been other reports of new methods to measure worm motility, they are largely based on modifications of Fetterer's method (Terada *et al.*, 1982; de Moura and Rozental, 1983; Fairweather *et al.*, 1983). There are several criticisms of these techniques. The drugs are applied to the outside of the usually intact worms and transport, metabolic and permeability factors may play a major role in the drug effects (Hillman, 1983). Strips of body wall musculature that allow easy access to the external environment are more sensitive and show more consistent motility responses than the intact proglottids of cestodes (Thompson and Mettrick, 1984). 5-HT and ACh differ in their effects on the circular and longitudinal musculature of trematodes and cestodes (Pax *et al.*, 1984; Sukhdeo *et al.*, 1984) and the motility responses of these worms often show complex patterns. The precise functioning roles of the various muscle groups in controlling worm behaviour have yet to be examined before a good neuromuscular preparation can be developed. Nevertheless, the present pharmacological evidence for neurotransmitters in parasites is based primarily upon these assays of worm response.

The ACh receptors of trematodes and cestodes do not bear any pharmacological resemblance to any known vertebrate type; they are neither purely nicotinic nor purely muscarinic as in vertebrates, but share characteristics of both (Hillman, 1983; Thompson *et al.*, 1986). ACh inhibits the motility of both *F. hepatica* and *S. mansoni* and this effect is mimicked by treatment with eserine (Chance and Mansour, 1953; Barker *et al.*, 1966; Holmes and Fairweather, 1984; Pax *et al.*, 1984; Hillman, 1983; Sukhdeo *et al.*, 1986). Carbachol, an analogue of ACh that operates at muscarinic sites, produces a larger and more consistent response than ACh in *F. hepatica*, yet muscarine itself has no effect while atropine, an ACh antagonist that blocks muscarinic receptor sites, stimulates motility and reverses the effect of carbachol and ACh (Holmes and Fairweather, 1984; Sukhdeo *et al.*, 1986). Nicotine, which directly stimulates nicotinic sites, had effects which were similar to ACh, yet d-tubocurarine, a specific blocker of these sites, was inactive (Holmes and Fairweather, 1984; Sukhdeo *et al.*, 1986). The more rapid responses of the worm to carbachol and nicotine than to ACh itself suggest that the ACh receptors in these worms are stearically different from those in vertebrates (Holmes and Fairweather, 1984). In schistosomes, the results are similar, with minor variations. Carbachol is more effective than ACh in paralysing the worms, and although muscarine has no effect, some muscarinic blockers have a stimulatory action (Barker *et al.*, 1966). In contrast to *F. hepatica*, nicotine has no effect on schistosomes (Barker *et al.*, 1966; Hillman, 1983).

2. *Amines*

Biogenic amines have been biochemically identified from several cestodes and trematodes and at least one of three biogenic amines, 5–HT, dopamine (DA) or noradrenaline (NA) was present in all the worms examined (Chou *et al.*, 1972). The presence of 5-HT was reported from the tissues of *F. hepatica* (Mansour and Stone, 1970). However, despite evidence of the biochemical effects 5-HT has on motor activity, carbohydrate metabolism, cyclic AMP levels and on the activities of adenyl cyclase and protein kinase (Mansour and Stone, 1970; Abrahams *et al.*, 1976; Gentleman *et al.*, 1976; Mansour, 1979), the presence of endogenous 5-HT was not confirmed by other investigations (Chou *et al.*, 1972; Andreini *et al.*, 1970; Tomosky-Sykes *et al.*, 1977). The biochemical determination of 5-HT was based on the measurement of a fluorescent product of ninhydrin reaction with 5-HT (Mansour and Stone, 1970). However, amino acids can produce fake positives in the determination of 5-HT; lysine was shown to be the amino acid responsible for the fake positives for 5-HT when the ninhydrin reaction was used in *F. hepatica* (Tomosky *et al.*, 1974). 5-HT has been demonstrated in the tissues of all schistosomes but with some interspecific differences in the concentration. *Schistosoma japonicum* yielded lower levels of 5-HT (1.3–1.7 μg/g wet weight) when compared to *S. mansoni* and *S. haematobium* (2.0–3.5 μg/g wet weight) (Bennet *et al.*, 1969; Chou *et al.*, 1972). In several cestodes, *H. diminuta*, *H. nana* and *Spirometra mansonoides*, 5-HT was also found in the tissue (0.59–1.8 μg/g wet weight) with regional differences in concentration (Chou *et al.*, 1972; Tomosky-Sykes *et al.*, 1977; Lee *et al.*, 1978).

Dopamine and noradrenaline have never been convincingly demonstrated in cestodes (Chou *et al.*, 1972; Tomosky-Sykes *et al.*, 1977). The only positives for these amines were reported from larval forms of *S. mansonoides* and it was believed that these results were fake positives based on tyrosine fluorescence (Tomosky-Sykes *et al.*, 1977). Early reports showed that dopamine is the only biogenic amine found in *F. hepatica* and although both DA and NA were found in schistosomes, there were some specific differences; DA was found in *S. haematobium* but not in *S. mansoni* (Chou *et al.*, 1972; Bennet and Gianutsos, 1977). A more sensitive radioenzymatic assay reported that DA and NA were present in both *F. hepatica* and *S. mansoni* (Gianutsos and Bennett, 1977). In *F. hepatica* NA was found in the head region (3.46 μg/g wet weight) and the highest concentrations of DA were central (2.5 μg/g wet weight). In *S. mansoni* the recovery of DA and NA was much smaller (1.1–7.4 ng/g wet weight and 1.3–10.9 ng/g wet weight, respectively) and there were considerable regional and sex differences in the distribution of these amines (Gianutsos and Bennett, 1977).

The histochemical localization of these biogenic amines has also been investigated in a number of these parasites. The basic method involves a formaldehyde treatment of freeze dried specimens—a yellow fluorescence indicates the presence of 5-HT and a green fluorescence indicates the presence of catecholamines (CA). In *S. mansoni*, strong green fluorescence was found in the cerebral ganglia and in two bilateral longitudinal nerve trunks from which arise numerous green, bulb-like structures and small green fibres that anastomose to form a green fluorescent network (Bennett and Bueding, 1971). This distribution closely parallels that of acetylcholinesterase in *S. mansoni* (Bueding *et al.*, 1966; Bennett and Bueding, 1971). The localization of CA in *F. hepatica* also correlates with the histochemical localization of acetylcholinesterase (Bennett and Gianutsos, 1977). In contrast to this discrete localization of CA, 5-HT distribution is more diffuse. 5-HT was found in structures near the cerebral ganglia, in numerous storage granules throughout the parenchyma of the worm and, in males, yellow fibres were connected to yellow knobs that are believed to be sensory endings in the gynaecophoric canal (Bennett and Bueding, 1971). This histochemical evidence suggests that CA may be the interneuronal transmitter and may induce the release of 5-HT from the storage sites. A radio-autographic method for visualizing incorporation of ^{3}H-5-HT and ^{3}H- dopamine revealed that in *S. mansoni*, muscle, digestive and excretory organs were not labelled; however, labelled 5-HT was found in nerve fibres containing granules of 660–1280 nm in diameter, while ^{3}H-dopamine was associated with nerve fibres containing synaptoid vesicles (Dei-Cas *et al.*, 1979). Both of these agents have pharmacological effects on worm movements.

In cestode nervous systems, the green fluorescence of CA has not been observed. In *D. caninum*, *H. diminuta* and *H. nana* yellow fluorescence was found in the scolex, longitudinal and transverse nerves, again closely paralleling the acetylcholinesterase localization in the nervous system (Wilson and Schiller, 1969; Shield, 1969, 1971; Lee *et al.*, 1978). The accurate localization of 5-HT using a sensitive immunohistochemistry technique that utilizes an antibody specific for 5-HT showed serotonin-containing unipolar and multipolar cell bodies in the rostellum, the germinative region and the cerebral ganglia and commissures of *H. diminuta* (Webb and Mizuhawa, 1985). However, despite these authors' findings that the terminals of these 5-HT-containing nerves abut the deep and superficial longitudinal muscles, and other germinative organs, recent evidence suggests that 5-HT may not act as a neurotransmitter (Thompson and Mettrick, in preparation).

As with ACh receptors, the pharmacological characteristics of 5-HT receptors in flatworms do not resemble any known vertebrate type. 5-HT stimulates the motility of *F. hepatica* and *S. mansoni*, and specific blockers of 5-HT receptors, including bromolysergic and diethylamide, yohimbine and methysergide, antagonize the stimulant action (Mansour, 1957; Tomosky *et al.*, 1974; Wilcockson and Hillman, 1984). Incubating these worms with a number of drugs that inhibit the uptake of or induce the release of 5-HT in mammalian nerve terminals also increases motility (Tomosky *et al.*, 1974; Holmes and Fairweather, 1984; Wilcockson and Hillman, 1984). It is believed that the 5-HT receptors lack a high degree of specificity because the motor activity is also stimulated by tryptamine and a number of tryptamine analogues other than 5-HT (Nimmo-Smith and Raison, 1968; Tomosky *et al.*, 1974). Vertebrate 5-HT receptors exist in a number of different conformations and the standard method of characterizing these receptors is by the order of potency of various antagonists. In an example cited by Wilcockson and Hillman (1984), in a typical vertebrate receptor the order of antagonism was spiroperidol > cyproheptadine > methysergide > mianserin > haloperidol. The order of antagonism to schistosome 5-HT receptors is haloperidol > cyproheptadine > nisoxetine > trazodone > mianserin > spiroperidol > methysergide (Wilcockson and Hillman, 1984). This order does not correspond to any known vertebrate 5-HT receptor and the high potency of haloperidol and low potency of spiroperidol are the most notable exceptions to the results of vertebrate 5-HT antagonist studies.

In the trematodes dopamine is also excitatory; this catecholemine increases motility and lengthening in *S. mansoni* and increases amplitude and contraction frequency in *F. hepatica* (Holmes and Fairweather, 1984; Wilcockson and Hillman, 1984). The lengthening response of the schistosome to DA may be due to a specific effect on the circular muscles (Tomosky *et al.*, 1974; Mellin *et al.*, 1983). Responses induced in schistosomes are not specific for DA but are also induced by NA and A, although not by specific alpha-adrenergic and beta-adrenergic agonists. More effective blocking of this response by apomorphine, a specific dopamine blocker, than by either alpha or beta adrenergic blockers suggests that these catecholamines all operate at the same DA receptor (Tomosky *et al.*, 1974). On the other hand, NA and A are inhibitory in *F. hepatica* and the effect is blocked by adrenergic antagonists (Holmes and Fairweather, 1984).

In the cestodes *D. caninum* and *H. diminuta*, 5-HT is excitatory (Lee *et al.*, 1978; Terada *et al.*, 1982; Thompson and Mettrick, 1984), although the excitatory role of 5-HT on *H. diminuta* is still not clear. 5-HT has more consistent excitatory effects on the circular muscles than on the longitudinal muscles of *H. diminuta* and it has significant inhibitory effects on the rate of sucker activity (Sukhdeo *et al.*, 1984). In addition, the motility responses to 5-HT by the strobila are concentration-dependent; 10^{-3} M 5-HT produces significant increases in spontaneous peristaltic motility, while 10^{-9} M 5-HT produces significant decreases in this motility (Sukhdeo *et al.*, 1984). Despite the overwhelming biochemical and histochemical evidence for a neurotransmitter role of 5-HT in cestodes, it appears that glutamate, and not 5-HT, acts as the excitatory substance in the longitudinal musculature of *H. diminuta* (Thompson and Mettrick, in preparation).

Glutamate is also believed to be the excitatory neurotransmitter in the cestodarian *Gyrocotyle fimbriata*, which belongs to a group that is more primitive than true cestodes. In the only neurophysiological study of flatworms, suction electrodes were attached to the isolated longitudinal nerve cords of this large worm. Although a wide variety of putative neurotransmitter drugs were tested on this preparation, changes in either spontaneous activity or evoked activity of these nerve cords were only found in response to the amino acids L-glutamate and L-aspartate, and the response was blocked by known glutamate blocking agents (Keenan and Koopowitz, 1982). The high levels of glutamate present in *S. mansoni* and *S. mansonoides* (Tomosky-Sykes *et al.*, 1977) suggests that this amino acid may also be important in other parasites. It is clear that further progress in the study of the neurobiology of these parasites depends on the development of good neuromuscular preparations.

IV. Conclusions

In this review we have stressed the importance of behavioural analyses to elucidate the mechanisms of orientation. In the free-living stages of parasitic platyhelminths the ability to orient to specific cues is crucial. The host finding behaviour of the free-living miracidia involves at least three sequential steps where, at a minimum, the parasites must be able to respond directionally to cues that characterize the host habitat and the specific host. Similar search patterns observed in other invertebrates, including food location behaviour of nematodes (Green, 1971; Ward, 1973) and the host finding behaviour of insect parasitoids (Lewis *et al.*, 1976; Bell and Cardé, 1984) reflects the conservative nature of a biologically successful strategy. Histological and morphological studies show that the miracidia is well supplied with a battery of mechanoreceptors, chemoreceptors, photoreceptors and gravity receptors connected to a neural network that includes a "brain" (Wilson, 1970; Fluks *et al.*, 1975). This of course is the basic equipment required for orientation and reflects the genetic investment in host finding.

The requirement for orientation ability may not be crucial during the site-finding behaviour of the parasitic stages. The host, although physiologically complex, provides a relatively more stable environment with fewer unknowns than the free-living environment. Gastrointestinal parasites without complex migration paths may only use releaser reactions, i.e. stereotyped patterns of behaviour stimulated by trigger cues. The activity of the oncospheres of *H. diminuta* is stimulated by the gut contents of the insect host. The hook movements of this larva allow its escape from the egg and the continuation of the same behaviour allows the larva to penetrate the gut wall and enter its final site in the body cavity (Anderson and Lethbridge, 1975). Thus, the "finding" of the final site in the body cavity does not require orientation to haemocoel-specific cues. This mechanism will work in the invariant environment of the host, where the minimum requirements would be a trigger cue and perhaps a "terminate" cue to signal arrival at the site and cessation of the behaviour. In the example of site finding by larval *H. diminuta*, the terminate cues are not obligatory since the larva runs out of energy for this behaviour by the time it penetrates the gut wall. Releaser reactions are commonly observed in the behavioural repertoire of several parasites and may even be responsible for circadian migration patterns. In the adult *H. diminuta*, the circadian migration pattern in the rat intestine does not result from an orientation response to the luminal contents, but is a function of activity modulation that is controlled by specific cues. Pancreatic and gastric secretions act as the trigger and terminate cues, respectively (Sukhdeo and Mettrick, 1984). However, releaser reactions to trigger cues do not account for site finding behaviour in trematodes with complex migrations through the host. Indeed, evidence shows that the adults of *S. mansoni* and *F. hepatica* can orient directionally to cues that may be important in site finding (Awad and Bell, 1982; Sukhdeo and Mettrick, 1986). The difficulties of isolating the specific stimuli to these responses have prevented precise characterization of the information processing systems. For example, chemoklinesis in miracidial host finding behaviour may be a response to one or more of over 50 possible cues. Pivotal to our understanding of behaviour, whether it be that of a site seeking trematode or a food seeking nematode, is that the organism will invest energy when stimulated by cues from favourable resources, but will withhold the investment when stimulated by cues from unfavourable resources or from resources to which the organism is indifferent. Thus, parasite responses to stimuli could be measured as positive or negative. Invertebrate responses are not simply negative or positive, but may be a function of the ratio of positive to negative factors in the stimulus (Dethier, 1982). An organism that may respond negatively to a stimulus, e.g. an unappealing food source, may respond positively under conditions that change the positive/negative ratio, e.g. when the organism is starved. Flexible and more adaptable behavioural responses to the environment result from such mechanisms and this may help explain some of the difficulties encountered in the determination of the specific cues of parasite behaviour. Carbon dioxide, reducing conditions and bile must be presented in the right sequence for the metacercariae of *F. hepatica* to excyst (Dixon, 1966), yet the excystment occurs even when worms are implanted into the abdominal cavity of mice (Dawes, 1961). Temperature, pH, pepsin, trypsin and bile all contribute to the excystment of *C. lingua*, but the absence of any one of these conditions does not prevent excystment (McDaniel, 1966). There have been no studies to determine if parasitic platyhelminths have a hierarchy in their responses to different cues or if cues may interact synergistically.

The best insights into the organization of behaviour in parasites may well come from studies of the nervous system. However, there is at present insufficient information, so that an effective integration between behavioural and neurobiological studies cannot yet be made. The evidence to date, based on studies of the morphology, cytology and histochemistry of the nervous system, and on the pharmacological effects of drugs on crude muscle preparations, suggests that platyhelminth nervous systems do not differ drastically from other closely related invertebrates, e.g. the turbellarians. However, a technological plateau has been reached and with the present methods we cannot answer questions relating to the types of neuronal circuitry that exist in the worms, how the circuitry is related to nervous control of behaviour and the levels of complexity that may be involved in the processing of sensory information. The first step towards answering these questions requires the ability to penetrate nerve cells with microelectrodes. Unfortunately, the techniques developed by neurobiologists do not work in small organisms with nerves that are impossible to visualize *in vitro* and which must be kept at host temperatures to maintain normal physiological function. For further progress in the study of the neurobiology of parasitic platyhelminths, new approaches will have to be devised.

Most of the major advances in neuroethology have been made using the "identified neuron approach", a method that utilizes the introduction of intracellular dyes to correlate specific muscle activity with nervous innervation (Hoyle, 1983). The approach being taken in our laboratory involves the determination of the nervous connections between the pharynx and the ventral sucker of *F. hepatica* using light and electron microscopy to localize the major nerve tracts and iontophoretic injection of Lucifer Yellow to trace nervous connections. The long-term goal is to explain the reciprocal inhibition between the behaviour of the pharynx (used in feeding) and the behaviour of the ventral sucker (used in attachment and locomotion). It is our opinion that the study of platyhelminth neurobiology will only advance through an approach that integrates behavioural analyses with neurobiology.

Acknowledgements

We thank Shigeru Kikukawa, Suzanne Sukhdeo, Jim Belanger and Steffanie Keith for reading the manuscript and for their critical discussions. This work was supported by Natural Sciences and Engineering Council of Canada grant A4667 to D. F. Mettrick.

References

Abrahams, S. L., Northup, J. K. and Mansour, T. E. (1976). Adenosine cyclic 3,5-monophosphate in the liver fluke *Fasciola hepatica*. I. Activation of adenylate cyclase by 5-hydroxytryptamine. *Molecular Pharmacology* **12,** 49–58.

Adler, J. (1983). Bacterial chemotaxis and molecular neurobiology. *Cold Spring Harbor Symposium of Quantitative Biology* **48,** 803–804.

Ahlman, H., Lundberg, J., Dahlstrom, A. and Keweuter, J. (1976). A possible vagal adrenergic release of serotonin from enterochromaffin cells in the cat. *Acta Physiologica Scandinavica* **98,** 336–375.

Alphey, T. J. W. (1970). Studies on the distribution and site location of *Nippostrongylus brasiliensis* within the small intestine of laboratory rats. *Parasitology* **61,** 449–460.

Alphey, T. J. W. (1971). Studies on aggregation behavior of *Nippostrongylus brasiliensis*. *Parasitology* **63,** 109–117.

Alphey, T. J. W. (1972). An *in vitro* study of the effect of oxygen tension upon the motility of *Nippostrongylus brasiliensis*. *Parasitology* **64,** 181–186.

Anderson, R. S. and Lethbridge, R. C. (1975). An experimental study of the survival characteristics, activity and energy reserves of the hexacanths of *Hymenolepis diminuta*. *Parasitology* **71,** 137–151.

Andreini, G. C., Beretta, C., Faustini, R. and Gallina, G. (1970). Spectroflurometric and chromatographic characterization of a butanol extract from *Fasciola hepatica*. *Experentia* **26,** 166–167.

Arai, H. P. (1980). Migratory activity and related phenomena in *Hymenolepis diminuta*. *In* "Biology of the Tapeworm *Hymenolepis diminuta*" (H. P. Arai, ed.), pp. 615–632. Academic Press Inc, New York.

Arme, C. (1966). Histochemical and biochemical studies on some enzymes of *Ligula intestinalis* (Cestoda: Pseudophyllidea). *Journal of Parasitology* **52,** 63–68.

Armstrong, J. C. (1965). Mating behaviour and development of schistosomes in the mouse. *Journal of Parasitology* **51,** 605–616.

Asangi, M. F. and Williams, M. O. (1974). Studies on the excystment of trematode metacercariae *in vivo*. *Journal of Helminthology* **48,** 85–91.

Awwad, M. and Bell, D. R. (1982). Faecal extract attracts copulating schistosomes. *Annals of Tropical Medicine and Parasitology* **72,** 389–390.

Bacq, Z. M. and Oury, A. (1937). Note sur la répartion de la cholinesterase chez les êtres vivants. *Académie Royale Belgique Bulletin Classe des Sciences* **23,** 891–893.

Bailey, G. M. A. (1971). *Hymenolepis diminuta*: circadian rhythm in movement and body length in the rat. *Experimental Parasitology* **29,** 285–291.

Bailey, W. S. (1972). *Spirocerca lupi*: a continuing enquiry. *Journal of Parasitology* **58,** 3–22.

Barker, L. R., Bueding, E. and Timms, A. R. (1966). The possible role of acetylcholine in *Schistosoma mansoni*. *British Journal of Pharmacology* **26,** 656–665.

Bawden, R. J. (1969). Some effects of the diet of mice on *Nematospiroides dubius* (Nematoda). *Parasitology* **59,** 203–213.

Bell, W. J. (1984). Chemo-orientation in walking insects. *In* "Chemical Ecology of Insects". (W. J. Bell and R. T. Cardé, eds.), pp. 93–110. Sinauer Associates Inc., Sunderland, Mass.

Bell, W. J. and Cardé, R. T. (1984). "Chemical Ecology of Insects". Sinauer Associates Inc., Sunderland, Mass. 524 pp.

Bell, W. J. and Tobin, T. R. (1982). Chemo-orientation. *Biological Reviews of the Cambridge Philosophical Society* **57,** 219–260.

Beernink, K. D., Nelson, S. D. and Mansour, T. E. (1963). Effect of lysergic acid derivatives on the liver fluke *Fasciola hepatica*. *International Journal of Neuropharmacology* **2,** 105–112.

Bennett, C. E. (1975a). *Fasciola hepatica*: Development of caecal epithelium during migration in the mouse. *Experimental Parasitology* **37,** 426–441.

Bennett, C. E. (1975b). Surface features, sensor structures and movement of the newly excysted juvenile *Fasciola hepatica* L. *Journal of Parasitology* **61,** 886–891.

Bennett, J. and Bueding, E. (1971). Localization of biogenic amines in *Schistosoma mansoni*. *Comparative Biochemistry and Physiology* **39A,** 859–867.

Bennett, J. and Gianutsos, G. (1977). Distribution of catecholamines in immature *Fasciola hepatica*: a histochemical and biochemical study. *International Journal for Parasitology* **7,** 221–225.

Bennett, J., Timms, A. R. and Engstrom, R. G. (1969). Occurrence and levels of 5-hydroxytryptamine in *Schistosoma mansoni*. *Molecular Pharmacology* **5,** 542–545.

Berntzen, A. K. and Voge, M. (1962). *In vitro* hatching of oncospheres of *Hymenolepis nana* and *Hymenolepis citelli* (Cestoda: Cyclophillidea). *Journal of Parasitology* **48,** 110–119.

Berntzen, A. K. and Voge, M. (1965). *In vitro* hatching of oncospheres of four hymenolepidid cestodes. *Journal of Parasitology* **51,** 235–242.

Berrie, A. D. (1969). Prolonged inhibition of growth in a natural population of the

fresh water snail *Biomphalaria sudanica tanganyicensis* in Uganda. *Annals of Tropical Medicine and Parasitology* **62,** 45–51.
Bettendorf, H. (1897). Ueber Muskulatur und Sinneszellen der Trematoden. *Zoologische Jahrbücher (Anatomie)* **10,** 307–358.
Black, J. W., Fisher, F. W. and Smith, A. N. (1958). The effects of 5-hydroxytryptamine on gastric secretion in anaesthetized dogs. *Journal of Physiology* **141,** 27–34.
Blitz, N. M. and Smyth, J. D. (1973). Tegumental ultrastructure of *Raillietina cesticillus* during the larval–adult transformation with emphasis on the rostellum. *International Journal for Parasitology* **3,** 561–570.
Blochmann, F. (1911). Die sogenannten freien Nervenendigungen bei Cestoden. *Zoologische Anzeiger* **38,** 87–88.
Bräten, T. and Hopkins, C. A. (1969). The migration of *Hymenolepis diminuta* in the rat's intestine during normal development and following surgical transplantation. *Parasitology* **59,** 891–905.
Brown, M. C., Norman, D. F., Bell, D. R. and Gilles, H. M. (1978). A multichannel ultrasonic activity monitor for *in vitro* screening of antischistosomal drugs. *Medical and Biological Engineering and Computing* **16,** 408–418.
Bruce, J. I., Pezzlo, F., Yajima Y. and McCarthy, J. E. (1974). *Schistosoma mansoni*: pulmonary phase of schistosomule migration studied by electron microscopy. *Parasitology* **35,** 150–160.
Bueding, E. (1952). Acetylcholinesterase activity of *Schistosoma mansoni. British Journal of Pharmacology* **7,** 563–566.
Bueding, E., Schiller, E. L. and Bourgeois, J. G. (1966). Some physiological, biochemical and morphologic effects of tris (p-aminophenyl) carbonium salts (TAC) on *S. mansoni. American Journal of Tropical Medicine and Hygiene* **16,** 500–515.
Bulbring, E., Lourie, E. M. and Pardoe, V. (1949). The presence of acetylcholine in *Trypanosoma rhodesiense* and its absence from *Plasmodium gallinaceum. British Journal of Pharmacology* **4,** 290–295.
Bullock, T. H. (1957). The trigger concept in biology. *In* "Physiological Triggers" (T. H. Bullock, ed.), pp. 1–8. American Physiological Society, Washington, D.C.
Bullock, T. H. and Horridge, G. A. (1965). "Structure and Function in the Nervous Systems of Invertebrates". Volume I. W. H. Freeman and Co., San Francisco pp. 535–577.
Buntning, P. (1927). Über den Mechanismus der Verwandlung des Cysticercus cellulosae in die *Taenia solium* und über die Wirdung der Verdaungsstafte auf diesen Prozess. *Zeitschrift für Morphologie und Ökologie der Tiere* **8,** 409–430.
Bursell, W. and Ewer, D. W. (1950). On the reactions to humidity of *Peripatopsis moseleyi* (Wood-Mason). *Journal of Experimental Biology* **26,** 335–353.
Caley, J. (1974). The functional significance of scolex retraction and subsequent cyst formation in the cysticercoid larva of *Hymenolepis diminuta. Parasitology* **68,** 207–228.
Campbell, W. C. (1961). Notes on the egg and miracidium of *Fascioloides magna* (Trematoda). *Transactions of the American Microscopical Society* **80,** 308–319.
Campbell, W. C. (1963). Efficacy of surface-active agents in stimulating evagination of cysticeri *in vitro. Journal of Parasitology* **49,** 81–84.
Campbell, W. C. and Richardson, T. (1960). Stimulation of cysticercus evagination by means of surfactants. *Journal of Parasitology* **46,** 490–495.
Campbell, W. C. and Todd, A. C. (1955). Behaviour of the miracidium of *Fascioloides magna* (Bassi 1875) Ward 1917 in the presence of a snail host. *Transactions of the American Mjcroscopical Society* **74,** 324–346.

Carvajal, J. and Dailey, M. D. (1975). Three new species of *Echeineibothrium* (Cestoda: Tetraphyllidea) from the skate *Raja chilensis* Guichenot, 1948, with comments on mode of attachment and host specificity. *Journal of Parasitology* **61**, 89–94.

Castro, G. A., Johnson, L. R., Copeland, E. M. and Dudrick, S. J. (1976). Course of infection with enteric parasites in hosts shifted from enteral to parenteral nutrition. *Journal of Parasitology* **62,** 353–359.

Chance, M. R. A. and Mansour, T. E. (1949). A kymographic study of the action of drugs on the liver fluke (*Fasciola hepatica*). *British Journal of Pharmacology* **4,** 7–13.

Chance, M. R. A. and Mansour, T. E. (1953). A contribution to the pharmacology of movement in the liver fluke. *British Journal of Pharmacology* **8,** 134–138.

Chandler, A. C. (1939). The effects of numbers and age of worms on development of primary and secondary infections with *Hymenolepis diminuta* in rats, and an investigation into the true nature of "premunition" in tapeworm infections. *American Journal of Hygiene* **29D,** 105–114.

Chapman, W. H. and Undeen, A. H. (1968). *In vivo* and *in vitro* hatching of eggs of *Trichosomoides crassicauda*. *Experimental Parasitology* **22,** 213–218.

Chappell, L. G., Arai, H. P., Dike, S. C. and Read, C. P. (1970). Circadian migration of *Hymenolepis* (Cestoda) in the intestine. I. Observations on *H. diminuta* in the rat. *Comparative Biochemistry and Physiology* **34,** 34–46.

Chavasse, C. J., Brown, M. C. and Bell, D. R. (1979). *Schistosoma mansoni*: ultrasonically detectable motor activity responses to 5-hydroxytryptamine *in vitro*. *Annals of Tropical Medicine and Parasitology* **73,** 363–368.

Chen, H. T. (1934). Reactions of *Ctenocephalides felis* to *Dipylidium caninum*. *Zeitschrift für Parasitienkunde* **6,** 603–637.

Cheng, T. C. (1968). The compatibility and incompatibility concept as related to trematodes and molluscs. *Pacific Science* **22,** 141–160.

Cheng, T. C. and Thakur, A. S. (1967). Thermal activation and inactivation of *Philopthalmus gralli* metacercariae. *Journal of Parasitology* **53,** 212–213.

Chernin, E. (1970). Behavioural responses of miracidia of *Schistosoma mansoni* and other trematodes to substances emitted by snails. *Journal of Parasitology* **56,** 287–296.

Chernin, E. and Dunavan, C. A. (1962). The influence of host–parasite dispersion upon the capacity of *Schistosoma mansoni* miracidia to infect *Australorbis glabratus*. *American Journal of Tropical Medicine and Hygiene* **11,** 455–471.

Ching, H. L. (1963a). The description and life cycle of *Maritrema aricola* sp.n. (Trematoda: Microphallidae). *Canadian Journal of Zoology* **41,** 881–888.

Ching, H. L. (1963b). The life cycle and bionomics of *Levinseniella charadriformis* Young 1949 (Trematoda: Microphallidae). *Canadian Journal of Zoology* **41,** 889–899.

Cho, C. H. and Mettrick, D. F. (1982). Circadian variation in worm distribution of *Hymenolepis diminuta* (Cestoda) and 5-HT (serotonin) levels in the gastrointestinal tract of the laboratory rat. *Parasitology* **84,** 431–443.

Christensen, W. O. (1980). A review of the influence of host- and parasite-related factors and environmental conditions on the host-finding capacity of the trematode miracidium. *Acta Tropica (Basel)* **37,** 303–318.

Chou, T-C. T., Bennett, J. and Bueding, E. (1972). Occurrence and concentrations of biogenic amines in trematodes. *Journal of Parasitology* **58,** 1098–1102.

Collings, S. B. and Hutchins, C. P. (1965). Motility and hatching of *Hymenolepis microstoma* oncospheres in sera, beetle extracts and salines. *Experimental Parasitology* **16,** 53–56.

Cooper, N. B., Allison, V. F. and Ubelaker, J. E. (1975). The fine structure of the cysticercoid of *Hymenolepis diminuta.* III. The scolex. *Zeitschrift für Parasitenkunde* **46,** 229–239.

Cooreman, I. and de Rycke, P. H. (1972). Migratory behaviour of *Hymenolepis diminuta. Zeitschrift für Parasitenkunde* **27,** 269–276.

Croll, N. A. (1970). "The Behaviour of Nematodes". Edward Arnold Ltd, London.

Croll, N. A. (1972). Behaviour of larval nematodes. *In* "Behavioural Aspects of Parasite Transmission" (E. U. Canning and C. A. Wright, eds.), pp. 31–52.

Croll, N. A. (1976a). "Organization of Nematodes". Academic Press, New York.

Croll, N. A. (1976b). The location of parasites within their hosts: the influence of host feeding and diet on the dispersion of adults of *Nipponstrongylus brasiliensis* in the intestine of the rat. *International Journal for Parasitology* **6,** 441–448.

Croll, N. A. and Smith, J. M. (1972). Mechanism of thermopositive behaviour in larval hookworms. *Journal of Parasitology* **58,** 891–896.

Crompton, D. W. T. (1973). The sites occupied by some parasitic helminths in the alimentary tract of vertebrates. *Biological Reviews* **48,** 27–83.

Crompton, D. W. T. (1976). Entry into the host and site selection. *In* "Ecological Aspects of Parasitology" (C. R. Kennedy, ed.), pp. 41–73. North-Holland Publ. Co., Amsterdam.

Crompton, D. W. T. and Whitfield, P. J. (1968). A hypothesis to account for the anterior migration of adult *Hymenolepis diminuta* (Cestoda) and *Moniliformis dubius* (Acanthocephala) in the intestine of rats. *Parasitology* **58,** 227–229.

Cyr, D., Gruner, S. and Mettrick, D. F. (1983). *Hymenolepis diminuta*: Uptake of 5-hydroxytryptamine (serotonin), glucose and changes in worm glycogen levels. *Canadian Journal of Zoology* **61,** 1469–1474.

Davenport, D. (1955). Specificity and behaviour in symbiosis. *Quarterly Review Biology* **30,** 29–46.

Davenport, D., Wright, C. A. and Causley, D. (1962). Technique for the study of the behaviour of motile micro-organisms. *Science* **135,** 1059–1060.

Dawes, B. (1961). On the early stages of *Fasciola hepatica* penetrating into the liver of an experimental host, the mouse: a·histological picture. *Journal of Helminthology.* R. T. Lieper Supplement pp. 41–52.

Dawes, B. (1963). The migration of juvenile forms of *Fasciola hepatica* L. through the wall of the intestines in the mouse, with some observations on food and feeding. *Parasitology* **53,** 109–122.

Dawes, B. and Hughes, D. L. (1964). *Fasciola* and fascioliasis. *Advances in Parasitology* **2,** 97–168.

Dei-Cas, E., Dhainaut-Courtois, N., Dhainant, A. and Vernes, A. (1979). Ultrastructural localization of tritiated 5-HT in adult *Schistoma mansoni. Biologie et Cellulaire* **35,** 321–324.

Dei-Cas, E., Dhainaut-Courtois, N. and Vernes, A. (1980). Contribution a l'étude du système nerveux des formes adultes et larvaires de Schistosoma mansoni Sambon 1907 (Trematode: Digenea). I. Aspects morphologiques: anatomie, histologie et ultrastructure chez la forme adulte. *Annales de Parasitologie Humaine et Comparée* **55,** 69–86.

de Moura, R. S. and Rozenthal, R. (1983). *Schistosoma mansoni*: new method for recording motor activity *in vitro. Experimental Parasitology* **56,** 314–317.

de Ryke, P. H. and van Grembergen, G. V. (1966). Étude sûr l'évagination de scolex d'*Echinococcus granulosus. Zeitschrift für Parasitenkunde* **25,** 518–525.

Despommier, D., Sukhdeo, M. V. K. and Meerovitch, E. (1978). *Trichinella spiralis*: site selection of the larva during its enteral phase of infection in mice. *Experimental Parasitology* **44,** 209–215.

Dethier, V. G. (1982). Mechanism of host–plant recognition. *Entomologia experimentalis et applicata* **31,** 49–50.

de Waele, A. (1934). Study of the function of bile in the evagination of the cysticerci of cestodes. *Annales de Parasitologie Humaine et Comparée* **12,** 492–510.

de Waele, A. (1940). Investigation on the biochemical mechanism of the influence of bile salts, acetylcholine, choline on the evagination of cysticerci of the cestodes. *Mededelingen van de K. Vlaarnsche Academie voor Wetenschapen* **1,** 3–19.

Dixon, K. E. (1964). Excystment of the metacercariae of *Fasciola hepatica* L. *in vitro. Nature* (Lond.) **202,** 1240–1241.

Dixon, K. E. (1965). The structure and histochemistry of the cyst wall of the metacercariae of *Fasciola hepatica* L. *Parasitology* **55,** 215–226.

Dixon, K. E. (1966). The physiology of excystment of the metacercariae of *Fasciola hepatica. Parasitology* **56,** 431–436.

Dixon, K. E. and Mercer, E. H. (1965). The fine structure of the nervous system of the cercaria of the liver fluke *Fasciola hepatica* L. *Journal of Parasitology* **51,** 967–976.

Dobson, C. (1961). Certain aspects of the host–parasite relationship of *Nematospiroides dubius* (Baylis). I. Resistance of male and female mice to experimental infections. *Parasitology* **51,** 173–179.

Dolani, H. A., Zaidman, E. and Gray, S. J. (1970). Hormonal and pharmacological influences on microcirculation in rat stomach. *American Journal of Physiology* **199,** 1157–1160.

Doutt, R. L. (1959). The biology of the parasitic Hymenoptera. *Annual Review of Entomology* **4,** 161–182.

Dunkely, L. C. and Mettrick, D. F. (1977). *Hymenolepis diminuta*: worm migration, intestinal and blood plasma glucose levels following host dietary carbohydrate intake. *Experimental Parasitology* **41,** 213–228.

Dusenbery, D. B. (1976). Chemotactic responses of male *Caenorhabditis elegans. Journal of Nematology* **8,** 352–355.

Edgar, S. A. (1940). Artificial evagination of larval tapeworms. *Transactions of the Kansas Academy of Science* **43,** 397–399.

Edgar, S. A. (1941). Use of bile salts for the evagination of tapeworm cysts. *Transactions of the American Microscopical Society* **60,** 121–128.

El-Sherif, M. A. and Mai, W. F. (1968). Thermotropic responses of *Pratylenchus penetrans* and *Ditylenchus dipsaci. Nematologica* **14,** 5–6.

El-Sherif, M. A. and Mai, W. F. (1969). Thermotactic response of some plant parasitic nematodes. *Journal of Nematology* **1,** 43–49.

Erasmus, D. A. (1962). Studies on the adult and metacercariae of *Holostephanus lühei* Szidat, 1936. *Parasitology* **52,** 353–374.

Erasmus, D. A. (1967). Histochemical observations on the structure and composition of the cyst wall enclosing the metacercaria of *Cyathocotyle bushiensis* Khan 1962 (Strigeoidea: Trematoda). *Journal of Helminthology* **41,** 11–14.

Erasmus, D. A. and Bennett, L. J. (1965). A study of the factors affecting excystation *in vitro* of the metacercarial stages of *Holostephanus lühei*, Szidat, 1936 and *Cyathocotyle bushiensis*, Kahn, 1962 (Strigeoida: Trematoda). *Journal of Helminthology* **39,** 185–196.

Etges, F. J., Carter, O. S. and Webbe, G. (1975). Behavioural and developmental physiology of schistosome larvae as related to their molluscan hosts. *Annals of the New York Academy of Science* **266,** 480–496.

Etges, F. J. and Decker, C. L. (1963). Chemosensitivity of the miracidium of *Schistosoma mansoni* to *Australorbis glabratus* and other snails. *Journal of Parasitology* **49,** 114–116.

Evans, D. S. and Wickham, M. G. (1971). The migratory behaviour of *Hymenolepis diminuta* in rats. *Proceedings of the West Virginia Academy of Science* **43,** 99–102.

Evans, W. S. (1980). The cultivation of hymenolepids *in vitro*. In "Biology of the Tapeworm *Hymenolepis diminuta*" (H. P. Arai, ed.), pp. 425–448. Academic Press, New York.

Eveland, L. K., Fried, B. and Cohen, L. M. (1983). *Schistosoma mansoni*: adult worm chemoattraction with barriers of specific molecular weight exclusions. *Experimental Parasitology* **56,** 255–258.

Ewer, D. W. and Bursell, E. (1950). A note on the classification of elementary behavioural patterns. *Behaviour* **34,** 40–47.

Fairweather, I., Holmes, S. D. and Threadgold, L. T. (1983). *Fasciola hepatica*: a technique for monitoring *in vitro* motility. *Experimental Parasitology* **56,** 369–380.

Fairweather, I., Holmes, S. D. and Threadgold, L. T. (1984). *Fasciola hepatica*: motility response to fasciolicides *in vitro*. *Experimental Parasitology* **57,** 209–224.

Fairweather, I. and Threadgold, L. T. (1983). *Hymenolepis nana*: the fine structure of the adult nervous system. *Parasitology* **86,** 89–103.

Faust, E. C. and Khaw, K. (1925). Excystment phenomena in *Clonorchis sinensis*. *Proceedings of the Society of Experimental Biology and Medicine* **23,** 245–248.

Faust, E. C. and Khaw, K. (1927). Studies on *Clonorchis sinensis* (Cobbold). *American Journal of Hygiene* Monograph Series No. 8.

Featherston, D. W. (1971). *Taenia hydatigena*. II. Evagination of cysticercus and establishment in dogs. *Experimental Parasitology* **29,** 242–249.

Fetterer, R. H., Pax, R. A. and Bennett, J. L. (1977). *Schistosoma mansoni*: direct method for simultaneous recording of electrical and motor activity. *Experimental Parasitology* **43,** 286–294.

Fluks, A. J., Scheerboom, J. E. M., Meuleman, E. A. (1975). The fine structure of the nervous system in the miracidium of *Schistosoma mansoni*. *Tropical and Geographical Medicine* **27,** 227–228.

Foreyt, W. J., Samuel, W. M. and Todd, A. C. (1977). *Fascioloides magna* in white-tailed deer (*Odocoileus virginianus*): observation on the pairing tendency. *Journal of Parasitology* **63,** 1050–1052.

Fraenkel, G. S. and Gunn, D. L. (1940). "The Orientation of Animals". Oxford University Press, Oxford.

Fraenkel, G. S. and Gunn, D. L. (1961). "The Orientation of Animals. Kineses, Taxes and Compass Reactions". Dover Publications Inc., New York.

Fried, B. (1970). Excystation of metacercariae of *Postodiplostomum minimum minimum* Hoffman 1958, and their development in the chick and on the choriallantois. *Journal of Parasitology* **56,** 944–946.

Fried, B. and Gioscia, R. M. (1976). Tentative identification of cholesterol as a chemoattractant for metacercarial pairing in *Leucochlordiomorpha constantiae* (Trematoda). *Journal of Parasitology* **62,** 326–327.

Fried, B. and Leiby, D. A. (1982). Intraspecific and interspecific pairing of *Haematoloechus medioplexus* (Trematoda) and *Echinostoma revolutum* (Trematoda) adults

in vivo and observations on *H. medioplexus* lipophilic excretory–secretory products. *Parasitology* **84,** 375–380.
Fried, B., Robbins, S. H. and Nelson, P. D. (1978). *In vivo* and *in vitro* excystation of *Zygocotyle lunata* (Trematoda) metacercariae and histochemical observations of the cyst. *Journal of Parasitology* **64,** 395–397.
Fried, B. and Robinson, G. A. (1981). Pairing and aggregation of *Amblosoma suwaense* (Trematoda: Brachylaimidae) metacercariae *in vitro* and partial characterization of lipids involved in chemo-attraction. *Parasitology* **82,** 225–229.
Fried, B. and Roth, R. M. (1974). *In vitro* excystment of the metacercariae of *Parorchis acanthus*. *Journal of Parasitology* **60,** 465.
Fried, B., Tancer, R. B. and Fleming, S. J. (1980). *In vitro* pairing of *Echinostoma revolutum* (Trematoda) metacercariae and adults, and characterization of worm products involved in chemoattraction. *Journal of Parasitology* **66,** 1014–1018.
Fripp, P. J. (1967). Histochemical localization of esterase activity in schistosomes. *Experimental Parasitology* **21,** 380–390.
Fuentes, B., Negrette, J. and Villalobo, R. (1960). Algunos factores físicos y químicos que afectan la evaginación de cysticercus cellulosae *in vitro*. *Revista del Instituto de Salubridad y Enfermedades Tropicales* **20,** 103–127.
Gainer, H. and Brownstein, M. J. (1981). Neuropeptides. *In* "Basic Neurochemistry" (G. J. R. Siegel, W. Albers, B. W. Agranoff and R. Katzman, eds.), pp. 269–296. Little Brown, Boston.
Gallati, W. W. (1959). Life history morphology and taxonomy of *Ariotaenia (Ershovia) procyonis* (Cestoda: Linstowiidae), a parasite of the raccoon. *Journal of Parasitology* **45,** 363–377.
Gear, N. R. and Fripp, P. J. (1974). Comparison of the characteristics of acetylcholinesterase present in four species of *Schistosoma*. *Comparative Biochemistry and Physiology* **47B,** 743–752.
Gentleman, S., Abrahams, S. L. and Mansour, T. E. (1976). Adenosine cyclic 3′,5′-monophosphate in the liver fluke *Fasciola hepatica*. II. Activation of protein kinase by 5-hydroxytryptamine. *Molecular Pharmacology* **12,** 59–68.
Gerber, J. H. (1952). Bilharzia in Boajibu. II. The human population. *Journal of Tropical Medicine and Hygiene* **55,** 79–93.
Gianutsos, G. and Bennett, J. (1977). The regional distribution of dopamine and norepinephrine in *Schistosoma mansoni* and *Fasciola hepatica*. *Comparative Biochemistry and Physiology* **58,** 157–159.
Goodchild, C. G. (1958). Transfaunation and repair of damage in the rat tapeworm *Hymenolepis diminuta*. *Journal of Parasitology* **44,** 345–351.
Goodchild, C. G. and Davis, O. B. (1972). *Hymenolepis microstoma* cystercoid activation and excystation *in vitro*. *Journal of Parasitology* **58,** 735–741.
Goodchild, C. G. and Harrison, D. L. (1961). The growth of the rat tapeworm *Hymenolepis diminuta* during the first five days in the final host. *Journal of Parasitology* **47,** 819–829.
Gordon, R. M. and Griffiths, R. B. (1951). Observations on the means by which cercariae of *Schistosoma mansoni* penetrate mammalian skin. *Annals of Tropical Medicine and Parasitology* **45,** 227–243.
Graff, D. S. and Kitzman, W. B. (1965). Factors influencing the activation of acanthocephalan cystacanths. *Journal of Parasitology* **51,** 424–429.
Green, C. D. (1971). Mating and host finding behaviour of plant nematodes. *In* "Plant Parasitic Nematodes" (B. M. Zuckerman, W. F. Mai and R. A. Rohde, eds.), Vol 2, pp. 247–266. Academic Press, New York.

Green, C. D. (1980). Nematode sex attractants. *Helminthological Abstracts Series A.* **49,** 327–339.

Gursch, O. F. (1948). Effect of digestion and refrigeration on the ability of *Trichinella spiralis* to infect rats. *Journal of Parasitology* **34,** 394–395.

Gustafsson, M. K. (1984). Synapses of *Diphylobothrium dendriticum* (Cestoda). An electron microscopical study. *Annales Zoologici Fennici* **21,** 167–175.

Halton, D. W. (1967). Histochemical studies of carboxylic esterase activity in *Fasciola hepatica. Journal of Parasitology* **53,** 1210–1216.

Hart, J. L. (1967). Studies on the nervous system of tetrathyridia (Cestoda: Mesocestoides). *Journal of Parasitology* **53,** 1032–1039.

Haslewood, G. A. D. (1978). "The Biological Importance of Bile Salts". Frontiers in Biology. North-Holland Publ. Co., Amsterdam.

Havet, J. (1900). Contribution a l'étude du système nerveuse des trématodes (*Distomum hepaticum*). *Cellule* **17,** 351–380.

Hemenway, M. (1948). Studies on excystment of *Clinostomum* metacercariae by use of artificial digestion. *Proceedings of the Academy of Science* **55,** 375–381.

Hillman, G. R. (1979). An improved electronic activity monitor for schistosomes. *Journal of Pharmacological Methods* **2,** 21–27.

Hillman, G. R. (1983). The neuropharmacology of schistosomes. *Pharmacological Therapy* **22,** 103–115.

Hillman, G. R., Gibler, A. M. and Anderson, J. B. (1978). Scanning microfluometric studies on anticholinergic drugs in *Schistosoma mansoni. Journal of Pharmacology and Experimental Therapy* **207,** 992–997.

Hillman, G. R. and Gibler, W. B. (1975). Acetylcholine receptors in *Schistosoma mansoni*: visualization and blockade by hycanthone. *Biochemical Pharmacology* **24,** 1911–1914.

Hillman, G. R., Gilber, W. B. and Chu, S. H. (1976). Fluorescent probes of acetylcholine binding sites—indicators of drug action in *Schistosoma mansoni. Biochemical Pharmacology* **25,** 2529–2535.

Hillman, G. R. and Senft, A. W. (1973). Schistosome motility measurements: response to drugs. *Journal of Pharmacology and Experimental Therapy* **185,** 177–184.

Hillman, G. R. and Senft, A. W. (1975). Anticholinergic properties of the antischistosomal drug hycanthone. *American Journal of Tropical Medicine and Hygiene* **24,** 827–834.

Hoffman, G. L. (1959). Studies on the life cycle of *Apatemon gracilis pellucidus* (Yamag.) (Trematoda: Strigeoidea). *Transactions of the American Fish Society* **88,** 96–99.

Holmes, J. C. (1961). Effects of concurrent infections on *Hymenolepis diminuta* (Cestoda) and *Moniliformis dubius* (Acanthocephala). I. General effects and comparison with crowding. *Journal of Parasitology* **47,** 209–216.

Holmes, J. C. (1962). Effects of concurrent infections on *Hymenolepis diminuta* (Cestoda) and *Moniliformis dubius* (Acanthocephala). III. Effect in hamsters. *Journal of Parasitology* **48,** 97–100.

Holmes, J. C. (1973). Site selection by parasitic helminths: interspecific interactions, site segregation, and their importance to the development of helminth communities. *Canadian Journal of Zoology* **51,** 333–347.

Holmes, J. C. (1976). Host selection and its consequences. *In* "Ecological Aspects of Parasitology" (C. R. Kennedy, ed.), pp. 21–39. North-Holland Publ. Co., Amsterdam.

Holmes, S. C. and Fairweather, I. (1984). *Fasciola hepatica*: the effects of neuropharmacological agents upon *in vitro* motility. *Experimental Parasitology* **58,** 194–208.

Hopkins, C. A. (1969). The influence of dietary methionine on the amino acid pool of *Hymenolepis diminuta* in the rat's intestine. *Parasitology* **59,** 407–427.

Hopkins, C. A. and Allen, L. M. (1979). *Hymenolepis diminuta*: the role of the tail in determining the position of the worm in the intestine of the rat. *Parasitology* **79,** 401–410.

Howell, M. J. (1970). Excystment of the metacercariae of *Echinoparyphium serratum* (Trematoda: Echinostomatidae). *Journal of Helminthology* **45,** 35–56.

Hoyle, G. (1983). On the way to neuroethology: The identified neuron approach. *In* "Neuroethology and Behavioral Physiology" (F. Huber and H. Mark, eds.), pp. 9–25. Springer-Verlag Berlin, Heidelberg.

Hsu, H. F. and Wang, L. S. (1938). Studies on certain problems of *Clonorchis sinensis*. IV. Notes on the resistance of cysts in fish flesh, the migration route and the morphology of the young worms in the final host. *Chinese Medical Journal* (Suppl) **2,** 385–400.

Hwang, J. C. (1960). Effects of pH, various proteolytic enzymes, amino acids and other substances on the eggs and larvae of *Ascaridia galli*. *Journal of Parasitology* **46,** 27 (Suppl).

Imperia, P. S. and Fried, B. (1980). Pheromonal attraction of *Schistosoma mansoni* females towards males in the absence of worm-tactile behaviour. *Journal of Parasitology* **66,** 682–684.

Ip, H. S. and Desser, S. S. (1984). Transmission electron microscopy of the tegumentary sense organs of *Cotylogaster occidentalis* (Trematoda: Aspidogastrea) *Journal of Parasitology* **70**, 563–575.

Irwin, S. W. B. (1983). *In vitro* excystment of the metacercariae of *Maritrema arenaria* (Digenea: Microphallidae). *International Journal for Parasitology* **13,** 191–196.

Jaffee, B. M., Kopem, D. F. and Lazan, D. Q. (1977). Endogenous serotonin in the control of gastric and secretion. *Surgery* **82,** 156–163.

Jewsbury, J. M., Homewood, C. A. and Marshall, I. (1977). Inexpensive apparatus for measuring activity of *Schistoma mansoni in vitro*. *Transactions of the Royal Society of Tropical Medicine and Hygiene* **71,** 115.

Johnson, C. D. and Stretton, A. O. W. (1980). Neural control of locomotion in *Ascaris*: anatomy, electrophysiology and biochemistry. *In* "Nematodes as Biological Models. Vol I. Behavioral and Developmental Models". (B. M. Żuckerman, ed.), pp. 159–195. Academic Press, New York.

Johnstone, J. (1912). *Tetrarhynchus erinaceus* van Beneden. I. Structure of larva and adult worm. *Parasitology* **4,** 364–415.

Kawashima, K., Tada, I. and Miyazaki, I. (1961). Host preference of miracidia of *Paragonimus ohira* Miyazaki 1939 among three species of snails of the genus *Assiminea* Kyushu. *Journal of Medical Science* **12,** 99–106.

Keenan, L. and Koopowitz, H. (1982). Physiology and *in situ* identification of putative aminergic neurotransmitters in the nervous system of *Gyrocotyle fimbriata*, a parasitic flatworm. *Journal of Neurobiology* **13,** 9–21.

Keshavarz-Valian, H. and Nollen, P. M. (1980). Responses of *Philopthalmus gralli* miracidia to gravity and light. *Journal of Parasitology* **66,** 684–686.

Keshavarz-Valian, H., Nollen, P. M. and Maynard, G. (1981). *Philopthalmus gralli*: chemosensitivity of miracidia. *Journal of Parasitology* **67,** 527–530.

Khalil, M. (1922). Thermotropism in ancyclostome larvae. *Proceedings of the Royal Society of Medicine* **15,** 6–8.

Kinoti, G. (1968). Observations on the infection of bulinid snails with *Schistosoma mattheei*. I. The susceptibility of *Bulinus africanus* and *Bulinus truncatus*. *Annals of Tropical Medicine and Parasitology* **62,** 382–392.

Kirchner, K. and Bacha, W. J. Jr. (1980). Excystment of *Himasthla quissetensis* (Trematoda: Echinostomatidae) metacercariae *in vitro*. *Journal of Parasitology* **66,** 263–267.

Kleinschuster, S. J., Hepler, D. I. and Voth, D. R. (1978). Attachment of *Nematospiroides dubius* in the murine intestine. *Veterinary Science Communications* **2,** 237–241.

Keenan, and Koopowitz (1982). Physiology and *in situ* identification of putative aminergic neurotransmitters in the nervous system of *Gyrocotyle fimbriata*, a parasitic flatworm. *Journal of Neurobiology* **13**, 9–21.

Kloetzel, K. (1958). Observacoes sobre a tropismo do miracidio de *S. manoni* pelo molusco A. glabratus. *Revista Brasileira de Biologia* **18,** 223–232.

Konturek, S., Radecki, T., Pawlik, W., Thor, P. and Biernat, S. (1974). Significance of vagus nerves in the regulation of pancreatic secretion. *Acta Physiologica Polonica* **25,** 423–433.

Kreig, C., Cole, T., Deppe, U., Schierenberg, E., Schmitt, D., Yoder, B. and von Ehrenstein, G. (1978). The cellular anatomy of embryos of the nematode *Caenorhabditis elegans*. *Developmental Biology* **65,** 193–215.

Kruger, S. P., Heitman, L. P., van Wyk, J. A. and McCully, R. M. (1969). The route of migration of *Schistosoma mattheei* from lungs to liver in sheep. *Journal of South African Veterinary Medical Association* **40,** 39–43.

Krull, W. H. and Price, H. F. (1932). Studies on the life history of *Diplodiscus temperatus* (Strafford) from the frog. *Occasional Papers of the Museum of Zoology. University of Michigan* **237,** 39.

Krvavica, S., Lui, A. and Becejac, S. (1967). Acetylcholinesterase and butyrylcholinesterase in the liver fluke (*Fasciola hepatica*). *Experimental Parasitology* **21,** 240–248.

Lackie, A. M. (1974). The activation of cystacanths of *Polymorphus minutus* (Acanthocephala) *in vitro*. *Parasitology* **68,** 135–146.

Lackie, A. M. (1975). The activation of infective stages of endoparasites of vertebrates. *Biological Reviews* **50,** 285–323.

Laing, J. (1937). Host finding by insect parasites. I. Observations on the finding of hosts by *Alysia manducator, Mormoniella vitropennis* and *Trichogramma evanescens*. *Journal of Animal Ecology* **6,** 298–317.

Lebowitz, H. E. and Feldman, J. M. (1973). Pancreatic amines and insulin release in health and disease. *Federation Proceedings* **32,** 1797–1802.

Lechin, F., Coll-Garcia, E., van der Dijs, F., Pena, F., Bentolita, A. and Rivas, C. (1975). The effects of serotonin in insulin secretion. *Acta Physiologica Latinoamericana* **25,** 339–346.

Lee, D. L. A., Rothman, A. H. and Senturia, J. B. (1963). Esterases in *Hymenolepis* and in *Hydatigera*. *Experimental Parasitology* **14,** 285–295.

Lee, M. B., Bueding, E. and Schiller, E. L. (1978). The occurence and distribution of 5-hydroxytryptamine in *Hymenolepis diminuta* and *H. nana*. *Journal of Parasitology* **64,** 257–264.

Lee, T. D. G. and Wright, K. A. (1978). The morphology of the attachment and probable feeding site of the nematode *Trichuris muris* (Schrank, 1788), Hall 1916. *Canadian Journal of Zoology* **86,** 1889–1905.

Leflore, W. B. and Bass, H. S. (1983). *In vitro* excystment of the metacercariae of

Cloactrema michiganensis (Trematoda: Philophalmidae). *Journal of Parasitology* **69,** 200–204.

Lethbridge, R. C. (1971). The hatching of *Hymenolepis diminuta* eggs and penetration of the hexacanths in *Tenebrio molitor* beetles. *Parasitology* **62,** 445–456.

Lethbridge, R. C. (1980). The biology of the oncosphere of cyclophyllidean cestodes. *Helminthological Abstracts Series A* **49,** 59–72.

Leuckart, K. G. F. R. (1894). "Die Parasiten des Menschen und die von ihnen Lerruhrenden Krankheiten". Vol. 1, part 5. Leipzig, Verlagshandlung.

Lewis, W. J., Jones, R. L., Gross, H. R. and Nordlund, D. A. (1976). The role of kairmones and other behavioral chemicals in host finding by parasitic insects. *Behavioural Biology* **16B,** 267–289.

Lumsden, R. D. and Specian, R. (1980). The morphology, histology and fine structure of the adult stage of the cyclophyllidean tapeworm *Hymenolepis diminuta*. *In* "Biology of the Tapeworm *Hymenolepis diminuta*" (H. P. Arai, ed.), pp. 157–280. Academic Press, New York.

Luria, W. M. and Kinney, J. A. S. (1970). Underwater vision. *Science* **167,** 1454–1461.

Lyons, K. M. (1972). Sense organs of monogeneans. *In* "Behavioural Aspects of Parasite Transmission" (E. U. Canning and C. A. Wright, eds.), pp. 181–199. Academic Press, New York.

MacInnis, A. J. (1965). Responses of *Schistosoma mansoni* miracidia to chemical attractants. *Journal of Parasitology* **51,** 731–746.

MacInnis, A. J. (1974). A general theory of parasitism. *Proceedings of the IIIrd International Congress of International Parasitology*: Facta, Vienna **3,** 1511–1512.

MacInnis, A. J. (1976). How parasites find hosts: some thoughts on the conception of host parasite integration. *In* "Ecological Aspects of Parasitology" (C. R. Kennedy, ed.), pp. 3–20. North-Holland Publ. Co., Amsterdam.

Macy, R. W., Berntzen, A. K. and Benz, M. (1968). *In vitro* excystation of *Sphaeridiotrema globulus* metacercariae structure of cyst and the relationship to host specificity. *Journal of Parasitology* **54,** 28–38.

Majumdar, A. P. N. and Nakhla, A. M. (1979). Effect of 5-hydroxytryptamine on protein synthesis in gastrointestinal and other tissues and in serum gastrin concentrations in rats. *British Journal of Pharmacology* **66,** 211–215.

Mansour, T. E. (1957). The effect of lysergic acid diethylamide, 5-hydroxytryptamine and related compounds on the liver fluke, *Fasciola hepatica*. *British Journal of Pharmacology* **12,** 406–409.

Mansour, T. E. (1964). The pharmacology and biochemistry of parasitic helminths. *In* "Advances in Pharmacology" (S. Garratina and P. A. Shore, eds.), pp. 129–165. Vol. 3. Academic Press, New York.

Mansour, T. E. (1979). Chemotherapy of parasite worms: new biochemical strategies. *Science* **25,** 464–469.

Mansour, T. E. and Stone, D. B. (1970). Biochemical effects of lysergic acid diethylamide on the liver fluke *Fasciola hepatica*. *Biochemical Pharmacology* **19,** 1137–1146.

Mapes, C. J. (1972). Bile and bile salts and exsheathment of the intestinal nematodes *Trichostrongylus colubriformis* and *Nematodirus battus*. *International Journal for Parasitology* **2,** 433–438.

Mason, P. R. and Fripp, P. J. (1976). Analysis of the movements of *Schistosoma mansoni* miracidia using dark ground photography. *Journal of Parasitology* **62,** 721–727.

Mason, P. R. and Fripp, P. J. (1977). The reactions of *Schistosoma mansoni* miracidia to light. *Journal of Parasitology* **63,** 240–244.

McCue, J. F. and Thornson, R. E. (1964). Behaviour of parasitic stages of helminths in a thermal gradient. *Journal of Parasitology* **50,** 67–71.

McDaniel, J. S. (1966). Excystment of *Crytocotyle lingua* metacercariae. *Biological Bulletin* **130,** 369–377.

McVicar, A. H. (1977). Intestinal helminth parasites of the ray *Raja naevus* in British waters. *Journal of Helminthology* **51,** 11–21.

McVicar, A. H. (1979). The distribution of cestodes within the spiral intestine of *Raja naevus* Mullar and Henle. *International Journal for Parasitology* **9,** 165–176.

Mead, R. W. (1976). Effect of abnormal intestinal glucose distribution on the migration of *Hymenolepis diminuta. Journal of Parasitology* **62,** 328–329.

Mead, R. W. and Roberts, L. S. (1972). Intestinal digestion and absorption of starch in the intact rat: effects of cestode (*Hymenolepis diminuta*) infection. *Comparative Biochemistry and Physiology* **41A,** 749–760.

Mellin, T. N., Busch, R. D., Wang, C. C. and Kath, G. (1983). Neuropharmacology of the parasitic trematode, *Schistosoma mansoni. American Journal of Tropical Medicine and Hygiene* **32,** 83–93.

Mettrick, D. F. (1970). Protein, amino acid and carbohydrate gradients in the rat intestine. *Comparative Biochemistry and Physiology* **37,** 517–541.

Mettrick, D. F. (1971a). *Hymenolepis diminuta*: effect of quantity of amino acid dietary supplement on growth. *Experimental Parasitology* **29,** 13–25.

Mettrick, D. F. (1971b). *Hymenolepis diminuta*: pH changes in rat intestinal contents and worm migration. *Experimental Parasitology* **29,** 386–401.

Mettrick, D. F. (1971c). Effect of host dietary constituents on intestinal pH and on the migrational behaviour of the rat tapeworm *Hymenolepis diminuta. Canadian Journal of Zoology* **29,** 1513–1525.

Mettrick, D. F. (1972). Changes in the distribution and chemical composition of *Hymenolepis diminuta* and the intestinal nutritional gradients of uninfected and parasitized rats following a glucose meal. *Journal of Helminthology* **46,** 707–729.

Mettrick, D. F. (1973). Competition for ingested nutrients between the tapeworm *Hymenolepis diminuta* and the rat host. *Canadian Journal of Public Health* **64,** 70–82.

Mettrick, D. F. (1975). Correlations between the amino acid pools of *Hymenolepis diminuta* and the rat intestine. *Canadian Journal of Zoology* **53,** 320–331.

Mettrick, D. F. (1980). The intestine as an environment for *Hymenolepis diminuta. In* "The Biology of *Hymenolepis diminuta*" (H. P. Arai, ed.), pp. 281–356. Academic Press, New York.

Mettrick, D. F. and Cho, C. H. (1981a). *Hymenolepis diminuta*; effect of electrical vagal stimulation on worm migration. *Journal of Parasitology* **67,** 386–390.

Mettrick, D. F. and Cho, C. H. (1981b). Migration of *Hymenolepis diminuta* (Cestoda) and changes in 5-HT (serotonin) levels in the rat host following parenteral and oral 5-HT administration. *Canadian Journal of Physiology and Pharmacology* **59,** 281–286.

Mettrick, D. F. and Cho, C. H. (1982). Changes in tissue and intestinal 5-HT (serotonin) levels in the laboratory rat following feeding and the effect of 5-HT inhibitors on the migrating response of *Hymenolepis diminuta* (Cestoda). *Canadian Journal of Zoology* **60,** 790–797.

Mettrick, D. F. and Dunkely, L. C. (1969). Variations in the size and position of *Hymenolepis diminuta* (Cestoda: Cyclophllidea) within the rats intestine. *Canadian Journal of Zoology* **47,** 1091–1101.

Mettrick, D. F. and Podesta, R. B. (1974). Ecological and physiological aspects of helminth–host interactions in the mammalian gastrointestinal canal. *Advances in Parasitology* **12,** 183–278.

Mettrick, D. F. and Podesta, R. B. (1982). Effect of gastrointestinal hormones and amines on intestinal mobility and the migration of *Hymenolepis diminuta* (Cestoda) in the rat small intestine. *International Journal for Parasitology* **12,** 151–154.

Mettrick, D. F., Rahman, M. S. and Podesta, R. B. (1981). Effect of 5-hydroxytryptamine (5-HT; serotonin) on *in vivo* glucose uptake and glycogen reserves in *Hymenolepis diminuta. Molecular and Biochemical Parasitology* **4,** 217–224.

Miller, P., Wilson, R. A. (1978). Migration of the schistosomula of *Schistosoma mansoni* from skin to lungs. *Parasitology* **77,** 281–302.

Morseth, D. J. (1967). Observations on the fine structure of the nervous system of *Echinococcus granulosus. Journal of Parasitology* **53,** 492–500.

Mueller, J. F. (1968). Growth stimulating effect of experimental sparganosis in thyroidectomized and hypophysectomized rats, and comparative activity of different species of *Spirometra. Journal of Parasitology* **54,** 795–801.

Neuhaus, W. (1953). Uber den chemischen Sinn der Miracidien von *Fasciola hepatica Zeitschrift für Parasitenkunde* **15,** 476–490.

Nimmo-Smith, R. H. and Raison, C. C. (1968). Monoamine oxidase activity of *Schistosoma mansoni. Comparative Biochemistry and Physiology* **24,** 403–416.

Ogren, R. E., Orgen, J. J. and Skarnulis, J. J. (1969). Effects of salt and neutral red solutions on movements of invasive oncospheres from the tapeworm *Hymenolepis diminuta. Proceedings of the Pennsylvania Academy of Science* **43,** 56–60.

Oshima, T., Yoshida, Y. and Kihata, M. (1958). Studies on the excystation of the metacercariae of *Paragonimus westermani.* II. Influence of pepsin pretreatment on the effect of bile salts. *Bulletin of the Institute of Public Health, Tokyo* **7,** 270–274.

Panitz, E. (1970). Histochemical localization of cholinesterase activity in *Fascioloides magna* (Bassi) 1875. *Comparative Genetics and Pharmacology* **1,** 372–374.

Pappas, P. W. and Mayer, L. P. (1976). The effect of transplanted *Hymenolepis microstoma*, the mouse bile duct tapeworm on CF-1 mice. *Journal of Parasitology* **6,** 329–332.

Patlak, C. S. (1953). Random walk with persistence and external bias. *Bulletin of Mathematical Biophysics* **15,** 311–338.

Pax, R. A., Siefker, C. and Bennet, J. L. (1984). *Schistosoma mansoni*: differences in acetylcholine, dopamine and serotonin control of circular and longitudinal parasite muscles. *Experimental Parasitology* **58,** 314–324.

Pennoit-de Cooman, E. and van Grembergen, G. (1942). Vergelijkend onderzoek van het fermentensysteem bij vrijlerende en parasitaire Plathelminthen. *Verhandelingen van de Koiniklijke Vlaamse Academie voor Wetenschapen* **4,** 7–77.

Pettersson, G. (1979). The neural control of serotonin content in mammaliam enterochromaffin cells. *Acta Physiologica Scandinavica*, Supplement **470,** 1–30.

Pintner, T. (1934). Bruchstücke zur Kenntnis der Rüsselbandwurmer. *Zoologische Jahrbücher (Anatomie)* **58,** 1–20.

Plempel, von M. (1964). Chemotaktische Anlockung der Miracidien von *Schistosoma mansoni* durch *Australorbis glabratus. Zeitschrift für Naturforschungen* **196,** 268–269.

Plempel, von M., Gounert, R. and Federmann, M. (1966). Versuche zur wirtsfindung von Miracidien. *Proceedings of the 1st International Congress of Parasitology* **1,** 32.

Plorin, G. G. and Gilbertson, D. E. (1981). Descriptive statistics of swimming behaviour of *Schistosoma mansoni* miracidia in artificial pond water. *Journal of Parasitology* **67,** 45–49.

Plorin, G. G. and Gilbertson, D. E. (1985). Behaviour of *Schistosoma mansoni* miracidia in gradients and in uniform concentrations of glucose. *Journal of Parasitology* **71,** 116.

Podesta, R. B. and Mettrick, D. F. (1981). A simple method for analysing oral and intravenous treatment effects on biomass re-distribution of *Hymenolepis diminuta* (Cestoda) in the rat intestine. *Canadian Journal of Zoology* **59,** 861–863.

Prah, S. K. and James C. (1977). The influence of physical factors on the survival and infectivity of miracidia of *Schistosoma mansoni* and *S. haematobium*. I. Effect of temperature and ultraviolet light. *Journal of Helminthology* **51,** 73–85.

Prah, S. K. and James, C. (1978). The influence of physical factors on the behaviour and infectivity of miracidia of *Schistosoma mansoni* and *S. haemotobium*. II. Effect of light and depth. *Journal of Helminthology* **52,** 115–120.

Prechel, D. P., Cain, G. P. and Nollen, P. M. (1976). Responses of *Megalodiscus temperatus* miracidia to amino and sialic acids found in snail-conditioned water. *Journal of Parasitology* **62,** 693–697.

Prechel, D. P. and Nollen, P. M. (1979). The effects of miracidial ageing and dilution of snail-conditioned water on responses of miracidia of *Megalodiscus temperatus*. *Journal of Parasitology* **65,** 446–450.

Pritchard, R. K., Bachmann, R., Hutchinson, G. W. and Kohler, P. (1982). The effect of praziquantel on calcium in *Hymenolepis diminuta*. *Molecular and Biochemical Parasitology* **5,** 297–308.

Probert, A. J. and Durrani, M. S. (1977). *Fasciola hepatica* and *Fasciola gigantica*: total cholinesterase, characteristics and effects of specific inhibitors. *Experimental Parasitology* **42,** 203–210.

Rahman, M. S., Mettrick, D. F. and Podesta, R. B. (1983). Effect of 5-hydroxytryptamine on carbohydrate intermediary metabolism in *Hymenolepis diminuta* (Cestoda). *Canadian Journal of Physiological Pharmacology* **61,** 137–143.

Ramisz, A. (1967). Studies on the nervous system of nematodes and cestodes by means of a histochemical method for active acetylcholinesterase. III. Nematodes of the genus *Capillaria* and cestodes of the genera *Dilepis* and *Choanotaenia*. *Acta Parasitologica Polonica* **14,** 365–385.

Read, C. P. (1950). The vertebrate small intestine as an environment for parasitic helminths. *Rice Institute Pamplet* **37,** 1–94.

Read, C. P. (1958). Status of behavioural and physiological "resistance". *Rice Institute Pamphlet* **45,** 36–54.

Read, C. P. (1971). The microcosm of intestinal helminths. *In* "Ecology and Physiology of Parasites" (A. M. Fallis, ed.), pp. 188–200. University of Toronto Press, Toronto.

Read, C. P. and Kilejian, A. Z. (1969). Circadian migratory behaviour of a cestode symbiote in the rat host. *Journal of Parasitology* **55,** 574–578.

Read, C. P. and Simmons, J. E. (1963). Biochemistry and physiology of tapeworms. *Physiological Reviews* **43,** 263–305.

Rees, G. (1951). The anatomy of *Cysticercus taeniae-taeniaeformis* (Batsch 1786) (*Cysticercus fasciolaris* Rud. 1808) from the liver of *Rattus norvegicus* (Eryx), including an account of spiral tension in the species and some minor abnormalities in structure. *Parasitology* **41,** 46–59.

Rees, G. (1956). The scolex of *Tetrabothrius affinis* (Lönnberg), a cestode from *Balaenoptera musculus* L., the blue whale. *Parasitology* **46,** 425–442.

Rees, G. (1958). A comparison of the structure of the scolex of *Bothriocephalus scorpii* (Muller 1776) and *Clestobothrium crassiceps* (Rud. 1819) and the mode of attachment of the scolex to the intestine of the host. *Parasitology* **48,** 468–492.

Rees, G. (1959). *Ditrachybothridium macrocephalum* gen nov., sp. nov., a cestode from some elasmobranch fishes. *Parasitology* **49,** 191–209.

Rees, G. (1966). Nerve cells in *Acanthobothrium coronatum* (Rud.) (Cestoda: Tetraphyllidae). *Parasitology* **56,** 45–54.

Rees, G. (1973). Cysticercoids of three species of *Tatria* (Cyclophyllidea: Amabiliidae) including *T. octacantha* sp. nov. from the haemocoele of the damsel-fly nymph *Pyrrhosoma nymphula*, Sulz and *Enallagma cyathigerum*, Charp. *Parasitology* **67,** 83–103.

Reid, W. M., Allaman, L. and Fitch, F. (1951). Some factors involved in the hatching of *Hymenolepis diminuta*. *Journal of Parasitology* **37,** 24.

Reid, W. M., Nice, S. J. and McIntyre, R. C. (1949). Certain factors which influence activation of the hexacanth embryo of fowl tapeworm *Raillietina cesticillus* (Molin). *Transactions of the Illinois Academy of Science* **42,** 165–168.

Reisinger, E. and Graak, B. (1962). Untersuchungen an *Codonocephalus* (Trematoda Digenea: Strigeidae), Nervensystem und Paranephridialer Plexus. *Zeitschrift für Parasitenkunde* **22,** 1–42.

Rew, R. S., Fetterer, R. H. and Martin, T. C. (1983). *Fasciola hepatica*: effects of diamfenetide free amine on *in vitro* physiology, biochemistry and morphology. *Experimental Parasitology* **55,** 159–167.

Ribeiro, P. and Webb, R. A. (1983). The occurrence and synthesis of octopamine and catecholamines in the cestode *Hymenolepis diminuta*. *Molecular and Biochemical Parasitology* **7,** 53–62.

Roberts, T. M., Ward, S. and Chernin, E. (1979). Behavioural responses of *Schistosoma mansoni* miracidia in concentration gradients of snail conditioned water. *Journal of Parasitology* **65,** 41–49.

Roche, M. (1966). Influence of male and female *Ancylostoma caninum* on each others distribution in the intestine of the dog. *Experimental Parasitology* **19,** 327–331.

Rogers, W. P. (1960). The physiology of infective processes of nematode parasites; the stimulus from the animal host. *Proceedings of the Royal Society (London) B* **152,** 367–386.

Rohde, K. (1968a). The nervous systems of *Multicotyle purvisi* Dawes 1941 (Aspidogastrea) and *Diaschistorchis multitesticularis* Rohde 1962 (Digenea). Implications for the ecology of the parasites. *Zeitschrift für Parasitenkunde* **30,** 78–94.

Rohde, K. (1986b). Lichtmikroskopische Untersuchungen and den Sinnesrezeptoren der Trematoden. *Zeitschrift für Parasitenkunde* **30,** 252–277.

Ross, E. M. and Gilman A. G. (1985). Pharmacodynamics: mechanisms of drug action and the relationship between drug concentration and effect. *In* "The Pharmacological Basis of Therepeutics" (A. G. Gilman, L. S. Goodman, T. W. Tall, F. Furad, eds.), pp. 35–48. MacMillan Publ. Co., New York.

Rothman, A. H. (1959). Studies on the excystment of tapeworms. *Experimental Parasitology* **8,** 336–364.

Saladin, K. S. (1979). Behavioural parasitology and perspectives on miracidial host-finding. *Zeitschrift für Parasitenkunde* **60,** 197–210.

Salt, G. (1935). Experimental studies in insect parasitism. III. Host selection. *Proceedings of the Royal Society (Lond) B* **117,** 4123–435.

Samuelson, J. C., Quinn, J. J. and Caulfield, J. P (1984). Hatching, chemokinesis and transformation of miracidia of *Schistosoma mansoni*. *Journal of Parasitology* **70,** 321–331.

Schardein, J. L. and Waitz, J. A. (1965). Histochemical studies of esterases in the cuticle and nerve cords of four cyclophyllidean cestodes. *Journal of Parasitology* **51,** 516–518.

Schwabe, C., Koussa, M. and Acra, A. (1961). Host–parasite relationships in echinococcosis. IV. Acetylcholinesterase and permeability regulation in the hyatid cyst wall. *Comparative Biochemistry and Physiology* **2,** 161–172.

Schiller, E. L. (1975). A simplified method for the *in vitro* cultivation of the rat tapeworm *Hymenolepis diminuta. Journal of Parasitology* **51,** 516–518.

Schumacher, W. (1938). Untersuchungen über den Wanderungsweg und die Entwicklung von *Fasciola hepatica* L. im Endwirt. *Zeitschrift für Parasitenkunde* **10,** 608–643.

Schwartz, T. W., Holst, J. J., Fahrenkrug, J., Lindkaer-Jensen, S., Nielsen, O. V., Rehfeld, J. F., Schaffalitzky de Muckadell, O. B. and Stadil, F. (1978). Vagal, cholinergic regulation of pancreatic polypeptide secretion. *Journal of Clinical Investigation* **61,** 781–789.

Shepherd, G. M. (1983). "Neurobiology." Oxford University Press, Oxford. 611 pp.

Sherman, I. W. (1981). A new look at the elephant. *In* "The Current Status and Future of Parasitology" (K. S. Warren and F. F. Purcell, eds.), pp. 174–183. Josiah Macy Jr. Foundation, New York.

Shield, J. M. (1969). *Dipylidium caninum, Echinococcus granulosus* and *Hydatigera taeniaeformis*: histochemical identification of cholinesterases. *Experimental Parasitology* **25,** 217–231.

Shield, J. M. (1971). Histochemical localization of monoamines in the nervous system of *Dipylidium caninum* (Cestoda) by the formaldehyde fluorescence technique. *International Journal for Parasitology* **1,** 135–138.

Shiff, C. J. (1968). Location of *Bulinus (Physopsis) globosus* by miracidia of *Schistosoma haematobium. Journal of Parasitology* **54,** 1133–1140.

Shiff, C. J. (1969). Influence of light and depth on localization of *Bulinus (Physopsis) globusus* by miracidia of *Schistosoma haematobium. Journal of Parasitology* **55,** 108–110.

Shiff, C. J. (1974). Seasonal factors influencing the location of *Bulinus (Physopsis) globusus* by miracidia of *Schistosoma haematobium. Journal of Parasitology* **60,** 578–583.

Shiff, C. J. and Kriel, R. L. (1970). A water soluble product of *Bulinus (Physopsis) globusus* attractive to *Schistosoma haematobium. Journal of Parasitology* **56,** 281–286.

Silk, M. H. and Spence, I. M. (1969). Ultrastructural studies of the blood fluke *Schistosoma mansoni.* III. The nerve tissue and sensory structures. *South African Journal of Medical Science* **34,** 93–104.

Silverman, P. H. (1954). Studies on the biology of some tapeworms of the genus *Taenia*. Factors affecting hatching and activation of taeniid ova, and some criteria of their viability. *Annals of Tropical Medicine and Parasitology* **48,** 207–215.

Smyth, J. D. (1969). "The Physiology of Cestodes". Oliver and Boyd, Edinburgh, 279 pp.

Smyth, J. D. and Haslewood, G. A. D. (1963). The biochemistry of bile as a factor in determining host specificity in intestinal parasites with particular reference to *Echinococcus granulosis. Annals of the New York Academy of Science* **113,** 234–260.

Sponholtz, G. M. and Short, R. B. (1976). *Schistosoma mansoni* miracidia: stimulation by calcium and magnesium. *Journal of Parasitology* **62,** 155–157.

Standen, O. D. (1953). The relationship of sex in *Schistosoma mansoni* to migration within the hepatic portal system of experimentally infected mice. *Annals of Tropical Medicine and Parasitology* **47,** 1139–145.

Steven, D. M. (1963). The dermal light sense. *Biological Reviews* **38,** 204–240.

Stibbs, H. H., Chernin, E., Ward, S. and Karnovsky, M. L. (1976). Magnesium emitted by snails alters the swimming behaviour of *Schistosoma mansoni* miracidia. *Nature (Lond.)* **260,** 702–703.

Stretton, A. O. W., Fishpool, R. M., Southgate, E., Donmoyer, J. E., Walrond, J. P., Moses, J. E. R. and Kass, I. S. (1978). Structure and physiological activity of motorneurons of the nematode *Ascaris. Proceedings of the National Academy of Science (USA)* **75,** 3493–3497.

Stretton, A. O. W., Davis, R. E., Angstadt, J. D., Donmoyer, J. E. and Johnson, C. D. (1985). Neural control of behavior in *Ascaris. Trends of Neuroscience* **84,** 294–300.

Stunkard, H. W. (1930). The life history of *Cryptocotyle lingua* (Creplin), with notes on the physiology of the metacercariae. *Journal of Morphological Physiology* **50,** 143–191.

Stunkard, H. W. (1934). Studies on the life cycle of anoplocephaline cestodes. *Zeitschrift für Parasitenkunde* **6,** 481–507.

Subramanian, M. K. (1940). The nervous system of a proglottid of *Tentacularia macropora. Current Science* **9,** 500–501.

Subramanian, M. K. (1941). Studies on cestode parasites of fishes. II. The nervous system of *Trylocephalum dierama* Shipley and Hornell. *Records of the Indian Museum* **43,** 269–280.

Sukhdeo, M. V. K. (1981). Studies on site selection of some gastrointestinal nematodes of mammals. Ph.D. Thesis, McGill University, Canada.

Sukhdeo, M. V. K., Hsu, S. C., Thompson, C. S. and Mettrick, D. F. (1984). *Hymenolepis diminuta*: Behavioural effects of 5-hydroxytryptamine, acetylcholine, histamine and somatostatin. *Journal of Parasitology* **70,** 682–688.

Sukhdeo, M. V. K. and Mettrick, D. F. (1983). Site selection by *Heligmosomoides polygyrus*: effect of surgical alterations of the gastrointestinal tract. *International Journal for Parasitology* **13,** 355–358.

Sukhdeo, M. V. K. and Mettrick, D. F. (1984). Migrational responses of *Hymenolepis diminuta* to surgical alterations of gastrointestinal secretions. *Parasitology* **88,** 421–430.

Sukhdeo, M. V. K. and Mettrick, D. F. (1985). Intestinal migration by *Hymenolepis diminuta*: 5-hydroxytryptamine, vagal stimulation and intestinal secretions. *Canadian Journal of Zoology* **63,** 1716–1719.

Sukhdeo, M. V. K. and Mettrick, D. F. (1986). Behaviour of the juvenile *Fasciola hepatica. Journal of Parasitology* **72,** 492–497.

Sukhdeo, S. C., Sangster, N. C. and Mettrick, D. F. (1986). Effects of cholinergic drugs on longitudinal muscle contractions of *Fasciola hepatica. Journal of Parasitology* **72,** 858–864.

Sulston, J. E. (1976). Postembryonic development in the ventral cord of *Caenorhabditis elegans. Philosophical Transactions of the Royal Society of London* **275B,** 287–297.

Takahashi, T., Mori, K. and Shigeta, Y. (1961). Phototactic, thermotactic and geotactic responses of miracidia of *Schistosoma japonicum. Japanese Journal of Parasitology* **6,** 686–691.

Tanaka, R. D. and MacInnis, A. J. (1975). An explanation of the apparent reversal of the circadian migration by *Hymenolepis diminuta* (Cestoda) in the rat. *Journal of Parasitology* **61,** 271–280.

Terada, M., Ishii, A. I., Kino, H. and Sano, M. (1982). Studies on chemotherapy of parasitic helminths (VI). Effects of various neuropharmacological agents on motility of *Dipylidium caninum. Japanese Journal of Parasitology* **32,** 479–488.

Thomas, A. P. (1883). The life history of the liver fluke (*Fasciola hepatica*). *Quarterly Journal of Microscopital Science* **23,** 99–133.

Thompson, C. S. and Mettrick, D. F. (1984). Neuromuscular physiology of *Hymenolepis diminuta* and *H. microstoma* (Cestoda). *Parasitology* **89,** 567–578.

Thompson, C. S., Sangster, N. C., and Mettrick, D. F. (1986). Cholinergic inhibition of muscle contraction in *Hymenolepis diminuta* (Cestoda. *Canadian Journal of Zoology* **64,** 2111–2115.

Thompson, J. H. (1971). Serotonin and the alimentary tract. *Research Communications in Chemical Pathology and Pharmacology* **2,** 687–781.

Thornson, R. E. (1969). Environmental stimuli and the response of parasitic helminths. *Bioscience* **19,** 126–130.

Thornson, R. E., Mueller, J. F. and McCue, J. F. (1964). Thermotactic responses of *Spirometra* plerocercoids. *Journal of Parasitology* **50,** 529–530.

Threadgold, L. T. and Read, C. P. (1970). Cell relationships in *Hymenolepis diminuta. Parasitology* **60,** 181–184.

Tomosky, K. T., Bennett, J. L. and Bueding, E. (1974) Tryptaminergic and dopaminergic response of *Schistoma mansoni. Journal of Pharmacology and Experimental Therapy* **190,** 260–271.

Tomosky-Sykes, Y. K. and Bueding, E. (1977). Effects of hycanthone on neuromuscular systems of *Schistosoma mansoni. Journal of Parasitology* **63,** 259–266.

Tower, W. L. (1900). The nervous system in the cestode *Monieza expansa. Zoologische Jahrbücher (Anatomie)* **13,** 359–384.

Turton, J. A. (1971). Distribution and growth of *Hymenolepis diminuta* in the rat, hamster and mouse. *Zeitschrift für Parasitenkunde* **37,** 315–329.

Ullyott, P. (1936). The behaviour of *Dendrocoelum lacteum.* II. Responses in non-directional gradients. *Journal of Experimental Biology* **13,** 265–278.

Ulmer, M. J. (1953). Studies on the nervous system of *Posthamostomum helicus* (Leidy 1847) Robinson, 1949 (Trematoda: Brachylaimatidae). *Transactions of the American Microscopic Society* **72,** 370–374.

Ulmer, M. J. (1971). Site finding behaviour in helminths in intermediate and definitive hosts. *In* "Ecology and Physiology of Parasites" (A. M. Fallis, ed.), pp. 123–160. University of Toronto Press, Toronto.

Upatham, E. S. (1972a). Exposure of caged *Biomphalaria glabrata* (Say) to investigate the dispersion of *S. mansoni* Sambon in outdoor habitats in St. Lucia. *Journal of Helminthology* **46,** 297–306.

Upatham, E. S. (1972b). Effects of physico-chemical factors on the infections of *Biomphalaria glabrata* (Say) by miracidia of *Schistosoma mansoni* Sambon in St. Lucia. *Journal of Helminthology* **46,** 305–315.

Upatham, E. S. (1972c). Effect of water depth on the infection of *Biomphalaria glabrata* by miracidia of St. Lucian *Schistosoma mansoni* under laboratory and field conditions. *Journal of Helminthology* **46,** 317–325.

Van Marck, E. A. E. and Gigasse, P.L. (1978). Effect of total portal vein ligation on the maturation of *Schistosoma mansoni* in mice. *Annales de la Société Belge de Médecine* **58,** 157–158.

Venard, C. E. (1938). Morphology, bionomics and taxonomy of the cestode *Dipylidium caninum. Annals of the New York Academy of Science (USA)* **37,** 207–237.

Vinson, S. B. (1975). Biochemical coevolution between parasitoids and their hosts. *In* "Evolutionary Strategies of Parasitic Insects and Mites" (P. W. Price, ed.), pp. 14–28. Academic Press, New York.

Ward, S. (1973). Chemotaxis by the nematode *Caenorhabditis elegans*: identification of attractants and analysis of the response by use of mutants. *Proceedings of the National Academy of Science (USA)* **70,** 817–821.

Ward, S. (1978). Nematode chemotaxis and chemoreceptors. *In* "Taxis and Behavior" (G. L. Hazelbauer, ed.). *In* "Elementary Systems in Biology. Receptors and Recognition, Series B" Vol. 5 (P. Cuatrecasas and M. F. Greaves, eds.), pp. 141–168. Chapman and Hall, London.

Ward, S., Thompson, N., White, J. G. and Brenner, S. (1975). Electron microscopical reconstruction of the anterior sensory anatomy of the nematode *Caenorhabditis elegans. Journal of Comparative Neurology* **160,** 313–318.

Wardle, R. A. and McLeod, J. A. (1952). "The Zoology of Tapeworms". University of Minnesota Press, Minneapolis. 780 pp.

Ware, R. W., Clark, D., Crossland, K. and Russell, R. L. (1975). The nerve ring of the nematode *Caenorhabditis elegans*: sensory input and motor output. *Journal of Comparative Neurology* **162,** 71–110.

Watson, E. E. (1911). The genus *Gyrocotyle* and its significance for problems of cestode structure and phylogeny. *University of California Publications in Zoology* **6,** 353–468.

Webb, R. A. (1976) Ultrastructure of synapses of the metacestode *Hymenolepis microstoma. Experentia* **32,** 99–100.

Webb, R. A. (1977). The organization and fine structure of the muscles of the scolex of the cysticerci of *Hymenolepis microstoma. Journal of Morphology* **154,** 339–356.

Webb, R. A. and Davey, K. G. (1974a). The gross anatomy and histology of the nervous system of the metacestode of *Hymenolepis microstoma. Canadian Journal of Zoology* **53,** 661–677.

Webb, R. A. and Davey, K. G. (1974b). Ciliated sensory receptors of the inactivated metacestode of *Hymenolepis microstoma. Tissue Cell* **6,** 587–598.

Webb, R. A. and Davey, K. G. (1976). The fine structure of the nervous tissue of the metacestode of *Hymenolepis microstoma. Canadian Journal of Zoology* **54,** 1206–1222.

Webb, R. A. and Mizukawa, K. (1985). Serotonin-like immunoreactivity in the cestode *Hymenolepis diminuta. Journal of Comparative Neurology* **234,** 431–440.

Webbe, G. (1966). The effect of water velocities on the infection of *Biomphalaria sudanica tanganycencis* exposed to different numbers of *Schistosoma mansoni* miracidia. *Annals of Tropical Medicine and Parasitology* **60,** 85–89.

Wheater, P. R. and Wilson, R. A. (1979). *Schistoma mansoni*: a histological study of migration in the laboratory mouse. *Parasitology* **75,** 49–62.

Wikerhauser, T. (1960). A rapid method for determining the viability of *Fasciola hepatica* metacercariae. *American Journal of Veterinary Research* **21,** 895–897.

Wilks, N. E. (1967). Lungs to liver migration of schistosomes in the laboratory mouse. *American Journal of Tropical Medicine and Hygiene* **16,** 599–605.

Willcockson, W. S. and Hillman, G. R. (1984) Drug effects on the 5-HT response of *Schistosoma mansoni. Comparative Biochemical Physiology* **77C,** 199–203.

Williams, H. H. (1959). The anatomy of *Kollikeria fillicolis* (Rudolp. i, 1819) Cobbold 1860 (Trematoda: Digenea). *Parasitology* **49,** 39–53.

Williams, H. H. (1966). The ecology, functional morphology and taxonomy of *Echeneibothrium* Beneden 1849 (Cestoda: Tetraphyllidea). A revision of the genus and comments on *Discobothrium* Beneden 1870, *Pseudanthobothrium* Baer 1956 and *Phormobothrium* Alexander 1963. *Parasitology* **56,** 227–285.

Williams, H. H., McVicar, A. H. and Ralph, K. (1970). The alimentary canal of fish as an environment for helminth parasites. *In* "Aspects of Fish Parasitology" (A. E. R. Taylor and R. Muller, eds.). *8th Symposium of the British Society of Parasitology* pp. 43–77.

Wilson, E. O. (1965). Chemical communication in social insects. *Science* **149,** 1064–1071.

Wilson, R. A. (1970). Fine structure of the nervous system and specialized nerve endings in the miracidium of *Fasciola hepatica. Parasitology* **60,** 399–410.

Wilson, R. A. and Denison, J. (1970a). Studies on the activity of the miracidium of the common liver fluke *Fasciola hepatica. Comparative Biochemical Physiology* **32,** 301–313.

Wilson, R. A. and Denison, J. (1970b). Short chain fatty acids as stimulants of turning activity by the miracidium of *Fasciola hepatica. Comparative Biochemical Physiology* **32,** 511–517.

Wilson, R. A., Draskan, T., Miller, P. and Lawson, J. R. (1978). *Schistosoma mansoni*: the activity and development of the schistosomulum during migration from the skin to the hepatic portal system. *Parasitology* **77,** 57–73.

Wilson, V. C. L. C. and Schiller, E. L. (1969). The neuroanatomy of *Hymenolepis diminuta. Journal of Parasitology* **55,** 261–270.

Wright, C. A. (1959). Host location by trematode miracidia. *Annals of Tropical Medicine and Parasitology* **53,** 288–292.

Wright, D. G. S., Lavigne, D. M. and Ronald, K. (1972). Responses of *Schistosoma douthitti* (Cort 1914) to monochromatic light. *Canadian Journal of Zoology* **50,** 197–200.

Wright, D. G. S. and Ronald, K. (1972). Effect of amino acids and light on the behavior of miracidia of *Schistosoma douthitti. Canadian Journal of Zoology* **50,** 855–860.

Wright, K. A. (1979). *Trichinella spiralis.* An intracellular parasite in the intestinal phase. *Journal of Parasitology* **65,** 441–445.

Wykoff, D. E. and Lepes, T. J. (1957). Studies on *Clonorchis sinensis.* I. Observations on the route of migration in the definitive host. *American Journal of Tropical Medicine and Hygiene* **6,** 1061–1065.

Yasuroaka, K., Kach, M., Hata, H. and Endo, T. (1974). Growth *in vitro* of *Parvatrema timondavidi* Bentoli 1963 (Trematoda: Gymnophallidae) from the metacercarial stage to egg production. *Parasitology* **68,** 293–302.

Yolles, T. K., Moore, D. V. and Meleney, H. E. (1949). Post cercarial development of *Schistosoma mansoni* in the rabbit and hamster after intraperitoneal and percutaneous infection. *Journal of Parasitology* **35,** 276–294.

Zailer, O. (1914). Zur Kenntnis der Anatomie der Muskulatur und des Nervensystems der Trematoden. *Zoologische Anzeiger* **44,** 385–396.

Zernecke, E. (1895). Untersuchungen über den feineren Ban den Cestoden. *Zoologische* **9,** 92–161.

Zuckerman, B. M. (1980). "Nematodes as Biological Models". Vol 1. Academic Press, New York.

Characterization of Species and Strains of *Theileria*

A. D. IRVIN*

International Laboratory for Research on Animal Diseases, PO Box 30709, Nairobi, Kenya

I. Introduction

Parasites of the genus *Theileria* are tick-transmitted intracellular protozoa which are important causes of disease in domestic livestock in the tropical and subtropical regions of the world. In this review attention will focus particularly on *Theileria parva*, *Theileria annulata* and other species which infect cattle, because of their economic importance and because they are the most intensively studied.

One area of study which commands particular attention at present is the immunology of theileriosis, because of the prospects of immunizing livestock against this disease. This area has been reviewed recently by Irvin (1985a),

**Present address:* Overseas Development Administration, Eland House, Stag Place, London, SW1E 5DH, U.K.

ADVANCES IN PARASITOLOGY VOL. 26
ISBN 0–12–031726–5

Copyright © 1987 Academic Press Inc. (London) Ltd.
All rights of reproduction in any form reserved.

Irvin and Morrison (in press) and Morrison *et al.* (1986a,b). A particular problem in immunization (especially in the case of East Coast fever—*T. parva* infection) is the existence of different strains of parasite which will not cross-protect. Thus, immunization of cattle against one strain will not necessarily protect them against challenge with an unrelated strain. In order for effective immunization programmes to be implemented, therefore, a better understanding of theilerial strain differences is required.

The advent of modern biochemical, molecular and immunological techniques offers the prospects and means of characterizing theilerial strains more precisely than was hitherto possible and this may lead to improved ways of identifying, *in vitro*, strains of potential use for immunization.

This review also discusses the different ways that theilerial parasites can be characterized, both at species and strain level, and considers the implications of improved methods of characterization in the development and application of immunization against theileriosis in the field. For more general coverage of theilerial parasites, the reader is referred, in addition to the reviews mentioned above, to those by Neitz (1957, 1959), Wilde (1967), Barnett (1968, 1977), Purnell (1977), Pipano (1977), Irvin and Cunningham (1981), Irvin *et al.* (1981b), Uilenberg (1981a,b), Robinson (1982), Saidu (1982) and Irvin (1985b).

II. Taxonomy

The taxonomic status of theilerial parasites has for many years been the subject of considerable controversy. This revolved particularly around the question of whether or not a sexual cycle occurred in the tick vector (Irvin and Boarer, 1980). The question is still not fully resolved, but recent descriptions of sexual forms of *Theileria* in vector ticks by Schein (1975), Schein *et al.* (1975, 1977), Mehlhorn and Schein (1977, 1984) and Mehlhorn *et al.* (1978) appear to have resolved some of the questions. The probable existence of sexual reproduction in *Theileria* was therefore accepted in the newly-revised classification of the Protozoa (Levine *et al.*, 1980), in which theilerial parasites are now classified as shown in Table 1.

Previously, a number of other genera such as *Gonderia* and *Haematoxenus* were included in the family Theileriidae, but parasites of these genera have mostly been absorbed into the genus *Theileria*. The only exception is the genus *Cytauxzoon*, which is retained for a parasite of North American Felidae (Wagner, 1976; Glenn *et al.*, 1982; Glenn and Stair, 1984). Parasites of African ungulates which were previously classified as *Cytauxzoon* have now been included in the genus *Theileria* (e.g. *Theileria taurotragi*: Grootenhuis *et al.*, 1979). The veil associated with the cattle parasite previously called

TABLE 1
Classification and features of Theileria

Subkingdom	Protozoa	Single celled eukaryotes
Phylum	Apicomplexa	Apical complex present in some stages; sexuality by syngamy
Class	Sporozoea	Sporogonic stage producing sporozoites
Subclass	Piroplasmia	Piriform, rod-shaped or amoeboid; parasitic in erythrocytes and sometimes other cells
Order	Piroplasmida	Asexual and probably sexual reproduction; vectors are ticks
Family	Theileriidae	Schizont stage in lymphocytes;
Genus	*Theileria*	piroplasm stage in erythrocytes lacks pigment

Haematoxenus veliferus (Uilenberg, 1964) has been shown to be a crystalline structure which is not part of the intra-erythrocytic parasite. The parasite itself has a similar ultrastructure to other theilerial parasites and is now called *T. velifera* (see Van Vorstenbosch *et al.*, 1978).

A further complication which may arise in the classification of theilerial parasites is the finding that sporozoites of the equine piroplasm *Babesia equi* can invade host lymphocytes and develop into *Theileria*-like schizonts (Schein *et al.*, 1981; Rehbein *et al.,* 1982; Moltmann *et al.*, 1983; Mehlhorn and Schein, 1984). Similar findings are reported for *Babesia microti* (H. Mehlhorn and E. Schein, unpublished results quoted by Mehlhorn and Schein, 1984). This raises the question whether such parasites should be classified as *Theileria*, *Babesia* or some other genus such as *Nicollia* (Young and Morzaria, 1986). However, further studies are needed before a final decision can be made.

III. SPECIES OF *THEILERIA*

Twenty-seven species of *Theileria* were listed by Levine (1971), but not all of these would be acceptable using the criteria applied today. However, the list provides a good summary of the species described. In the current paper, only the more important species are considered. Fuller descriptions of these and others can be found in papers by Barnett (1968), Uilenberg (1981a,b), Uilenberg *et al.* (1982) and Irvin and Morrison (in press).

A. *THEILERIA ANNULATA* (DSCHUNKOWSKY AND LUHS, 1904)

T. annulata is a parasite of cattle and domestic buffalo (*Bubalus bubalis*) and *bubalis*) and is transmitted by ticks of the genus *Hyalomma*. It causes the disease known as tropical theileriosis, or Mediterranean Coast fever, which is widespread in northern Africa and southern Europe, extending through the Middle East to India and southern Russia. Reviews by Sergent *et al.* (1945), Pipano (1977) and Robinson (1982) give further details.

B. *THEILERIA HIRCI* (DSCHUNKOWSKY AND URODSCHEVICH, 1924)

T. hirci is a highly pathogenic parasite of sheep and goats which occurs in south-east Europe, northern Africa, the Middle East and southern Russia. This species is also transmitted by *Hyalomma* ticks. Morel and Uilenberg (1981) believed that the name *T. hirci* was invalid and proposed renaming the parasite *T. lestoquardi*. Further details can be found in the papers by Hooshmand-Rad and Hawa (1973a,b) and Hawa *et al.* (1981).

C. *THEILERIA MUTANS* (THEILER, 1906)

T. mutans is a widespread, but normally avirulent, parasite of cattle and buffalo (*Syncerus caffer*) in Africa. It has recently also been found in the Caribbean (Uilenberg *et al.*, 1983). *Amblyomma* ticks act as vectors. The review by Saidu (1982) gives further details.

D. *THEILERIA ORIENTALIS* (YAKIMOFF AND SOUDATSCHENKOFF, 1931)

Uilenberg *et al.* (1985) have recently presented strong evidence to indicate that *T. orientalis* and *T. sergenti* are the same species, and that the former name has preference. However, Morel and Uilenberg (1981) indicated that *T. buffeli* may have priority over *T. orientalis*. The parasite affects cattle and domestic buffalo (*B. bubalis*) and appears to occur worldwide, although pathogenic strains are encountered mainly in Russia, Japan and the Far East. *Haemaphysalis* spp. ticks are the principal vectors but, in Africa, *Amblyomma* may be important (Kiltz *et al.,* 1986).

E. *THEILERIA PARVA* (THEILER, 1904)

T. parva is the causative agent of east coast fever (ECF), a highly pathogenic disease of cattle in East and Central Africa. The parasite also affects buffalo (*S. caffer*), and cattle infected by parasites derived from buffalo show a characteristic disease syndrome. At one time parasites causing such infections were given species status (*T. lawrencei*); this is no longer accepted and the name *T. parva lawrencei* is preferred (Uilenberg, 1976). Similar nomenclature is applied to the parasite *T. parva bovis*, which causes a distinct disease syndrome of cattle in Zimbabwe and neighbouring countries. Under this system, parasites causing classical ECF are called *T. parva parva*. This trinomial system is regarded as one of convenience rather than biological accuracy, since the three parasites can be separated only on the basis of clinical and epidemiological criteria; morphologically and serologically they are indistinguishable. Furthermore, intermediate parasite forms can occur, and if *T. parva lawrencei* is artificially passaged through cattle it becomes indistinguishable from *T. parva parva* (Barnett and Brocklesby, 1966b; Young and Purnell, 1973; Young *et al.*, 1973a). The implications concerning the origins of *T. parva parva* infections of cattle are thus obvious. Preliminary attempts similarly to modify *T. parva bovis* have been unsuccessful (Uilenberg *et al.*, 1982).

Rhipicephalus appendiculatus is the normal vector of all three forms of *T. parva*, although the newly-described *Rhipicephalus zambeziensis* (Walker *et al.*, 1981) probably acts as a vector of *T. parva lawrencei* in Zimbabwe (Lawrence *et al.*, 1983).

F. *THEILERIA SERGENTI* (YAKIMOFF AND DEKHTEREFF, 1930)

The name *T. sergenti* has previously been used to describe a moderately pathogenic parasite of cattle found in Russia, Japan and the Far East. As discussed above, it now appears that *T. sergenti* and *T. orientalis* are the same, the only difference being one of virulence; the former is the more virulent and the latter generally apathogenic. The review by Uilenberg (1981b) discusses the question more fully.

G. *THEILERIA TAUROTRAGI* (MARTIN AND BROCKLESBY, 1960)

T. taurotragi is normally a mildly pathogenic parasite affecting cattle and other Bovidae in Africa. Occasionally, severe infections can arise. The parasite appears to occur naturally in antelopes (particularly eland—*Taurotragus oryx*), but may have quite a wide host range as infections have been established *in vitro* in lymphoid cells of at least 11 different species (Stagg *et al.*, 1983). The vectors are *Rhipicephalus* spp., particularly *R. appendiculatus* and *R. pulchellus*.

H. *THEILERIA VELIFERA* (UILENBERG, 1964)

T. velifera is an apathogenic parasite of cattle and buffalo (*S. caffer*) in Africa. The vectors are *Amblyomma* ticks. This parasite has also recently been described from the Caribbean (Uilenberg *et al.*, 1983), having apparently been introduced from West Africa, together with its vector and *T. mutans*, by importation of infected cattle in the latter part of the last century.

I. OTHER *THEILERIA* SPECIES

Other theilerial species of domestic animals include *T. ovis*, *T. recondita*, *T. buffeli* and *T. separata*; these have been reviewed by Uilenberg (1981b) and Morel and Uilenberg (1981), and their status and validity discussed.

IV. LIFE CYCLE

Comprehensive reviews of the life cycle of theilerial parasites have been given by Barnett (1968, 1977) and by Mehlhorn and Schein (1984). A simplified life cycle is given in the paper by Irvin and Cunningham (1981). Essentially, the cycle has two components: one in the vector and one in the vertebrate host. A larval or nymphal tick which feeds on a mammal carrying the intra-erythrocytic piroplasm stage of *Theileria* can acquire infection which can then be transmitted trans-stadially when the next instar of the tick feeds on a susceptible host. Shortly after a tick becomes infected by taking up piroplasm-infected blood, gametes can be seen in the gut lumen (Mehlhorn and Schein, 1984). Sexually disparate forms apparently fuse to produce a zygote, which develops in an epithelial cell of the tick gut wall; a motile kinete is formed, which passes via the haemolymph to the salivary glands where sporogony takes place and infective sporozoites are ultimately produced.

When an infected tick feeds on a susceptible host sporozoites are injected in the saliva and rapidly invade host lymphocytes (Fawcett *et al.*, 1982); here they develop into schizonts (also called macroschizonts) which cause host cell transformation and lymphoproliferation. A proportion of schizonts transforms to microschizonts which release merozoites; these, in turn, invade erythrocytes and develop to piroplasms, thus completing the parasite life cycle. The pathogenicity of the respective parasite stages is related to their ability to divide within host cells; this varies with different theilerial species. Thus, in *T. parva* infection, the schizont stage is pathogenic, whereas with *T.*

mutans and *T. orientalis* the piroplasm stage is more important. In the case of *T. annulata*, both schizont and piroplasm are pathogenic.

V. Nomenclature

A variety of methods is used to characterize theilerial species and strains. However, because the parasites exhibit a number of different forms in both vector and host, and because the availability of these forms for study and analysis varies, one needs to be selective in the characterization method used and the parasite form studied. Furthermore, precise characterization of a parasite can be made only when several methods are used. In the past, when the available methods of characterization were limited, parasites were accorded strain and even species status on poorly-defined criteria, and some erroneous conclusions were reached. Now that more precise methods of characterization are available, it should be easier to avoid such mistakes.

Apart from confusion caused by inadequate and imprecise characterization, problems have also arisen because the nomenclature used to describe different populations of parasite was poorly defined. In particular, the use of the word "strain" has caused confusion, and there are many instances where a parasite population has been accorded strain status simply because it was isolated from a new area, when no other characterization was carried out beyond species identification. This can cause obvious problems, since the same parasite strain can quite clearly occur in a number of different areas and countries. Similar confusion arose with trypanosomes and a committee was convened by the World Health Organization to recommend appropriate nomenclature (WHO, 1978). Irvin *et al.* (1983) and Irvin and Morrison (in press) have urged that similar nomenclature be applied to theilerial parasites and proposed the following definitions:

Isolate. Viable organisms isolated on a single occasion from a field sample into experimental hosts or culture systems, or by direct preparation of a stabilate.

Stock. All the populations of a parasite derived from an isolate without any implication of homogeneity or characterization. Populations comprising a single stock thus include cell lines and tick stabilates, and subsequent parasite preparations derived from them.

Line. A laboratory derivate of a stock maintained under defined physical conditions, e.g. as a culture of parasitized bovine lymphoid cells.

Parasite clone. Theileria species line derived from a single parasite.

Cell clone. Theileria species line derived from a single parasitized cell.

Strain. A population of homogeneous organisms possessing a set of defined characters. Unambiguous characterization of a strain can be assured only if the population of organisms was initiated from a parasite clone.

Stabilate. A sample of organisms preserved alive (usually in replicate) on a single occasion.

In accordance with these definitions the term "strain" should be reserved for cloned parasite populations which have been precisely defined; where such definition has not been carried out, the terms "isolate" or "stock" should be used according to the appropriate circumstances.

For practical purposes, strain characterization should be based on biologically relevant characters (e.g. cross-immunity patterns). Trivial differences, which may be useful as markers, can have negligible biological relevance. Thus, the degree of characterization required will be determined by the circumstances in which the parasite characters are being applied.

VI. Cloning

As discussed above, precise characterization of parasites can be achieved only when cloned populations of organisms are analysed. Many field isolates are likely to contain mixed populations of parasites, comprising different strains and even different species. Although laboratory manipulation may achieve some degree of selection, this can be achieved more reliably by cloning.

The first cloned populations of *Theileria* were obtained by Nelson and Hirumi (1981) and Munderloh and Kurtti (1982), who applied single cell cloning techniques to cultures of bovine lymphoblastoid cells infected with schizonts of *T. parva*. These were important developments, but it must be appreciated that such cell clones may not be synonymous with parasite clones, since the single cell from which the clone was derived may have been initially infected by more than one sporozoite. Cells containing more than one schizont are sometimes seen in culture and, although these may be detectable by phase or interference microscopy, multiply-infected cells may on occasions be inadvertently used to initiate lines.

The mechanism of entry of sporozoites into host cells has been closely studied by Fawcett *et al.* (1982), Jura *et al.* (1983a), and Webster *et al.* (1985), and it is clear that multiple invasion of a single cell by several sporozoites can occur. Although each sporozoite may then develop to a separate schizont within the cell, when that cell divides the integrity of the separate schizonts may be lost and schizonts of mixed "parentage" could be formed. Studies by both light and electron microscopy have shown that, when the host cell divides, the integrity of schizonts is lost as their nuclear particles become aligned along the host cell spindle. This could allow mixing of nuclei from different schizonts to occur before reconstruction of the daughter cells (Hulliger *et al.*, 1964; Stagg *et al.*, 1980; Vickerman and Irvin, 1981; Musisi *et al.*, 1981a; Jura *et al.*, 1983b). Furthermore, there is clearly no blocking or exclusion mechanism which prevents entry of sporozoites into a schizont-infected cell since Buscher *et al.* (1984a) and Stagg *et al.* (1984) could superinfect schizont-infected cells with sporozoites *in vitro*.

Because of the uncertainty relating to the genetic purity of parasites within cloned cell lines, attention is now being turned towards obtaining parasite clones derived unequivocally from single organisms. With malarial and coccidian parasites, cloned populations can be derived from infections established with a single sporozoite (Downs, 1947; Shirley and Millard, 1976; Walliker, 1972). *Theileria* sporozoites are much smaller, and clones derived from single sporozoite infections have not so far been obtained. The possibility of obtaining cloned parasites from other stages is now being explored. Young *et al.* (1983) have shown that interference contrast microscopy can be used to identify *Theileria*-infected acinar cells in viable salivary glands freshly removed from live ticks. Sporozoites from infected acinar cells can then be used to establish theilerial infections by injection into cattle or by cultivation with lymphocytes *in vitro* using the technique of Brown *et al.* (1973). Recently, Young *et al.* (in press) have shown that such infections can be established with sporozoites from single acini. In ticks showing very low salivary gland infection rates (e.g. only one or two infected acini per gland), there is a strong probability that infection of a single acinus represents invasion by a single kinete (Irvin *et al.*, 1981a; Young *et al.*, 1983). Thus, infections derived from sporozoites from a single infected acinus should be derived from a parasite clone. However, two possibilities still have to be faced: firstly, that the sporozoites initiating infection may have been derived from an acinus that was multiply infected; secondly, that contamination may have occurred with sporozoites from an adjacent infected acinus, not detected by interference contrast microscopy, which ruptured during manipulation of the salivary gland releasing its sporozoites into the medium.

Another approach to cloning is described by Fujisaki *et al.* (in press), who transplanted kinetes of *T. parva*, derived from the haemolymph of newly-moulted infected *R. appendiculatus* ticks, into clean unfed adult ticks. The recipient ticks were then fed on rabbits to induce parasite maturation, salivary glands were dissected and infection rates established. Transplantation of 40–60 kinetes per tick into female ticks resulted in infection of one or more salivary gland acini. Single infected acini could then be used to obtain parasite clones using the techniques described by Young *et al.* (1983) and Young *et al.* (in press).

Fujisaki *et al.* (in press) were unable to infect recipient ticks with single kinetes, but this approach should be technically feasible. It might also be possible to achieve such infections *in vitro* by infecting salivary glands of backless tick explant preparations (Bell, 1980); clones might then be obtained provided maturation of parasites within such a system could subsequently be achieved.

A micro-injection technique has been used to inject single sporozoites of *T. parva* into cells which form monolayers and remain fixed to their substrate; the presence of intracellular parasites was confirmed by specific immunofluorescence, although no schizont development was recorded (G. Huez and S. P. Morzaria, unpublished data). However, the technical difficulties of infecting lymphocytes, which are more difficult to immobilize, have not yet been resolved.

The ultimate means of obtaining a parasite clone is by infecting a single lymphocyte with a single sporozoite and then deriving a cell line *in vitro*. To obtain cloned sporozoites, this line should be used to infect cattle; clean nymphal ticks would be fed on the cattle during their reaction, while piroplasms are present in the circulation (Bailey, 1960; Irvin and Brocklesby, 1970). The resultant adult ticks could then be used as a source of cloned sporozoites, either immediately or else after preparation of cryopreserved stabilates (Cunningham *et al.*, 1973). Currently, the single sporozoite/single cell technique has not been developed, but it seems likely that by using a combination of a technique available now, e.g. establishment of a line from lymphocytes infected with sporozoites from a single acinus, followed by single cell cloning of the line, a reliable means of obtaining a parasite clone could be achieved. Stabilates of cloned sporozoites could then be obtained following infection of cattle with the cell line as described above. However, consideration may have to be given to choosing between autologous or allogenic cattle when infecting with the cell line, since the level of successful infection with cells in the host depends on the degree of histocompatibility between the cell donor and the recipient (Brown *et al.*, 1978b; Dolan *et al.*, 1984a; Buscher *et al.*, 1984b; Morrison *et al.*, 1986a,b).

The mechanism whereby theilerial parasites undergo meiotic or reduction division to form haploid gametes is unknown, but Irvin and Boarer (1980) suggested that the process might be analogous to that which occurs in *Plasmodium* and *Eimeria*, in which the first post-zygotic division represents meiosis (Canning and Anwar, 1968; Sinden *et al.*, 1985). If this also occurs in *Theileria*, then all subsequent stages in both the tick and the mammalian host are haploid. Furthermore, in *Plasmodium* and *Eimeria*, since sexually dimorphic forms can arise in clones derived from single sporozoites or erythrocytic forms (i.e. haploid stages) (Downs, 1947; Walliker, 1972; Shirley and Millard, 1976), it follows that "male" and "female" differentiation arises phenotypically. The implications of a similar process occurring in *Theileria* should be considered when cloned populations of parasites are used, particularly when it becomes feasible to conduct controlled matings of theilerial clones to produce hybrids possessing selected characters (Irvin and Boarer, 1980). Further advances in this area are likely to follow the lines adopted for malaria (Walliker, 1983).

VII. Species and Strain Characterization

Five approaches to species and strain characterization of *Theileria* are described; these increase in complexity but, at the same time, higher levels of precision can be achieved. Thus, biological and morphological criteria are normally sufficient to resolve species differences, but, to separate strains, more precise immunological, biochemical and genetic techniques are required.

As the precision of the techniques increases, so the requirement for pure parasite preparations becomes more acute. Methods for obtaining parasite clones have already been discussed and it is important to be aware of their current limitations, since no technique, irrespective of its elegance, will produce meaningful results if the purity of the starting material is suspect.

A. Biology

1. *Geographical distribution*

The distribution of the more pathogenic species of *Theileria* is now well-known and correlates closely with the distribution of the specific vectors. There is, for example, virtually no overlap in the distribution of *T. parva* and *T. annulata*, so the possibility of confusing these parasites should be excluded on geographical grounds alone. The presence of the specific vector also provides a good indication of the theilerial parasites likely to be present in a particular area, although presence of the vector does not always correlate with the presence of the parasite. An obvious example is *R. appendiculatus*, which is present over wide areas of southern Africa (Morel, 1969) where *T. parva parva* no longer occurs, having been previously eradicated (Anonymous, 1981; Lawrence and Norval, 1979; Irvin and Mwamachi, 1983).

The use of geographical distribution to separate theilerial species can be complicated in situations where similar parasites coexist and where communication difficulties arise. Such situations have made it very difficult, for example, to classify parasites from Russia and eastern Asia which fall into the *T. orientalis*/*T. sergenti* group, particularly where they overlap with *T. annulata*, quite apart from the difficulties which face western scientists when grappling with Russian, Chinese, Korean or Japanese literature. Papers by Uilenberg (1981b) and Uilenberg *et al.* (1985) have made important advances in resolving these difficulties and complexities.

A further problem that arises in using geographical distribution as a means of classifying *Theileria* species is that it is all too easy to give a parasite a new label because it is isolated from a new area. This caused much of the confusion surrounding the speciation of *T. orientalis*, which now appears to be much more cosmopolitan than previously suspected (Uilenberg *et al.*, 1985). Another important aspect of this problem is that newly isolated parasites of a particular species are often accorded "strain" status purely on geographical grounds. Often this simply raises a semantic problem which can be resolved by more critical use of appropriate nomenclature, as discussed above. Sometimes it can lead to a situation where geographical criteria become prime considerations in classifying parasite strains, overriding more rational and precise methods of characterization. This may cause problems in moving parasite stocks or vaccine strains across national borders, as it may be difficult to convince authorities that parasites observe ecological rather than political boundaries.

2. *Vector specificity*

Attention was drawn by Brocklesby (1978) to the close (sometimes exclusive) association between a theilerial species and a specific genus or species of tick. Although this vector specificity can often be broken down artificially (Barnett, 1968), the specificity tends to be fairly rigid under field conditions, largely because immature stages of certain potential vector ticks do not normally feed on cattle and cannot therefore acquire infection, even though the adult ticks themselves may feed on cattle.

3. *Host specificity and susceptibility*

In general, theilerial parasites appear to have a narrow host range in which host and parasite live in reasonable harmony. Pathogenic manifestations normally arise when parasites spill over to other hosts such as cattle. An apparently common situation is that a wild bovid (e.g. buffalo) is the natural host but, as a result of cattle/buffalo contact, the parasite is transferred to cattle, initially rather irregularly, but subsequently to the extent that the parasite can be maintained in a tick/cattle cycle without recourse to the natural host (Barnett and Brocklesby, 1966b; Young *et al.*, 1973a; Young and Purnell, 1973). As the parasite is maintained in cattle, further adaptation can arise and generations of indigenous cattle can become increasingly inured to the presence of the parasite (Moll *et al.*, 1981). A situation then arises where the susceptibility of indigenous and exotic cattle to the same parasite is totally different. Similar differences in susceptibility of indigenous and exotic sheep to *T. hirci* infection have been noted by Khayyat and Gilder (1947) and Hooshmand-Rad and Hawa (1973a). Unless these differences in susceptibility are considered, the erroneous assumption can be made that different parasites are implicated.

The behaviour of *T. parva parva* and *T. parva lawrencei* in cattle and buffalo (*S. caffer*) clearly demonstrates the host influence on parasite pathogenicity. Both parasites cause severe infections in cattle, but identical stocks of each cause mild infections in buffalo (Barnett and Brocklesby, 1966a,b; Young *et al.*, 1978a). With *T. parva parva* infection, buffalo cells undergo transformation less readily *in vitro* than cattle cells infected with the same parasite under identical conditions. However, the transformation frequency of cells infected with *T. parva lawrencei* is similar in both buffalo and cattle (Baldwin *et al.*, 1986), demonstrating that buffalo have some other mechanism for containing infection at the invasion and transformation stage. Similarly, *Bos indicus* cattle appear to be innately more resistant than *Bos taurus* cattle to both *T. parva* (Guilbride and Opwata, 1963; Stobbs, 1966; Radley, 1978a; Dolan *et al.*, 1982) and *T. annulata* (Rafyi *et al.*, 1965).

The variation in the response of fully susceptible individuals to an identical disease challenge is well recognized, and it now appears that specific immune responsiveness can sometimes be linked to genes of the host's major histocompatibility complex regulating immune response (Benacerraf and Germain, 1978; Van Dam, 1981; Adams and Brandon, 1981). Antigens coded by genes closely linked to these regulating genes can then serve as specific immune response markers. Examples are the bovine lymphocyte antigens (BoLAs) of cattle which can be identified and classified by screening against batteries of specific alloantisera (Stone, 1981; Anonymous, 1982). The possibility that cattle differ in their response to theilerial infections according to their BoLA specificity is currently being examined (Teale *et al.*, 1981; Dolan *et al.*, 1984a; Morrison *et al.*, 1986b).

The possibility of host age affecting susceptibility to theilerial infections has been explored by Barnett (1957) and reviewed by Irvin and Morrison (in press). Under natural conditions the picture can be confused by the possible presence of acquired immunity, either from maternal colostrum or as a result of low-level challenge; it may therefore be hard to draw any meaningful conclusions. However, when groups of fully susceptible cattle of different ages were given identical *T. parva parva* stabilate challenge, no evidence of different age susceptibilities was detected (Irwin *et al.*, in press a). In Zimbabwe, however, there is strong circumstantial evidence from field observations that calves have a higher innate resistance to *T. parva bovis* than do older cattle (J. A. Lawrence and R. A. I. Norval, personal communication).

Whilst the host specificity of most *Theileria* parasites appears to be fairly narrow, that of *T. taurotragi* may be different. The parasite was originally described from eland (Martin and Brocklesby, 1960; Brocklesby, 1962; Irvin *et al.*, 1972b), but experimentally it can readily infect cattle (Young *et al.*, 1977a; Grootenhuis *et al.*, 1979, 1981) and sheep (P. N. Ngumi, D. A. Stagg, B. L. Leitch and A. S. Young, personal communications) and has, on a number of occasions, been isolated from naturally infected cattle in eland-free areas (Burridge *et al.*, 1974a; Lawrence and Mackenzie, 1980; De Vos and Roos, 1981b; De Vos *et al.*, 1981; Uilenberg *et al.*, 1977b, 1982). This suggests that cattle or some other wild bovid can also act as reservoir hosts. A wide range of African ungulates carry apparently benign infections of *Theileria* (Brocklesby and Vidler, 1966; Barnett and Brocklesby, 1968; Burridge, 1975) but, although their possible infectivity for cattle may have been tested, their relationship to *T. taurotragi* is largely unexplored. In general, such parasites have been given names indicating their host of origin, e.g. *Theileria sylvicaprae* from the duiker (*Sylvicapra grimmia*) (Neitz and Thomas, 1948) and *Theileria gorgonis* from the wildebeest (*Connochaetes taurinus*) (Brocklesby and Vidler, 1961) (the latter name was applied for convenience rather than because its specific identity was definitely established). Now that improved methods of characterization are available, it should be possible to identify parasites more precisely, and many of the theilerial parasites of African ungulates may show a greater degree of synonymy than has hitherto been accepted. One example of such a parasite given species status is *Theileria barnetti* (Brocklesby, 1965), isolated from a buffalo (*S. caffer*). When opportunities arose to study this parasite more closely, it was found to be indistinguishable from *T. mutans* (Young *et al.*, 1978a,c). As described above, Stagg *et al.* (1983) have shown that cells from a variety of ungulate species can be infected with *T. taurotragi in vitro*, but whether this wide host range applies *in vivo* remains to be explored.

As can be seen, a number of innate factors can affect host susceptibility to the theilerial parasites. These factors are quite distinct from any immunological factors which may be acquired as a result of exposure to theilerial infections. However, both innate and acquired resistance can affect host susceptibility to *Theileria* and complicate attempts to identify parasites on the basis of host susceptibility.

4. *Pathogenicity*

Apart from host factors, discussed above, which can affect the apparent virulence of parasites, different strains of the parasites themselves may vary in pathogenicity. Thus, although *T. mutans* is normally regarded as a benign parasite, virulent strains may be encountered which result in occasional fatal infections (Irvin *et al.*, 1972a; Moll *et al.*, 1981), and in some areas *T. mutans* appears to be an important cause of chronic theileriosis in calves (Moll *et al.*, 1986). However, it appears that some of the virulent strains of *T. mutans* described from South Africa, notably at Tzaneen in the Transvaal (De Kock *et al.*, 1937; Flanagan and Le Roux, 1957), may have been confused with *T. taurotragi* which was unknown at the time of the early reports (De Vos and Roos, 1981a,b). Similarly, virulent strains of *T. orientalis* were previously classified as a separate species, *T. sergenti* (see above). Only when a variety of isolates was compared serologically did the true identity emerge (Uilenberg *et al.*, 1985).

With *T. parva* and *T. annulata*, certain apparently virulent or mild strains may be encountered, in which enhanced or reduced virulence appear to be inherent in the strain, rather than the result of a dose effect. Barnett and Brocklesby (1961, 1966a), for example, isolated a mild strain (Icely) of *T. parva* which caused 25% mortality in susceptible cattle (as opposed to 96% seen with more virulent strains such as Muguga); recovered cattle were solidly immune when challenged with virulent *T. parva* (Muguga). More recently, Irvin *et al.* (in press, b) showed that the Boleni stock of *T. parva bovis* (Lawrence and Mackenzie, 1980) caused a mild reaction in *B. indicus* cattle and that recovered cattle were resistant to virulent challenge with *T. parva parva* and *T. parva lawrencei* stocks. However, it has been clearly established that the severity of *T. parva* infection increases as the dose of sporozoites rises (Barnett, 1957; Wilde *et al.*, 1968; Dolan *et al.*, 1984b), and it may therefore be difficult to determine whether the pathogenicity of a strain is due to inherent factors or simply to dose levels. Barnett and Brocklesby (1966a) found, for example, that the virulence of *T. parva* (Icely) was increased if the challenge level was raised. Certain *T. parva* stocks which produce high infection rates in ticks have low virulence for cattle, indicating that their virulence may be strain-dependent rather than dose-dependent. Also, some stocks consistently produce high piroplasm parasitaemias.

The possibility must also be considered that the virulence of theilerial parasites can be modified by the strain of tick involved. This may be particularly important when comparisons are made between the same parasite stock in different laboratories or countries, if parasites are passaged through different tick strains. The inherent virulence of a strain is a difficult characteristic to measure, particularly as it is currently not possible to quantitate sporozoite preparations, except rather crudely. However, recent work by Morzaria *et al.* (1985) has shown that sporozoites, directly labelled with fluorescently tagged antisporozoite antibody (Dobbelaere *et al.*, 1984), can be counted in a fluorescence-activated cell sorter. This raises the possibility of using known numbers of sporozoites of different stocks in an infectivity assay *in vitro* (Brown *et al.*, 1973), or *in vivo*, and thus directly comparing the pathogenicity of the respective stocks. However, since the antibody labels both live and dead sporozoites, the method still has some limitations as a means of counting infective sporozoites.

The *T. parva* "sub-species" produce sufficiently distinct clinical syndromes to enable them to be regarded as separate entities. Thus, in susceptible cattle, *T. parva parva* produces an acute, normally fatal disease in which schizonts and piroplasms are abundant; *T. parva lawrencei* also produces an acute, often fatal disease, but parasite numbers are few; *T. parva bovis* normally produces less severe disease, from which recovery is common, and few to moderate numbers of parasites are seen. However, within this spectrum intermediate syndromes may be encountered. To explain such variation Jarrett *et al.* (1969) suggested that different clones of parasite existed, with different replication times. However, Radley *et al.* (1974) showed that variation in disease response was primarily dose-dependent, rather than strain-dependent. Resolution of this question will have to await further studies with cloned and quantified sporozoites as outlined above, but clearly parasite pathogenicity cannot be reliably used on its own as a means of characterization; other methods must be used in support.

A further factor which can add to the confusion is that the virulence of parasites can apparently be altered by passage *in vitro*. This is particularly true of *T. annulata* (Pipano, 1977, 1981), in which production of vaccine strains of parasite is based on attentuation by *in vitro* culture with minimal loss of immunogenicity. Similarly, reduced virulence of *T. parva* has been recorded following prolonged passage *in vitro* (Brown *et al.*, 1978a; Brown, 1981). The nature of this reduction in virulence has not been explained, and all observations appear to have been made with uncloned material, so that it is not possible to say whether mutations are involved or whether different clones are being selected. Apparent alteration of parasite pathogenicity on passage through ticks and cattle, as, for example, observed with *T. parva lawrencei* (Barnett and Brocklesby, 1966b; Young and Purnell, 1973; Young *et al.*, 1973a) or with *T. parva* (Icely) (Barnett and Brocklesby, 1966a), may simply be due to selection of different parasite populations rather than to more fundamental changes in parasite biology or genetic make-up.

5. *Pathology*

The pathology of theileriosis was recently reviewed by Irvin and Morrison (in press). In general, pathological features are too variable to be of value in parasite strain characterization, but detailed comparative studies between *T. parva lawrencei* and *T. parva parva* have shown consistent pathological differences (Jura and Losos, 1980; Maxie *et al.*, 1982). These possibly arise as a result of the different parasite loads to which the host is exposed. Also, with infections of *T. parva parva*, different strains appear to cause different degrees of pulmonary, renal or ocular involvement (Cowdry and Danks, 1933; De Kock, 1957; Neitz, 1959; Barnett, 1960; Irvin and Morrison, in press).

B. MORPHOLOGY

The structure of parasites is usually the first criterion to be applied in speciation. Thus, for *Theileria*, Giemsa-stained blood or lymph node biopsy smears are examined to determine the size, shape and structure of parasites (Barnett *et al.*, 1961) and the presence of associated structures such as rods, bars or veils (Uilenberg, 1981b). Such features provide an initial indication of the parasite species involved. More critical analysis of schizont structure and nuclear number may be possible if preparations are stained by the Giemsa-acid hydrolysis method (Kurtti *et al.*, 1981; Irvin *et al.*, 1982). With Giemsa-stained preparations of schizonts, clear morphological differences can be seen between, for example, *T. mutans* and *T. parva*, where schizont nuclear particles of the former are fewer in number and larger than those seen in *T. parva* (Fig. 1). There is considerable diversity in shape and size of piroplasms, so that identification of *Theileria* species simply on the basis of piroplasm morphology can be unreliable. Also, mixed infections are common in animals exposed in the field and blood smears from such animals can concurrently show infections with three or more species of *Theileria*, e.g. *T. parva*, *T. mutans* and *T. velifera*. However, some degree of specific identifica-

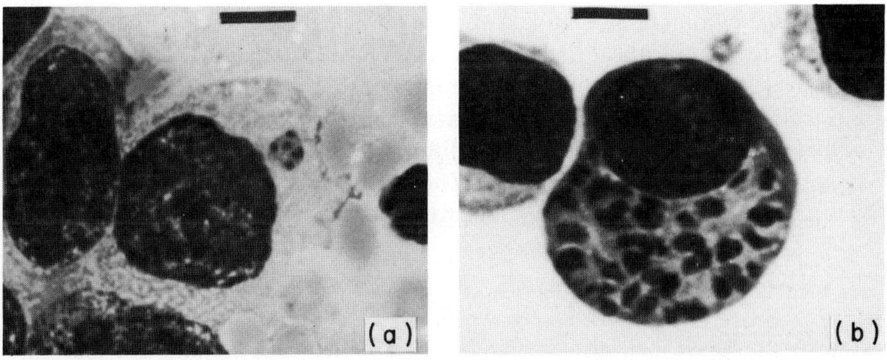

FIG. 1. Giemsa-stained preparations to show morphological differences between schizonts of (a) *Theileria parva* and (b) *Theileria mutans*. Scale bar = 10μm. (By courtesy of S. P. Morzaria and A. S. Young.)

tion can be achieved, as *T. parva* piroplasms are normally small and often rod-like. Those of *T. mutans* are large, variable in morphology, and often piriform in shape, whereas those of *T. velifera* usually show an associated veil. In *T. annulata*, as the name implies, the piroplasms are normally annular or ring-shaped. A. S. Young (personal communication) has found that structural differences in piroplasms are even more striking in fresh blood viewed by interference contrast microscopy (Fig. 2).

When salivary gland stages of *Theileria* are studied in ticks, a variety of stains can be used in addition to Giemsa; these include Giemsa-colophonium (Shortt and Cooper, 1948; Purnell and Joyner, 1968; Binnington *et al.*, 1983), Feulgen (Blewett and Branagan, 1973) and methyl green–pyronin (Walker *et al.*, 1979; Irvin *et al.*, 1981a). The use of histochemical techniques to study changes induced by parasites in tick salivary glands may also be applicable (Martins, 1978; Walker *et al.*, 1985). Structural differences between the salivary glands of *Theileria* are hard to detect at the light microscope level, but Young *et al.* (1983) used interference contrast microscopy to identify *Theileria* infections in fresh salivary glands of ticks and showed that morphological differences could be detected between those infected with *T. parva*, *T. taurotragi* or *T. mutans*.

Other stages in the tick have been less intensively studied, but Young *et al.* (1980) found that kinetes of *T. mutans*, *T. annulata*, and *T. taurotragi* could be differentiated on the basis of size, *T. annulata* being the smallest and *T. taurotragi* the largest. Development times of the different parasite stages in the tick also varied with different theilerial species (Young *et al.*, 1980).

The structure of parasites can be greatly influenced by the methods of preparation and fixation used. Thus, identification of parasites purely on the basis of light microscopic observation of limited Giemsa-stained material may be unreliable. With some species, such as *T. taurotragi* which forms distinctive cytomeres, examination of histological sections may be a useful adjunct to identification (Brocklesby, 1962; Barnett and Brocklesby, 1968). However, more precise morphology of parasites can be resolved with the electron microscope, where appropriate facilities exist. For example, Fawcett *et al.* (1985) detected ultrastructural differences between the sporozoites of *T. parva parva*, *T. parva lawrencei* and *T. taurotragi.* Ultrastructural features of *Theileria* have been extensively reviewed by Mehlhorn and Schein (1984).

C. IMMUNOLOGY

1. *Diagnostic serology*

Serology is probably the single most definitive method for determining

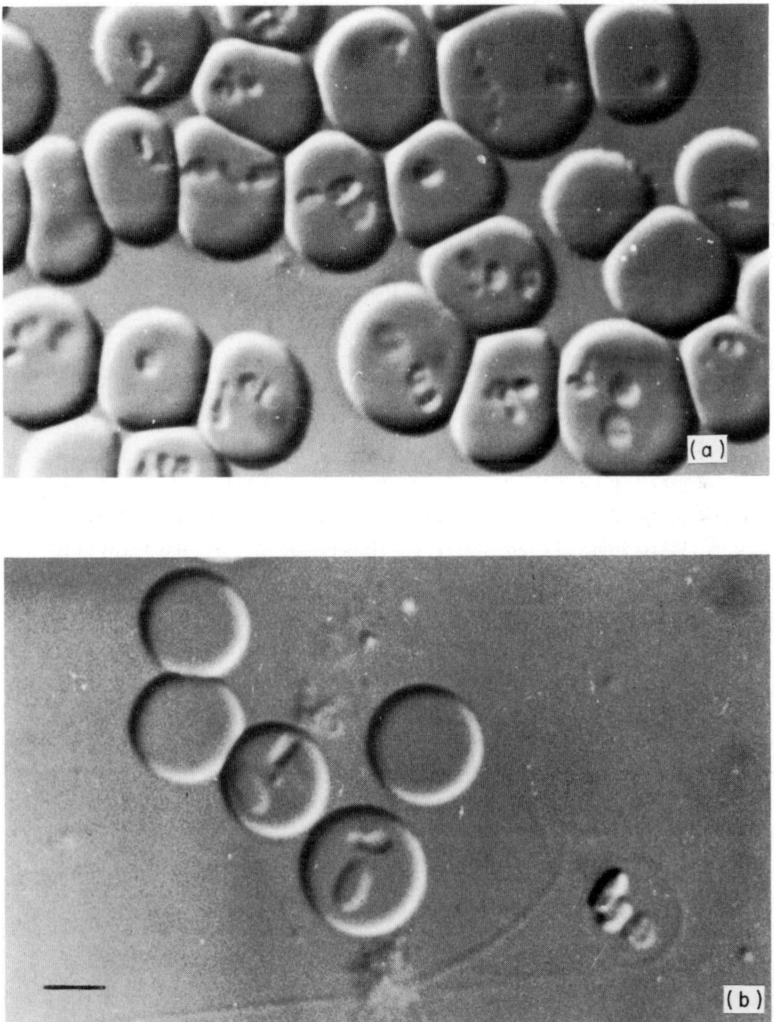

FIG. 2. Bovine erythrocytes infected with (a) *Theileria parva* and (b) *Theileria taurotragi* viewed by interference contrast microscopy of unstained blood. Piroplasms appear as sunken areas in this three-dimensional representation. The raised structures seen in *Theileria taurotragi*-infected erythrocytes would appear as bars in Giemsa-stained preparations. Scale bar = 3μm. (By courtesy of A. S. Young.)

specific differentiation in *Theileria*. Sera collected from animals which have recovered from theilerial infections can be screened against a range of species-specific antigens, and the causative parasite of the initial infection can thus be identified. The indirect fluorescent antibody (IFA) tests developed for schizont antigens (Pipano and Cahana, 1969; Burridge and Kimber, 1972; Goddeeris *et al.*, 1982) or piroplasm antigens (Schindler and Wokatsch, 1965; Lohr and Ross, 1969; Burridge, 1971) form the basis of tests used in the routine serological identification of all the *Theileria* species including *T. parva* (Burridge, 1971; Burridge and Kimber 1972; Goddeeris *et al.*, 1982), *T. annulata* (Pipano and Cahana, 1969; Burridge *et al.*, 1974b; Pipano, 1977), *T. mutans* (Perié *et al.*, 1979; Kimber and Young, 1977), *T. hirci* (Hawa *et al.*, 1976) and the *T. sergenti* / *T. orientalis* complex (Takahashi *et al.*, 1976; Minami *et al.*, 1980; Fujinaga and Minami, 1981; Uilenberg *et al.*, 1985). The IFA test has also played a key role in confirming the homology between *T. parva parva*, *T. parva lawrencei* and *T. parva bovis* (Burridge *et al.*, 1973; Lawrence, 1977; Uilenberg *et al.*, 1982). In terms of differential diagnosis, the IFA test has again been predominant (Burridge *et al.*, 1974a; Mpangala *et al.*, 1976; Morzaria *et al.*, 1977; Uilenberg *et al.*, 1977a, 1982, 1985; Grootenhuis *et al.*, 1979; Joyner *et al.*, 1979; Minami *et al.*, 1980; De Vos and Roos, 1981b; Norval *et al.*, 1985).

Other serological tests which have been used for diagnosis of *Theileria* include indirect haemagglutination assay (IHA), complement fixation, capillary agglutination and immunodiffusion. Duffus and Wagner (1980) compared and reviewed the efficacy and specificity of these tests and concluded that IFA and IHA tests were the most reliable. Gray *et al.* (1980) explored the use of the enzyme-linked immunosorbent assay (ELISA) and concluded that this too was a reliable test which was more rapid than the IFA test and was not constrained by subjective bias. The use of an immunoperoxidase test was examined by Cowan *et al.* (1984); if this test were exploited it would also provide another means of obviating the need for fluorescence microscopy. However, despite the potential of other tests, the use of the IFA test still tends to predominate for general diagnostic purposes.

The specificity of the IFA test is very good, although some cross-reactivity has been recorded between *T. parva* and *T. annulata* (Burridge *et al.*, 1974b) and between *T. parva* and *T. taurotragi* (Grootenhuis *et al.*, 1979). However, provided appropriate controls are included in the test, the possibility of confusion arising between species is reduced. It is likely that the limited cross-reactivity is due to the presence of some common antigens between the different species (Minami *et al.*, 1983; Shiels *et al.*, 1986 a), rather than to any shortcoming of the test (see below).

2. *Monoclonal antibodies*

Animals infected with theilerial parasites respond immunologically by producing antibodies against the whole spectrum of parasite antigens to which they are exposed. These antibodies can be detected by screening sera against crude antigen preparations in IFA and similar tests, as described above. Such tests are valuable diagnostic tools at the parasite species level, but are unsuitable for detecting minor antigenic changes which may be associated with strain variation, since the presence of common antigens within strains will mask any minor antigenic change which might be detectable by conventional serological tests. However, an elegant way to overcome this difficulty is to use monoclonal antibodies (MAbs) which recognize single antigenic determinants (Kohler and Milstein, 1975; Milstein, 1981). Such antibodies have been derived for studying parasite antigens (Pearson *et al.*, 1980) and have been used extensively in the characterization of parasitic protozoa, including *Plasmodium* (McBride *et al.*, 1982, 1984; Knowles *et al.*, 1984), *Leishmania* (Pratt and David, 1981; Pratt *et al.*, 1982; Handman and Hocking, 1982; Jaffe and Pratt, 1983) and *Theileria* (Pinder and Hewett, 1980; Minami *et al.*, 1983; Shiels *et al.*, 1986 a,b). In the case of *Theileria*, MAbs have been raised against schizont-infected cells and sporozoites. Those raised against sporozoites appear to detect common antigen(s) which occur(s) on the surface of sporozoites of different strains (Dobbelaere *et al.*, 1984; Musoke *et al.*, 1984); such MAbs are therefore unsuitable for strain differentiation. However, those raised against schizonts detect antigen diversity amongst different isolates of *T. parva* (Pinder and Hewett, 1980; Minami *et al.*, 1983) and *T. annulata* (Shiels *et al.*, 1986a) and appear to offer considerable scope for strain characterization since, when different stocks of parasite are tested against a series of such MAbs, a profile of reactivity can be prepared for each stock. This MAb profile remains essentially the same, irrespective of antigen source or host cell origin. In this context Minami *et al.* (1983) examined a number of features and showed that the best source of antigen was schizont-infected cells grown *in vitro*, but that cells derived from infected cattle, provided they contained sufficient schizonts, could also be used. When cell lines were derived from a number of different cattle, each infected with the same *T. parva* stock, the lines all showed the same MAb profile, indicating that host cell background did not affect the composition of the profile. Similarly, clones of cells derived from a single culture all showed the same MAb profile as the parent stock, and parasite stocks passaged through ticks retained their original profiles. Thus, antigenic profiles appear to be fixed characters which identify strain-associated phenotypic diversity among populations of theilerial parasites. Minami *et al.* (1983) found that the percentage of cells fluorescing with a specific labelled MAb was generally in close agreement with the percentage of cells showing schizonts in Giemsa-stained smears; however one MAb in particular produced irregular staining which, they suggested, might be related to variable antigenic expression associated with cell cycle changes. In subsequent studies by Shiels *et al.* (1986 a), working with *T. annulata*, and by Conrad *et al.* (in press), working with *T. parva lawrencei*, the percentage of fluorescing cells was often much lower than the percentage of schizont-containing cells and considerable variation existed between different isolates. This variation was subsequently shown to be due to the presence of mixed strains within an isolate. Conrad *et al.* (in press), for example, obtained one isolate from a buffalo (*S. caffer*) from which four distinct parasite lines could be derived. When those isolates were cloned, the reactivity of the clones with specific MAbs correlated closely with the percentage of schizont-infected cells within the culture. After passage of such clones and further cloning, all subclones retained the same profile as the parent clone.

Conrad *et al.* (in press) demonstrated considerable diversity in the MAb profiles of cell clones derived from buffalo; this agrees with the extent of antigenic diversity that is apparent *in vivo* (Lohr, 1978; Young *et al.*, 1978a,b; Radley *et al.*, 1979). However, the fact that the antigenic character of individual clones appears to remain fixed suggests that the diversity demonstrated by *T. parva lawrencei* is due to the presence of a multiplicity of strains rather than to antigenic "drift" or mutation within an individual strain. However, further work is required to settle this question and experiments are currently in progress to follow the MAb profiles of sequential isolates from cattle and buffalo infected initially with cloned lines of cells infected with *T. parva lawrencei*. The results of these experiments should provide greater insight into the mechanism of antigenic variation within this parasite.

Minami *et al.* (1983) found that the anti-schizont MAbs they used were all stage-specific (Fig. 3), but, in subsequent work, MAbs have been produced which recognize common antigen determinants on different parasite stages—e.g. between schizonts and piroplasms, or between schizonts and merozoites (Shiels *et al.*, 1986b; S. P. Morzaria, unpublished data). MAbs have also detected some common antigen determinants between *T. parva* and *T. taurotragi* (Minami *et al.*, 1983) and between *T. annulata* and *T. parva* (Shiels *et al.*, 1986a; P. A. Conrad, unpublished data), indicating why cross reactions sometimes occur between these parasites in diagnostic serology, as described above.

The presence or absence of binding by specific MAbs enabled Minami *et al.* (1983) and Shiels *et al.* (1986a) to assign different parasite stocks to particular groups on the basis of MAb profiles. Subsequent work, particularly with *T. parva lawrencei*, indicates that group diversity appears to be wider than initial studies indicated, but certain MAbs are valuable markers

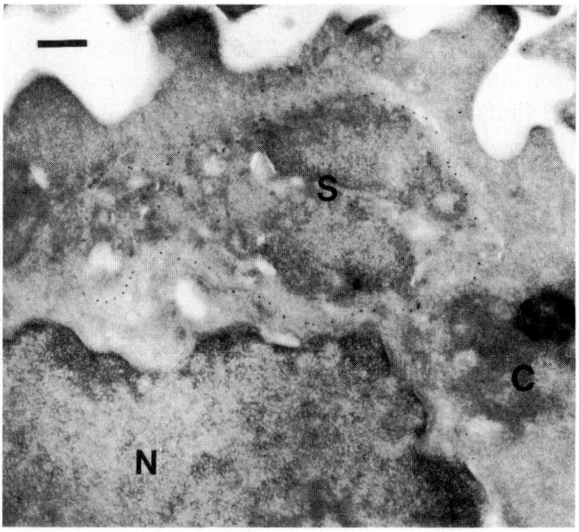

FIG. 3. Intracellular schizont of *Theileria parva* (Marikebuni) binding protein A gold-labelled (PAG) anti-schizont monoclonal antibody. C = host cell cytoplasm, N = host cell nucleus, S = schizont. Scale bar = 1 μm; average particle size = 12 nm. (By courtesy of P. Webster.)

of strain differences. For example, Minami *et al.* (1983) found that the presence or absence of binding with their MAbs 2 and 3, and 15 and 16, provided a useful means of grouping different *T. parva parva* stocks. Also, MAb 19 appeared to be specific for *T. parva lawrencei* stocks, since it reacted with most *T. parva lawrencei*-type isolates, but not with any *T. parva parva* types (Conrad *et al.*, in press). Furthermore, binding with MAb 7 was absent from most *T. parva bovis* stocks from Zimbabwe (Koch *et al.*, in press). This latter finding is the first indication that MAb profile type may be segregated geographically; studies by Minami *et al.* (1983) and Shiels *et al.* (1986a) failed to find any such segregation. Further advances in the use of MAb profiles could be made if specific MAbs for *T. parva parva* and *T. taurotragi* were identified.

Apart from their potential value in characterizing theilerial strains, MAbs might also provide markers for hybridization studies (Irvin and Boarer, 1980; Minami *et al.*, 1983), using the types of approach outlined for malarial parasites (Greenberg and Trembley, 1954; Walliker, 1976, 1983; Walliker *et al.*, 1971). For example, cloned stabilates derived from ticks would be prepared as described above from two strains of parasite; one strain would bind MAb A but not B; the other strain would bind B but not A. The two strains would be injected concurrently into a bovid; when this reacted, nymphal ticks would be fed on its ears in expectation that piroplasms of the two strains would be present together in the circulation and that a proportion of them would fuse during gametogony in the tick gut to produce hybrid zygotes. The resultant kinetes would be cloned or single infected acini derived from them would be isolated and used to initiate schizont-infected cell lines; these would subsequently be screened with the respective MAbs to detect hybrid lines expressing both A and B markers. Such lines could then be injected into cattle to derive stabilates. If such an approach could be established, resulting in the production of hybrid lines, it would provide convincing evidence of genetic recombination as well as being a means of creating hybrid parasites with defined and selected characteristics.

A potentially valuable application of MAbs would be in the prediction of cross immunity patterns *in vivo* between parasites of different MAb profiles. Preliminary studies by Irvin *et al.* (1983) showed that, if cattle were immunized with a *T. parva* stock and then challenged with one of identical MAb profile, good protection ensued, but if cattle were challenged with a stock with a different profile, responses were variable, and no prediction could be made. If such correlations can be validated and extended by further work, MAb profiles may provide useful *in vitro* markers for selecting appropriate strains for immunization of cattle in particular situations and areas, as discussed by Morzaria *et al.* (in press a). However, as pointed out (Minami *et al.,* 1983; Irvin *et al.,* 1983; Shiels *et al.,* 1986a), MAb profiles do not identify antigens which are necessarily involved in immunogenesis; they merely define sets of antigenic determinants expressed on schizonts of different stocks. The majority of the anti-schizont MAbs in current use apparently detect only antigenic determinants associated directly with schizonts (Fig. 3); generation of the genetically restricted cytotoxic cells involved in cell-mediated immunity in theileriosis (Eugui and Emery, 1981; Emery *et al.*, 1982; Preston *et al.*, 1983), appears to depend on recognition of antigenic changes on the surface of parasitized cells. The nature of these changes is still not clear, but current indications are that parasite antigens, or parasite-induced antigens, are presented on the surface of infected cells in conjunction with host major histocompatibility (MHC) antigens (Morrison *et al.*, 1986a); these activate immune mechanisms similar to those responsible for the cell-mediated control of other infectious agents (Zinkernagel, 1979; Zinkernagel and Doherty, 1979; Townsend and McMichael, 1985). Early studies (e.g. by Creemers, 1981) failed to demonstrate any parasite or parasite-associated antigen on the surface of infected cells, but two recent publications indicate that such antigens may be present and detectable by MAbs (Newson *et al.*, 1986; Shiels *et al.,* 1986b). If these findings are validated, they increase the prospects of identifying parasite-associated cell surface antigens of direct relevance to immunogenesis and possibly detecting diversity similar to that recorded with current MAb profiles. This would mean that *in vitro* profiles might correlate directly with cross-protection patterns seen *in vivo*, and thereby provide more reliable means of selecting appropriate stocks for immunization.

A further application of the present MAbs might be in determining the antigenic profile of parasite strains responsible for field outbreaks of disease, particularly if techniques to prepare antigen directly from infected cattle can be improved. A rapid test to characterize such strains could enable prophylactic immunization to be initiated with appropriately selected parasite stocks at an early stage in disease outbreaks.

3. *Cross-immunity*

Cattle immune to one species of *Theileria* generally show no protection when challenged with an unrelated species; thus, no significant cross-protection exists between *T. parva* and *T. annulata* (Sergent *et al.*, 1945; Neitz, 1957). Similarly, immunity to mildly pathogenic parasites such as *T. mutans* and *T. taurotragi* does not protect cattle against challenge with virulent parasites such as *T. parva* (Theiler, 1912; Neitz, 1957; Irvin *et al.*, 1972a; Burridge *et al.*, 1974a; Young *et al.*, 1977a; Grootenhuis *et al.*, 1979; Uilenberg *et al.*, 1982), *T. annulata* (Sergent *et al.*, 1945; Neitz, 1957) or *T. orientalis* (=*T. sergenti*) (Ishihara, 1968).

Cross-immunity patterns between different species of *Theileria* are generally not used for species differentiation as more convenient definitive methods of differentiation are available. However, where different strains of parasite exist, cross-challenge experiments provide the most valid data in terms of practical characterization. With *T. parva parva*, animals immunized against one stock, when challenged with a heterologous stock, may be resistant or partially or fully susceptible (Radley *et al.*, 1975a; Paling and Geysen, 1981; Irvin *et al.*, 1983). If the heterologous stock is of *T. parva lawrencei* type, breakthroughs are more common (Young *et al.*, 1973b, 1977b; Cunningham *et al.*, 1974; Radley *et al.*, 1975b,c, 1979). However protection of cattle against this diversity of strains can be achieved by using a mixture or "cocktail" of stocks for immunization by infection and treatment (Radley *et al.*, 1975c; Robson *et al.*, 1977; Uilenberg *et al.*, 1977c; Radley, 1978a,b, 1981; Dolan *et al.*, 1980). The level of protection that is achieved does not depend on the severity of the immunizing reaction, and cattle which undergo mild or inapparent reactions are solidly immune to homologous challenge, even when an artificially massive challenge is given (Morzaria *et al.*, in press b).

Cross-immunity trials between different stocks of parasite provide valuable data for selecting appropriate stocks or groups of stocks for field immunization programmes, but the data they provide may be rather imprecise since the immune status of the host and the sporozoite dose in the inoculum are difficult to quantify, and levels of cross protection may be nil, partial or absolute. In these circumstances, precise characterization is clearly impossible; nevertheless, the value of cross-challenge experiments for practical purposes should not be underestimated, despite their lack of precision.

Variations in cross-protection patterns between different stocks of *T. annulata* are also recorded (Pipano, 1977); thus, some stocks from different areas show good cross-protection (Rafyi *et al.*, 1965; Gill *et al.*, 1980), while others show little or no cross-protection (Adler and Ellenbogen, 1935; Sergent *et al.*, 1945). However, in many of these studies, the parasite stocks used were poorly characterized or quantified, making interpretation of results difficult. The advent of more precise methods of characterization should enable future cross-challenge experiments with *T. annulata* stocks to provide more meaningful data on strain diversity of this parasite.

4. *Cytotoxicity*

Genetically restricted cytotoxic cells specific for parasitized target cells are transiently detected in the peripheral blood of cattle recovering from *T. parva* and *T. annulata* infections, either spontaneously or as a result of infection and treatment immunization (Eugui and Emery, 1981; Emery *et al.*, 1981, 1982; Preston *et al.*, 1983; Morrison *et al.*, 1986a). These cytotoxic cells appear to play a major role in immunity in theileriosis, particularly in protection against re-infection with homologous parasites. Eugui *et al.* (1981) pointed out that if specific cytotoxicity is correlated with resistance, the effector cells should kill not only autologous cells infected with parasites homologous with those which initiated the immune reaction, but also cells infected with heterologous parasites which cross-protect *in vivo*. Conversely, heterologous parasites which are not cross-protective, or only partially so, should elicit a reduced cytotoxic response. To examine this premise, Eugui *et al.* (1981) infected cells from individual animals with different theilerial stocks *in vitro* and obtained parasitized cell lines. The animals were then immunized against *T. parva parva* (Muguga) and cytotoxic cells obtained. As expected, autologous cytotoxic cells killed target cells infected with the homologous parasite stock or with a stock (Kilifi) which gave good cross-protection *in vivo*, but the killing of cells infected with poorly cross-protecting stocks of parasites (Kiambu 5 or Serengeti-transformed) was variable. Thus, the level of cytotoxic response appeared to be both genetically restricted and parasite strain-specific. However, this work was conducted with uncloned cell populations and cytotoxic cells had to be raised *in vivo*, which limited the possible application of the technique as a means of parasite strain characterization. Previous work by Pearson *et al.* (1979, 1982) showed that cytotoxic cells which were both genetically restricted and parasite-specific could be generated *in vitro*, but problems of non-specific cytotoxicity arose. Recently, however, Goddeeris *et al.* (in press) have taken this work further and isolated cytotoxic T cell clones with specificity for target cells infected with *T. parva*; this was achieved by repeated *in vitro* stimulation of bovine peripheral blood mononuclear cells from an immune animal with a cloned autologous lymphoblastoid cell line, infected *in vitro* with *T. parva* (Muguga). Killing by these cytotoxic clones was restricted to autologous target cells or allogeneic targets closely matched for class I MHC A locus-specificity. Killing was also parasite strain restricted, as autologous cells infected with *T. parva* (Muguga) were killed, whereas cells derived from the same original clone but infected with *T. parva* (Marikebuni) were not. This elegant work therefore raises the prospect of developing an *in vitro* cytotoxicity assay for parasite strain characterization which is not only strain-specific but also of direct relevance to immunity and cross-protection *in vivo*, since the antigenic changes detected on the surface of parasitized cells by cytotoxic cells *in vitro* appear to be identical to those which the immune host recognizes when exposed to challenge *in vivo*.

Preliminary studies with buffalo (*S. caffer*) have shown that cell-mediated cytotoxicity can be generated *in vitro* against autologous cells infected with *T. parva lawrencei*. Potent cytotoxicity was specific for parasitized cells and also partially strain-specific (C. L. Baldwin *et al.*, unpublished data). This work therefore indicates that cytotoxic cells derived from buffalo could be used to investigate strain diversity in *T. parva lawrencei*.

D. BIOCHEMISTRY

1. *Isoenzymes*

Parasite enzyme polymorphisms, arising as a result of genetic variation between parasite strains, can be studied by electrophoresis or isoelectric focusing, if the molecular differences between isoenzymes of different strains are associated with differences in electric charge (Gibson *et al.*, 1980; Allsopp and Gibson, 1983). The enzymes selected for study of polymorphisms are those easily identified on the basis of their substrate specificity. The majority of forms (isoenzymes) of a specific enzyme are controlled by nuclear genes which undergo a Mendelian type of inheritance, and specificities appear to remain stable over many passages (Walliker, 1983). Isoenzyme patterns (zymograms) can therefore be used to group parasite stocks, which show similar patterns, into zymodemes. Isoenzyme polymorphisms have been used to demonstrate parasite diversity and as strain markers to study patterns of inheritance for a variety of parasitic protozoa, including coccidia (Shirley and Rollinson, 1979), *Leishmania* (Chance, 1979), trypanosomes (Gibson *et al.*, 1980) and *Plasmodium* (Walliker, 1976, 1983; Carter and Voller, 1975; Carter and Walliker, 1977).

Zymograms have been prepared from isolates of *T. parva*, *T. taurotragi* and *T. annulata* using schizonts and piroplasms as the source of enzyme. Glucose phosphate isomerase (EC 5.3.1.9) and hexokinase (EC 2.7.1.1) were the most variable enzymes, and species differences were readily detected (Melrose and Brown, 1979; Melrose *et al.*, 1980, 1984; Musisi *et al.*, 1981b; Van der Meer *et al.*, 1981; Nyormoi and Bwayo, 1981; Allsopp *et al.*, 1985). With *T. annulata*, differences between stocks were found, and isoenzyme polymorphisms could play a role in strain characterization of this species (Melrose *et al.*, 1980, 1984), but with *T. parva* no differences between zymograms of different stocks could be detected and Musisi *et al.* (1981b), for example, could not differentiate between *T. parva parva* and *T. parva lawrencei*.

Allsopp *et al.* (1985) found that piroplasm lysates were a better source of enzymes than schizonts, because of the problem of contamination with host cell enzymes in the latter preparations. Furthermore, expression of schizont-derived isoenzymes could be affected by the host cell background; polymorphisms were less readily detectable in schizonts derived from *B. taurus* cattle than those derived from *B. indicus* cattle.

Zymograms, despite their use in other parasite systems, do not currently appear to offer advantages in characterizing theilerial stocks, particularly *T. parva*. Furthermore, there is no evidence that differences that have been detected can be correlated with different cross-protection patterns *in vivo*.

The reasons why *T. parva* shows negligible isoenzyme polymorphism could be twofold: firstly, the piroplasm stage which is used for analysis is rather inert and may lack significant enzyme activity; secondly, compared to *T. annulata*, *T. parva* appears to have been a parasite of cattle for only a short time in evolutionary terms, and thus has had less opportunity to diversify.

2. *Protein analysis*

Immunochemical characterization of schizont and piroplasm antigens of *Theileria* was first described by Wagner *et al.* (1974,a,b). More recently, proteins of purified theilerial piroplasms and schizonts have been analysed by Allsopp (1981) and Creemers (1981, 1983), using sodium dodecylsulphate polyacrylamide gel electrophoresis. These authors identified a number of parasite polypeptides, and Creemers (1981, 1983) detected minor differences in protein bands between *T. parva parva*, *T. parva lawrencei* and *T. taurotragi*, but most bands were common to all three. Some specific binding of anti-schizont antibodies, raised in rabbits or obtained from recovered cattle, was detected in immune precipitation studies. In subsequent work, Shapiro *et al.* (in press) used Western blotting techniques to analyse proteins of different stocks of *T. parva* with several different MAbs. The major findings were, firstly, that the molecular weight (MW) of the schizont protein of a specific stock appeared to be the same irrespective of the MAb used, indicating that the MAbs used in that study were recognizing different epitopes on the same protein and, secondly, that the MW of this protein differed in different stocks. This diversity in MW might therefore provide a means of characterizing stocks. However, parasite groupings on the basis of MW did not appear to correlate with the MAb profile groupings previously described (Minami *et al.*, 1983; Irvin *et al.*, 1983). Shapiro *et al.* (in press) suggested that protein size polymorphisms detected in *T. parva* may be due to variation in the number of tandem repeats of specific nucleotide sequences, analogous to that seen in the genes coding for the circumsporozoite protein and other strain-specific antigens of malarial parasites (Weber and Hockmeyer, 1985; Nussenzweig and Nussenzweig, 1985).

Another method of analysing parasite proteins that is being explored is high resolution, two-dimensional polyacrylamide gel electrophoresis (Anderson *et al.*, 1985). Preliminary results indicate that the technique can be used to separate host and parasite proteins and that species and strain differences may be detectable (T. W. Pearson and C. Sugimoto, personal communication).

Although these various studies are still in their early stages, they do indicate that differences in parasite proteins of *Theileria* can be detected and that these differences may correlate with strain and species diversity, thus allowing the possibility of defining species and strain differences very precisely at the biochemical level.

3. *Other approaches*

Taracha (1985) has detected infection-specific glycoproteins on the surface of cells infected with *T. annulata* by means of lectin affinity chromatography. Since such glycoproteins are likely to show both species and strain diversity, they could be used for parasite characterization.

Drug resistance has been widely used as a marker in genetic recombinant studies of a number of parasitic protozoa, including *Plasmodium* and coccidia (Beale, 1980; Walliker, 1983; Joyner and Norton, 1975, 1977). No such approach has been used for *Theileria* and no convincing evidence of drug resistance has been reported (Dolan, 1981), although Munderloh and Kurtti (1982) were able to isolate a *T. parva*-infected cell line with reduced sensitivity to aminopterin. However, now that the therapeutic compounds parvaquone and halofuginone (Schein and Voigt, 1979; McHardy, 1984; Humke, 1985; Musisi *et al.*, 1985; Chema *et al.*, 1986) are available for treatment of theileriosis, it can be expected that drug resistant strains of *Theileria* will emerge, and ultimately the necessity of characterizing strains on the basis of this resistance may arise.

E. MOLECULAR BIOLOGY

Most of the methods of parasite characterization that have been considered so far relate largely to detection of phenotypic differences, the expression of which may vary according to external factors and influences. The most precise level of characterization that can be achieved is at the genetic level, and very rapid progress is being made along these lines with a number of parasites; this is particularly the case with *Plasmodium*, where gene mapping, sequencing and manipulation are being extensively applied in order to understand the genetic basis of immunity, for the purpose of vaccine development and in the investigation of species and strain differences (Goman *et al.*, 1982; Coppel *et al.*, 1983, 1985; Dame *et al.*, 1984; Enea *et al.*, 1984; Vincenzo *et al.*, 1984; Hope *et al.*, 1985; Barker *et al.*, 1986). Similar approaches are being adopted with *Theileria*, and those associated with strain characterization are described below.

1. *Deoxyribonucleic acid (DNA) probes*

Theileria parva DNA has been obtained from piroplasm-infected blood (Iams, 1985; B. A. Allsopp, personal communication). DNA fragments, obtained either by shearing or mung bean nuclease digestion (McCutchan *et al.*, 1984b), was inserted into the genome of the bacteriophage lambda (gt 11). Hybrid virus was cloned in *Escherichia coli* and expression of theilerial proteins detected by screening gene banks with anti-schizont MAbs (Iams, 1985; Conrad, 1985). A number of clones has now been identified which produce proteins recognized by these MAbs, indicating that these clones contain genes coding for schizont antigen (Conrad, 1985; K. Iams *et al.*, unpublished data). As this work develops and the repertoire of specific gene probes is extended, the possibility of using such probes for parasite strain characterization becomes very real. Probes are being sought which contain strain-specific sequences of theilerial DNA and, under appropriate conditions, these probes will hybridize to DNA or RNA strands that have a complementary sequence of nucleotide bases (Southern, 1975; Post, 1985). When radiolabelled probes are used, hybridization can be detected autoradiographically or by related techniques. Thus, a battery of probes containing different strain-specific sequences of parasite DNA can be used to screen parasite DNA of unknown specificity and hence identify the parasite strain under test (Post, 1985). This approach is now being used very successfully for the identification of trypanosomes (Massamba and Williams, 1984; Majiwa *et al.*, 1985), and *Plasmodium* and *Leishmania* species in samples collected from infected patients (Wirth and Pratt, 1982; Franzen *et al.*, 1984; Pollack *et al.*, 1985). Preliminary studies indicate that a similar approach can be used for strain characterization in *Theileria* (B. A. Allsopp, K. Iams and P. A. Conrad, personal communications) (Fig. 4). Since the hybridization technique is extremely sensitive (Pollack *et al.*, 1985), it is possible to obtain the requisite amount of test DNA from schizont-infected lymphoid cells or piroplasm-infected erythrocytes circulating in the peripheral blood of infected cattle. In this way the specificity of the infecting strain(s) of parasite can be rapidly determined.

Another approach which might be feasible (P. A. Conrad, K. Iams and G. Desai, personal communication) is to use the strain-specific probes for production of fusion proteins containing specific antigens. A battery of these

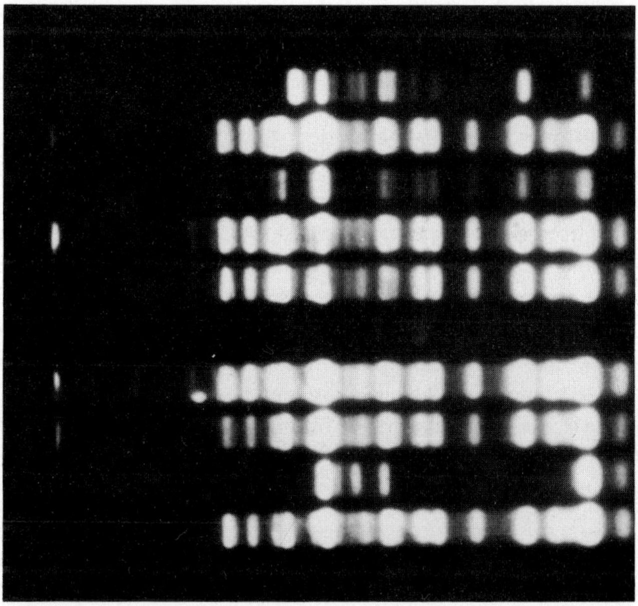

FIG. 4. Autoradiograph of a Southern blot of *Theileria* DNA probed with a ^{32}P-labelled recombinant genomic DNA element cloned from *Theileria parva* (Kiambu 4). The blot was obtained from one sample of *Theileria mutans* and 11 of *Theileria parva* piroplasm DNA digested with the restriction enzyme Hinf 1 and separated on a 2.0% agarose gel. (By courtesty of B. A. Allsopp.)

antigens could then be screened against field sera of unknown specificity (for example in an ELISA test), to determine the nature of the infecting strain(s) in the cattle from which the sera were derived.

Both these putative approaches have the advantages that they provide data which relate specifically to the strain(s) of parasite present in the animals at the time of testing and that large numbers of samples can be handled. This is in contrast to the current MAb profile test (Minami *et al.*, 1983), which relies on the isolation and cultivation of the parasite *in vitro*, with possible concomitant modification of antigenicity, before the test can be applied.

The majority of DNA probes developed for studies on strain characterization in *Theileria* have been derived from genomic libraries, where the whole parasite genome has been obtained (usually from piroplasms) and then cleaved with restriction enzymes. However, the use of complementary DNA (cDNA) libraries is also being explored (Hall, 1985). These are derived from messenger RNA (mRNA) sequences which, in the presence of reverse transcriptase, are copied to give cDNA. This cDNA can then be used for the construction of gene probes in the same way as genomic DNA. The advantage of using cDNA is that it is derived from only that part of the parasite genome which is transcriptionally active, and much non-expressed DNA can be excluded. Thus, with *Theileria*, it may be possible to utilize stage or strain-specific mRNA sequences to construct cDNA libraries for the production of probes to monitor strain variation as described above.

Much attention is currently being devoted to obtaining repetitive nucleotide sequences of protozoan parasites, for a number of reasons; they appear to be commonly present, and some play an important role in coding for immunogenic epitopes or peptides; in contrast to structural genes, they appear to undergo considerable evolutionary diversity which can be relevant to species and strain characterization; also, because they have a high copy number, they give a strong signal and can be readily detected (Godson *et al.*, 1983; Coppel *et al.*, 1984; Vincenzo *et al.*, 1984). A number of genes coding for repetitive sequences in *Theileria* has now been isolated and they are being characterized (P. A. Conrad and K. Iams, personal communication).

2. *Restriction enzyme patterns*

Restriction endonucleases are enzymes of bacterial origin which recognize specific nucleotide sequences in DNA and then cleave it at those sites. For example, the restriction endonuclease EcoR1 (derived from a strain of *E. coli*) recognizes the nucleotide sequence GAATTC and cleaves it between G and A (Roberts, 1983). This sequence is very common in DNA, so that treatment with EcoR1 endonuclease produces numerous DNA fragments of different lengths which can be separated by agarose gel electrophoresis. The resultant restriction enzyme banding patterns show a high level of specificity for different species and strains of organism. Preliminary studies have been conducted with *Theileria* DNA cleaved with EcoR1 (Guerin-Marchand and Lambiotte, 1984; K. Iams, personal communication), and differences in the banding patterns of different isolates of *T. parva* have been detected (K. Iams, personal communication). This work indicates that restriction enzyme patterns can be used to differentiate theilerial strains, but perhaps more importantly the technique provides a means of identifying strain-specific bands of parasite DNA.

3. *Pulse-field gradient gel electrophoresis*

Pulse-field gradient (PFG) gel electrophoresis is a technique which enables chromosome-sized molecules (in the range of 30–3000 kilobase pairs) to be separated electrophoretically in agarose gel (Cox, 1985; Gibson, 1985). The technique was originally applied to the analysis of yeast chromosomes (Schwarts and Cantor, 1984), but has recently been successfully applied to the analysis of chromosomes of other eukaryotic organisms such as trypanosomes and *Plasmodium*, in which chromosomal condensation does not occur and hence direct cytogenetic analysis is impossible (Van der Ploeg *et al.*, 1984a, 1984b, 1985; Majiwa *et al.*, 1985; Kemp *et al.*, 1985). Preliminary studies with *Theileria* have also been conducted (O. ole-Moi Yoi and K. Iams, personal communication); these have shown that if *T. parva* DNA obtained from piroplasms is cleaved with the restriction enzymes Sfi 1 and Not 1 and then subjected to PFG electrophoresis, the different DNA fragments can be identified because they migrate at different rates in the gel. Such gel patterns can be used to differentiate the molecular karyotypes of malarial parasites (Kemp *et al.*, 1985), and may soon be applicable for the differentiation of *Theileria*.

In addition to comparative karyotyping, the technique may also be used to map the location of specific genes and to determine gene linkages on chromosomes, by using hybridization techniques with specific probes.

4. *Other approaches*

The deoxyguanosine:deoxycytidine (dG:dC) content of DNA from malaria parasites differs greatly from that of mammalian DNA (Gutteridge *et al.*, 1971; Pollack *et al.*, 1982), and parasite and host DNA can subsequently be separated by caesium chloride centrifugation (Simpson, 1979). Recently, however, McCutchan *et al.* (1984a) have also shown that different dG:dC levels are detectable in different malarial species and that evolutionary relatedness between species can be determined on this basis. Preliminary attempts to characterize theilerial DNA in this way have given a dC:dG content of 36.7% for *T. parva* (Geurin-Marchand and Lambiotte, 1984). A similar result has been obtained by B. A. Allsopp, and by O. ole-Moi Yoi and K. Iams (personal communications), but the latter workers noted that their preparation was contaminated with bovine DNA and felt that this gave an erroneously high value. The availability of improved reagents should allow more precise characterization to be achieved.

Another approach to DNA analysis is that used for *Trypanosoma cruzi* by Dvorak *et al.* (1982), who found variation between different stocks in which DNA was coupled to mithramycin and different levels of fluorescence detected by flow cytometry. This technique has not so far been applied to *Theileria*, but may be another means of detecting strain diversity.

Geysen *et al.* (1984) and Geysen (1985) have recently shown that peptides can be synthesized which simulate the antigenic epitopes recognized by MAbs. Starting with a specific MAb it is possible to build up the molecule corresponding to the epitope which the MAb recognizes, without the necessity of synthesizing the whole protein on which the epitope is located. This approach can obviously be very useful for synthesizing immunogenic peptides for vaccination, but it may also be applicable as a means of producing a battery of monospecific antigens for screening test sera in parasite strain characterization.

VIII. Summary and Conclusions

A variety of methods is now available for characterizing species and strains of *Theileria*. For many practical purposes involving field control of theileriosis, characterization on a broad basis may be sufficient, but in other areas much more precise characterization is required. Such precision can be usefully exploited only when cloned parasite populations are involved, and methods to improve parasite characterization and parasite cloning should be developed concurrently.

The current methods of immunization against theileriosis involve the use of live parasite populations which are generally poorly defined and, in addition, have the capacity to undergo biological change (by selection, mutation or genetic recombination) within hosts and vectors. Such changes may be difficult to define and identify, but could have profound effects on immunization strategies. Improved methods of parasite characterization and selection, which are now becoming available, will enable parasite stocks for immunization to be identified and selected more precisely, and any biological changes that occur can be monitored.

Improved methods of parasite characterization will also open the way to a better understanding of *Theileria* genetics and the mechanisms of heritability, which appear to differ in some fundamental ways from patterns of Mendelian inheritance. Controlled matings between selected and defined populations of parasites can be envisaged, with the aim of producing hybrid parasites for immunization. In addition, the prospects of modifying the theilerial genome by genetic manipulation become very real: transfection vectors tailored by restriction enzymes could be used to insert or modify gene sequences to develop parasites with appropriate sets of characters. It may also be possible to identify parasite genes which trigger the cytotoxic response which is so important in immunity (Eugui and Emery, 1981; Emery *et al.*, 1981; Preston *et al.*, 1983). Such genes might then be transfected into bovine host lymphocytes to generate immunity against the whole parasite (Iams, 1985). The gene products which are responsible for stimulating immune responses could also be synthesized artificially and used for vaccination.

Methods of characterizing *Theileria* range from Giemsa's staining to DNA hybridization; all have a role to play, and by judicious selection of appropriate methods for particular circumstances, it is becoming possible to characterize theilerial parasites very precisely. Improved methods of characterization can, in turn, lead to a better understanding of parasite biology and to the development of improved methods of immunization and control.

Acknowledgements

I am most grateful to the following people for helpful discussions, advice and criticism, and for access to unpublished data: B. A. Allsopp, P. A. Conrad, K. Iams, O. ole-Moi Yoi, W. I. Morrison, S. P. Morzaria, S. Z. Shapiro, G. Uilenberg and A. S. Young. Photographs have been kindly supplied by B. A. Allsopp, S. P. Morzaria, P. Webster and A. S. Young.

References

Adams, T. E. and Brandon, M. R. (1981). Genetic aspects of disease resistance in cattle. *In* "The Ruminant Immune System" (J. E. Butler, ed.), pp. 451–473. Plenum Press, New York.

Adler, S. and Ellenbogen, V. (1935). Observations on theileriosis in Palestine. *Archives de l'Institut Pasteur d'Algérie* **13**, 451–471.

Allsopp, B. A. (1981). Membrane antigens of *Theileria* piroplasms. *In* "Advances in the Control of Theileriosis" (A. D. Irvin, M. P. Cunningham and A. S. Young, eds), pp. 358–361. Martinus Nijhoff Publishers, The Hague.

Allsopp, B. A. and Gibson, W. C. (1983). Isoelectric focusing in agarose: a highly discriminatory method for the detection of enzyme heterogeneity. *Annals of Tropical Medicine and Parasitology* **77,** 169–173.

Allsopp, B. A., Gibson, W. C. and Stagg, D. A. (1985). Characterization of some East African *Theileria* species isolates by isoenzyme analysis, with particular reference to *T. parva. International Journal for Parasitology* **15,** 272–276.

Anderson, N. L., Parish, N. M., Richardson, J. P. and Pearson, T. W. (1985). Comparison of African trypanosomes of different antigenic phenotypes, subspecies and life cycle stages by two dimensional gel electrophoresis. *Molecular and Biochemical Parasitology* **16,** 299–314.

Anonymous (1981). The eradication of east coast fever in South Africa. *Journal of the South African Veterinary Association* **52,** 71–73.

Anonymous (1982). Proceedings of the second international bovine lymphocyte (BoLA) workshop. *Animal Blood Groups and Biochemical Genetics* **13,** 33–63.

Bailey, K. P. (1960). Notes on the rearing of *Rhipicephalus appendiculatus* and their infection with *Theileria parva* for experimental transmission. *Bulletin of Epizootic Diseases of Africa* **8,** 33–43.

Baldwin, C. L., Malu, M. N., Kinuthia, S. W., Conrad, P. A. and Grootenhuis, J. G. (1986). Comparative analysis of infection and transformation of lymphocytes from African buffalo and Boran cattle with *Theileria parva parva* and *T. p. lawrencei. Infection and Immunity* **53,** 186–191.

Barker, D. C., Gibson, L. J., Kennedy, W. P. K., Nasser, A. A. A. A. and Williams, R. H. (1986). The potential of using recombinant DNA species-specific probes for the identification of tropical *Leishmania. Parasitology* **91,** S139–S174.

Barnett, S. F. (1957). Theileriasis control. *Bulletin of Epizootic Diseases of Africa* **5,** 343–357.

Barnett, S. F. (1960). Connective tissue reactions in acute fatal East Coast fever (*Theileria parva*) of cattle. *Journal of Infectious Diseases* **107,** 253–282.

Barnett, S. F. (1968). Theileriasis. *In* "Infectious Blood Diseases of Man and Animals" (D. Weinmann and M. Ristic, eds), pp. 269–328. Academic Press, New York.

Barnett, S. F. (1977). Theileria. *In* "Parasitic Protozoa" (J. P. Kreier, ed.), Vol. 4, pp. 77–113. Academic Press, New York.

Barnett, S. F. and Brocklesby, D. W. (1961). A mild form of east coast fever. *Veterinary Record* **73,** 43.

Barnett, S. F. and Brocklesby, D. W. (1966a). Recent investigations into Theileriidae of cattle and buffalo in Africa. A mild form of east coast fever (*Theileria parva*) with persistence of infection. *British Veterinary Journal* **122,** 361–371.

Barnett, S. F. and Brocklesby, D. W. (1966b). The passage of "*Theileria lawrencei*" (Kenya) through cattle. *British Veterinary Journal* **122,** 396–409.

Barnett, S. F. and Brocklesby, D. W. (1968). Some piroplasms of wild mammals. *Symposium of the Zoological Society of London* **24,** 159–176.

Barnett, S. F., Brocklesby, D. W. and Vidler, B. O. (1961). Studies on macroschizonts of *Theileria parva. Research in Veterinary Science* **2,** 11–18.

Beale, G. H. (1980). The genetics of drug resistance in malaria parasites. *Bulletin of the World Health Organization* **58,** 799–804.

Bell, L. J. (1980). Organ culture of *Rhipicephalus appendiculatus* with maturation of *Theileria parva* in tick salivary glands *in vitro. Acta Tropica* **37,** 319–325.

Benacerraf, B. and Germain, R. M. (1978). The immune response genes of the major histocompatibility complex. *Immunological Reviews* **38,** 70–119.

Binnington, K. C., Young, A. S. and Obenchain, F. D. (1983). Morphology of normal and *Theileria parva*-infected salivary glands of *Rhipicephalus appendiculatus* (Acari: Ixodoidea). *Journal of Parasitology* **69,** 421–424.

Blewett, D. A. and Branagan, D. (1973). The demonstration of *Theileria parva* infection in intact *Rhipicephalus appendiculatus* salivary glands. *Tropical Animal Health and Production* **5,** 27–34.

Brocklesby, D. W. (1962). *Cytauxzoon taurotragi* Martin & Brocklesby 1960, a piroplasm of the eland (*Taurotragus oryx pattersonianus* Lydekker, 1906). *Research in Veterinary Science* **3,** 334–344.

Brocklesby, D. W. (1965). A new theilerial parasite of the African buffalo (*Syncerus caffer*). *Bulletin of Epizootic Diseases of Africa* **13,** 325–330.

Brocklesby, D. W. (1978). Recent observations on tick-borne protozoa. *In* "Tick-born Diseases and their Vectors" (J. K. H. Wilde, ed.), pp. 263–286. University of Edinburgh, Edinburgh, Scotland.

Brocklesby, D. W. and Vidler, B. O. (1961). Haematozoa of the blue wildebeest. *Bulletin of Epizootic Diseases of Africa* **9,** 245–249.

Brocklesby, D. W. and Vidler, B. O. (1966). Haematozoa found in wild members of the order Artiodactyla in East Africa. *Bulletin of Epizootic Diseases of Africa* **14,** 285–299.

Brown, C. G. D. (1981). Application of *in vitro* techniques to vaccination against theileriosis. *In* "Advances in the Control of Theileriosis" (A. D. Irvin, M. P. Cunningham and A. S. Young, eds), pp. 104–119. Martinus Nijhoff Publishers, The Hague.

Brown, C. G. D., Stagg, D. A., Purnell, R. E., Kanhai, G. K. and Payne, R. C. (1973). Infection and transformation of bovine lymphoid cells *in vitro* by infective particles of *Theileria parva*. *Nature* **245,** 101–103.

Brown, C. G. D., Crawford, J. G., Kanhai, G. K., Njuguna, L. M. and Stagg, D. A. (1978a). Immunization of cattle against east coast fever with lymphoblastoid cell lines infected and transformed by *Theileria parva*. *In* "Tick-borne Diseases and their Vectors" (J. K. H. Wilde, ed.), pp. 331–333. University of Edinburgh, Edinburgh, Scotland.

Brown, C. G. D., Cunningham, M. P., Joyner, L. P., Purnell, R. E., Branagan, D., Corry, G. L. and Bailey, K. P. (1978b). *Theileria parva*: significance of leukocytes for infecting cattle. *Experimental Parasitology* **45,** 55–64.

Burridge, M. J. (1971). Application of the indirect fluorescent antibody test in experimental east coast fever (*Theileria parva* infection of cattle). *Research in Veterinary Science* **12,** 338–341.

Burridge, M. J. (1975). The role of wild mammals in the epidemiology of bovine theileriosis in East Africa. *Journal of Wildlife Diseases* **11,** 68–75.

Burridge, M. J. and Kimber, C. D. (1972). The indirect fluorescent antibody test for experimental east coast fever (*Theileria parva* infection of cattle): evaluation of a cell culture schizont antigen. *Research in Veterinary Science* **13,** 451–455.

Burridge, M. J., Kimber, C. D. and Young, A. S. (1973). Use of the indirect fluorescent antibody technique in serologic studies of *Theileria lawrencei* infections in cattle. *American Journal of Veterinary Research* **34,** 897–900.

Burridge, M. J., Brown, C. G. D., Crawford, J. G., Kirimi, I. M., Morzaria, S. P., Payne, R. C. and Newson, R. M. (1974a). Preliminary studies on an atypical strain of bovine *Theileria* isolated in Kenya. *Research in Veterinary Science* **17,** 139–144.

Burridge, M. J., Brown, C. G. D. and Kimber, C. D. (1974b). *Theileria annulata*: cross reactions between a cell culture schizont antigen and antigens of East African

Theileria species in the indirect fluorescent antibody test. *Experimental Parasitology* **35,** 374–380.
Buscher, G., Katende, J., Otim, B. and Morrison, W. I. (1984a). Infection of the host cells of *Theileria annulata* with *T. parva. Zeitschrift für Parasitenkunde* **70,** 687–689.
Buscher, G., Morrison, W. I. and Nelson, R. T. (1984b). Titration in cattle of infectivity and immunogenicity of autologous cell lines infected with *Theileria parva. Veterinary Parasitology* **15,** 29–38.
Canning, E. U. and Anwar, M. (1968). Studies on meiotic division in coccidial and malarial parasites. *Journal of Protozoology* **15,** 290–298.
Carter, R. and Voller, A. (1975). The distribution of enzyme variation in populations of *Plasmodium falciparum* in Africa. *Transactions of the Royal Society of Tropical Medicine and Hygiene* **69,** 371–376.
Carter, R. and Walliker, D. (1977). Biochemical markers for strain differentiation in malarial parasites. *Bulletin of the World Health Organization* **55,** 339–345.
Chance, M. (1979). The identification of *Leishmania. Symposia of the British Society for Parasitology* **17,** 55–74.
Chema, S., Waghela, S., James, A. D., Dolan, T. T., Young, A. S., Masiga, W. N., Irvin, A. D., Mulela, G. H. M. and Wekesa, L. S. (1986). Clinical trial of parvaquone for the treatment of East Coast fever in Kenya. *Veterinary Record* **118,** 588–589.
Conrad, P. A. (1985). Use of monoclonal antibodies and DNA probes for theilerial strain/species characterization. *In* "Parasite Antigens" (Summary Proceedings of an International Workshop), p. 42. International Laboratory for Research in Animal Diseases, Nairobi.
Conrad, P. A., Stagg, D. A., Grootenhuis, J. G., Irvin, A. D., Newson, J., Njamunggeh, R. E. G., Rossiter, P. B. and Young, A. S. (in press). Isolation of *Theileria* from African buffalo (*Syncerus caffer*) and characterization with anti-schizont monoclonal antibodies. *Parasitology.*
Coppel, R. L., Cowman, A. F., Lingelbach, K. R., Brown, G. V., Saint, R. B., Kemp, D. J. and Anders, R. F. (1983). Isolate specific S-antigen of *Plasmodium falciparum* contains a repeated sequence of eleven amino acids. *Nature* **306,** 751–756.
Coppel, R. L., Cowman, A. F., Anders, R. F., Bianco, A. E., Saint, R. B., Lingelbach, K. R., Kemp, D. J. and Brown, G. V. (1984). Immune sera recognise on erythrocytes *Plasmodium falciparum* antigen composed of repeated amino acid sequences. *Nature* **310,** 789–791.
Coppel, R. L., Saint, R. B., Stahl, H. D., Langford, C. J., Brown, G. V., Anders, R. F. and Kemp, D. J. (1985). *Plasmodium falciparum*: differentiation of isolates with DNA hybridisation using antigen gene probes. *Experimental Parasitology* **60,** 82–89.
Cowan, K. M., Dolan, T. T., Teale, A. J., Young, A. S., Stagg, D. A. and Groocock, C. (1984). Detection of antibody to *Theileria parva* schizonts and cell surface membrane antigens of infected lymphoblastoid cells by immunoperoxidase techniques. *Veterinary Parasitology* **15,** 223–237.
Cowdry, E. V. and Danks, W. B. C. (1933). Studies on east coast fever. II. Behaviour of the parasite and the development of distinctive lesions in susceptible animals. *Parasitology* **25,** 1–63.
Cox, F. E. G. (1985). Chromosomes of malaria parasites and trypanosomes. *Nature* **315,** 280–281.
Creemers, P. (1981). Characterization of antigens of *Theileria* macroschizonts and

immune precipitation studies. *In* "Advances in the Control of Theileriosis" (A. D. Irvin, M. P. Cunningham and A. S. Young, eds), p. 357. Martinus Nijhoff Publishers, The Hague.

Creemers, P. (1983). Protein antigens of *Theileria parva* macroschizonts and immune precipitation studies. *Journal of Parasitology* **69,** 54–59.

Cunningham, M. P., Brown, C. G. D., Burridge, M. J. and Purnell, R. E. (1973). Cryopreservation of infective particles of *Theileria parva. International Journal for Parasitology* **3,** 583–387.

Cunningham, M. P., Brown, C. G. D., Burridge, M. J., Irvin, A. D., Kirimi, I. M., Purnell, R. E., Radley, D. E. and Wagner, G. G. (1974). Theileriosis: the exposure of immunized cattle in a *Theileria lawrencei* enzootic area. *Tropical Animal Health and Production* **6,** 39–43.

Dame, J. B., Williams, J. L., McCutchan, T. F., Weber, J. L., Wirtz, R. A., Hockmeyer, W. T., Maloy, W. L., Haynes, J. D., Schneider, I., Roberts, D., Sanders, G. S., Reddy, E. P., Diggs, C. L. and Miller, L. H. (1984). Structure of the gene encoding the immunodominant surface antigen on the sporozoite of the human malaria parasite *Plasmodium falciparum. Science* **225,** 593–599.

De Kock, G. (1957). Studies on the lesions and pathogenesis of east coast fever (*Theileria parva* infection) in cattle, with special reference to the lymphoid tissue. *Onderstepoort Journal of Veterinary Research* **27,** 431–452.

De Kock, G., van Heerden, C. J., du Toit, R. and Neitz, W. O. (1937). Bovine theileriosis in South Africa with special reference to *Theileria mutans. Onderstepoort Journal of Veterinary Science and Animal Industries* **8,** 9–125.

De Vos, A. J. and Roos, J. A. (1981a). Observations on the transmission of *Theileria mutans* in South Africa. *Onderstepoort Journal of Veterinary Research* **48,** 1–6.

De Vos, A. J. and Roos, J. A. (1981b). The isolation of *Theileria taurotragi* in South Africa. *Onderstepoort Journal of Veterinary Research* **48,** 149–153.

De Vos, A. J., Bessenger, R. and Banting, L. F. (1981). *Theileria ?taurotragi*: a probable agent of bovine cerebral theileriosis. *Onderstepoort Journal of Veterinary Research* **48,** 177–178.

Dobbelaere, D. A. E., Spooner, P. R., Barry, W. C. and Irvin, A. D. (1984). Monoclonal antibody neutralizes the sporozoite stage of different *Theileria parva* stocks. *Parasite Immunology* **6,** 361–370.

Dolan, T. T. (1981). Progress in the chemotherapy of theileriosis. *In* "Advances in the Control of Theileriosis" (A. D. Irvin, M. P. Cunningham and A. S. Young, eds), pp. 186–208. Martinus Nijhoff Publishers, The Hague.

Dolan, T. T., Radley, D. E., Brown, C. G. D., Cunningham, M. P., Morzaria, S. P. and Young, A. S. (1980). East coast fever. 4. Further studies on the protection of cattle immunized with a combination of theilerial strains. *Veterinary Parasitology* **6,** 325–332.

Dolan, T. T., Njuguna, L. N. and Stagg, D. A. (1982). The response of *Bos taurus* and *Bos indicus* cattle types to inoculation of lymphoblastoid cell lines infected with *Theileria parva* schizonts. *Tropenmedizin und Parasitologie* **33,** 57–62.

Dolan, T. T., Teale, A. J., Stagg, D. A., Kemp, S. J., Cowan, K. M., Young, A. S., Groocock, C. M., Leitch, B. L., Spooner, R. L. and Brown, C. G. D. (1984a). An histocompatibility barrier to immunization against east coast fever using *Theileria parva*-infected lymphoblastoid cells. *Parasite Immunology* **6,** 243–250.

Dolan, T. T., Young, A. S., Losos, G. J., McMillan, I., Minder, C. E. and Soulsby, K. (1984b). Dose dependent responses of cattle to *Theileria parva* stabilate. *International Journal for Parasitology* **14,** 89–95.

Downs, W. G. (1947). Infections of chicks with single parasites of *Plasmodium gallinaceum* Brumpt. *American Journal of Hygiene* **46,** 41–44.

Duffus, W. P. H. and Wagner, G. G. (1980). Comparison between certain serological tests for diagnosis of east coast fever. *Veterinary Parasitology* **6,** 313–324.

Dvorak, J. A., Hall, T. E., Crane, M. S. J., Engel, J. C., McDaniel, J. P. and Uriegas, R. (1982). *Trypanosoma cruzi*: flow cytometric analysis. I. Analysis of total DNA/organism by means of mithramycin-induced fluorescence. *Journal of Protozoology* **29,** 430–435.

Emery, D. L., Eugui, E. M., Nelson, R. T. and Tenywa, T. (1981). Cell-mediated immune responses to *Theileria parva* (east coast fever) during immunization and lethal infections in cattle. *Immunology* **43,** 323–336.

Emery, D. L., Morrison, W. I., Buscher, G. and Nelson, R. T. (1982). Generation of cell-mediated cytotoxicity to *Theileria parva* (east coast fever) after inoculation of cattle with parasitized lymphoblasts. *Journal of Immunology* **128,** 195–200.

Enea, V., Ellis, J., Zavala, F., Arnot, D. E., Asavanich, A., Masuda, A., Quakyi, I. and Nussenzweig, R. S. (1984). DNA cloning of *Plasmodium falciparum* circumsporozoite gene: amino acid sequence of repetitive epitope. *Science* **225,** 628–630.

Eugui, E. M. and Emery, D. L. (1981). Genetically-restricted cell-mediated cytotoxicity in cattle immune to *Theileria parva*. *Nature* **290,** 251–254.

Eugui, E. M., Emery, D. L., Buscher, G. and Khaukha, G. (1981). Specific and non-specific cellular immune response to *Theileria parva* in cattle. *In* "Advances in the Control of Theileriosis" (A. D. Irvin, M. P. Cunningham and A. S. Young, eds), pp. 289–294. Martinus Nijhoff Publishers, The Hague.

Fawcett, D. W., Doxsey, S., Stagg, D. A. and Young, A. S. (1982). The entry of sporozoites of *Theileria parva* into bovine lymphocytes *in vitro*. Electron microscope observations. *European Journal of Cell Biology* **27,** 10–21.

Fawcett, D. W., Young, A. S. and Leitch, B. L. (1985). Sporogony in *Theileria* (Apicomplexa: Piroplasmida): a comparative study. *Journal of Submicroscopical Cytology* **17,** 299–314.

Flanagan, H. O. and Le Roux, J. M. W. (1957). Bovine cerebral theileriosis—a report on two cases occurring in the Union. *Onderstepoort Journal of Veterinary Research* **27,** 453–461.

Franzen, L., Westin, G., Shabo, R., Aslund, L., Perlman, H., Persson, T., Wigzell, H. and Petersonn, U. (1984). Analysis of clinical specimens by hybridization with probes containing repetitive DNA from *Plasmodium falciparum*: a novel approach to malaria diagnoses. *Lancet* **i,** 525–528.

Fujinaga, T. and Minami, T. (1981). Indirect fluorescent antibody and complement fixation tests in the diagnosis of bovine theileriosis and babesiosis in Japan. *Veterinary Parasitology* **8,** 115–126.

Fujisaki, K., Irvin, A. D., Voigt, W. P., Leitch, B. L. and Morzaria, S. P. (in press). The establishment of infection in the salivary glands of *Rhipicephalus appendiculatus* ticks by transplantation of kinetes of *Theileria parva* and the potential use of the method for parasite cloning. *International Journal for Parasitology*.

Geysen, H. M. (1985). *In vitro* peptide synthesis. *In* "Parasite Antigens" (Summary Proceedings of an International Workshop), pp. 18–19. International Laboratory for Research in Animal Diseases, Nairobi.

Geysen, H. M., Moloen, R. H. and Barteling, S. J. (1984). Use of peptide synthesis to probe viral antigens for epitopes to a resolution of a single amino acid. *Proceedings of the National Academy of Sciences, USA* **81,** 3998–4002.

Gibson, W. C. (1985). Molecular karyotyping. *Parasitology Today* **1,** 64–65.

Gibson, W. C., Marshall, T. F. de C. and Godfrey, D. G. (1980). Numerical analysis of enzyme polymorphism: a new approach to the epidemiology and taxonomy of trypanosomes of the sub-genus *Trypanozoon*. *Advances in Parasitology* **18,** 175–246.

Gill, B. S., Bansal, G. C., Bhattacharyulu, Y., Kaur, D. and Singh, A. (1980). Immunological relationships between strains of *Theileria annulata* Dschunkowsky and Luhs 1904. *Research in Veterinary Science* **29,** 93–97.

Glenn, B. L. and Stair, E. L. (1984). Cytauxzoonosis in domestic cats: report of two cases in Oklahoma, with a review and discussion of the disease. *Journal of the American Veterinary Medical Association* **184,** 822–825.

Glenn, B. L., Rolley, R. E. and Kocan, A. A. (1982). Cytauxzoon-like piroplasms in erythrocytes of wild-trapped bobcats (*Lynx rufus rufus*) in Oklahoma. *Journal of the American Veterinary Medical Association* **181,** 1251–1253.

Goddeeris, B. M., Katende, J. M., Irvin, A. D. and Chumo, R. S. (1982). Indirect fluorescent antibody test for experimental and epizootiological studies on east coast fever (*Theileria parva* infection of cattle). Evaluation of a cell culture schizont antigen fixed and stored in suspension. *Research in Veterinary Science* **33,** 360–365.

Goddeeris, B. M., Morrison, W. I., Teale, A. J., Bensaid, A. and Baldwin, C. L. (in press). Bovine cytotoxic T cell clones specific for cells infected with *Theileria parva*: parasite strain specificity and class I MHC restriction. *Proceedings of the National Academy of Sciences, USA*.

Godson, G. N., Ellis, J., Svec, P., Schlesinger, D. H. and Nussenzweig, V. (1983). Identification and chemical synthesis of a tandemly repeated immunogenic region of *Plasmodium knowlesi* circumsporozoite protein. *Nature* **306,** 29–33.

Goman, M., Langsley, G., Hyde, J. F., Nankousky, N. K., Zolg, J. W. and Scaife, J. G. (1982). The establishment of genomic DNA libraries for the human malaria parasite *Plasmodium falciparum* and identification of individual clones by hybridization. *Molecular and Biochemical Parasitology* **5,** 391–400.

Gray, M. A., Luckins, A. G., Rae, P. F. and Brown, C. G. D. (1980). Evaluation of an enzyme immunoassay for serodiagnosis of infections with *Theileria parva* and *T. annulata*. *Research in Veterinary Science* **29,** 360–366.

Greenberg, J. and Trembley, H. L. (1954). Infections produced by mixed strains of *Plasmodium gallinaceum* in chicks. *Journal of Parasitology* **40,** 336–340.

Grootenhuis, J. G., Young, A. S., Dolan, T. T. and Stagg, D. A. (1979). Characteristics of *Theileria* species (eland) infections in eland and cattle. *Research in Veterinary Science* **27,** 59–68.

Grootenhuis, J. G., Young, A. S. and Uilenberg, G. (1981). The relationship between *Theileria taurotragi* from eland and *Theileria* sp. (Idobogo) from cattle. *Veterinary Parasitology* **8,** 39–47.

Guerin-Marchand, C. and Lambiotte, M. (1984). The genome of *Theileria parva*: some structural properties. *FEBS Letters* **169,** 305–308.

Guilbride, P. D. L. and Opwata, B. (1963). Observations on the resistance of Jersey/Nganda calves to east coast fever (*Theileria parva*). *Bulletin of Epizootic Diseases of Africa* **11,** 289–298.

Gutteridge, W. E., Trigg, P. I. and Williamson, D. H. (1971). Properties of DNA from some malarial parasites. *Parasitology* **62,** 209–219.

Hall, R. (1985). Progress in theileriosis: 2. Identification of genes encoding important protective antigens of sporozoites of *Theileria parva*. *In* "Parasite Antigens"

(Summary Proceedings of an International Workshop), p. 31. International Laboratory for Research in Animal Diseases, Nairobi.

Handman, E. and Hocking, R. E. (1982). Stage-specific, strain-specific and cross-reactive antigens of *Leishmania* species identified by monoclonal antibodies. *Infection and Immunity* **37,** 28–33.

Hawa, N. J., Latif, B. M. A. and Bakir, F. A. (1976). Application of the indirect fluorescent antibody test for diagnosis of *Theileria hirci* infection of sheep using cell culture schizont antigen. *Tropical Animal Health and Production* **8,** 97–101.

Hawa, N. J., Latif, B. M. A. and Ali, S. R. (1981). Immunization of sheep against *Theileria hirci* infections with schizonts propagated in tissue culture. *Veterinary Parasitology* **9,** 91–97.

Hooshmand-Rad, P. and Hawa, N. J. (1973a). Malignant theileriosis of sheep and goats. *Tropical Animal Health and Production* **5,** 97–102.

Hooshmand-Rad, P. and Hawa, N. J. (1973b). Transmission of *Theileria hirci* in sheep by *Hyalomma anatolicum anatolicum. Tropical Animal Health and Production* **5,** 103–109.

Hope, I. A., Mackay, M., Hyde, J. E., Goman, M. and Scaife, J. (1985). The gene for an exported antigen of the malaria parasites *Plasmodium falciparum* cloned and expressed in *Escherichia coli. Nucleic Acids Research* **13,** 369–380.

Hulliger, L., Wilde, J. K. H., Brown, C. G. D. and Turner, L. (1964). Mode of multiplication of *Theileria* in cultures of bovine lymphocytic cells. *Nature* **203,** 728–730.

Humke, R. (1985). Halofuginone: toxicology, kinetics, efficacy. *In* "Immunization against Theileriosis in Africa" (A. D. Irvin, ed.), p. 89. International Laboratory for Research in Animal Diseases, Nairobi.

Iams, K. (1985). Progress in theileriosis: 1. Construction of *Theileria parva* genomic libraries and identification of sporozoite and macroschizont-specific genes. *In* "Parasite Antigens" (Summary Proceedings of an International Workshop), p. 30. International Laboratory for Research in Animal Diseases, Nairobi.

Irvin, A. D. (1985a). Immunity in theileriosis. *Parasitology Today* **1,** 124–128.

Irvin, A. D., ed. (1985b). "Immunization against Theileriosis in Africa". International Laboratory for Research in Animal Diseases, Nairobi.

Irvin, A. D. and Boarer, C. D. H. (1980). Some implications of a sexual cycle in *Theileria. Parasitology* **80,** 571–579.

Irvin, A. D. and Brocklesby, D. W. (1970). Rearing and maintaining *Rhipicephalus appendiculatus* in the laboratory. *Journal of the Institute of Animal Technicians* **21,** 106–112.

Irvin, A. D. and Cunningham, M. P. (1981). East coast fever. *In* "Diseases of Cattle in the Tropics" (M. Ristic and W. I. M. McIntyre, eds), pp. 393–410. Martinus Nijhoff Publishers, The Hague.

Irvin, A. D. and Morrison, W. I. (in press). Immunopathology, immunology and immunoprophylaxis of *Theileria* infections. *In* "Immunopathology, Immunology and Immunoprophylaxis of Parasitic Infections" (E. J. L. Soulsby, ed.). CRC Press, Boca Raton.

Irvin, A. D. and Mwamachi, D. M. (1983). Clinical and diagnostic features of east coast fever (*Theileria* parva infection of cattle). *Veterinary Record* **133,** 192–198.

Irvin, A. D., Brown, C. G. D., Burridge, M. J., Cunningham, M. P., Musoke, A. J., Peirce, M. A., Purnell, R. E. and Radley, D. E. (1972a). A pathogenic theilerial syndrome of cattle in the Narok District of Kenya. 1. Transmission studies. *Tropical Animal Health and Production* **4,** 220–229.

Irvin, A. D., Peirce, M. A., Purnell, R. E. and King, J. M. (1972b). The possible role of the eland (*Taurotragus oryx*) in the epidemiology of east coast fever and other bovine theilerioses. *Veterinary Record* **91,** 513–517.

Irvin, A. D., Boarer, C. D. H., Dobbelaere, D. A. E., Mahan, S. M., Masake, R. and Ocama, J. G. R. (1981a). Monitoring *Theileria parva* infection in adult *Rhipicephalus appendiculatus* ticks. *Parasitology* **82,** 137–147.

Irvin, A. D., Cunningham, M. P. and Young, A. S., eds (1981b). "Advances in the Control of Theileriosis". Martinus Nijhoff Publishers, The Hague.

Irvin, A. D., Ocama, J. G. R. and Spooner, P. R. (1982). Cycle of bovine lymphoblastoid cells parasitized by *Theileria parva*. *Research in Veterinary Science* **33,** 298–304.

Irvin, A. D., Dobbelaere, D. A. E., Mwamachi, D. M., Minami, T., Spooner, P. R. and Ocama, J. G. R. (1983). Immunization against east coast fever: correlation between monoclonal antibody profiles of *Theileria parva* stocks and cross immunity *in vivo*. *Research in Veterinary Science* **35,** 341–346.

Irvin, A. D., Dobbelaere, D. A. E., Morzaria, S. P., Spooner, P. R., Goddeeris, B. M., Chumo, R. S., Taracha, E. L. N., Dolan T. T. and Young, A. S. (in press, a). East coast fever: the significance of host age in infection or immunization of cattle with *Theileria parva*. *Veterinary Parasitology*.

Irvin, A. D., Morzaria, S. P., Munatswa, F. C. and Koch, H. T. (in press, b) Preliminary studies on immunization of cattle with a mild *Theileria parva bovis* stock from Zimbabwe and challenge with virulent *T. p. parva* stocks (east coast fever) from Kenya. *Veterinary Parasitology*.

Ishihara, T. (1968). Bovine piroplasmosis in Japan. *Japanese Agricultural Research Quarterly* **3,** 23–31.

Jaffe, C. L. and Pratt, D. M. (1983). Monoclonal antibodies specific for *Leishmania tropica*. *Journal of Immunology* **131,** 1987–1993.

Jarrett, W. F. H., Crighton, G. W. and Pirie, H. M. (1969). *Theileria parva*: kinetics of replication. *Experimental Parasitology* **24,** 9–25.

Joyner, L. P. and Norton, C. C. (1975). Transferred drug resistance in *Eimeria maxima*. *Parasitology* **71,** 385–392.

Joyner, L. P. and Norton, C. C. (1977). Further observations on the genetic transfer of drug resistance in *Eimeria maxima*. *Parasitology* **74,** 205–213.

Joyner, L. P., Payne, R. C., Takahashi, K., Brocklesby, D. W. and Irvin, A. D. (1979). Serological comparison of British *Theileria mutans* and Japanese *T. sergenti*. *Research in Veterinary Science* **26,** 387–388.

Jura, W. G. Z. O. and Losos, G. J. (1980). A comparative study of the diseases in cattle caused by *Theileria lawrencei* and *Theileria parva*. 1. Clinical signs and parasitological examinations. *Veterinary Parasitology* **7,** 275–286.

Jura, W. G. Z. O., Brown, C. G. D. and Kelly, B. (1983a). Fine structure and invasive behaviour of the early development stages of *Theileria annulata in vitro*. *Veterinary Parasitology* **12,** 31–44.

Jura, W. G. Z. O., Brown, C. G. D. and Rowland, A. C. (1983b). Ultrastructural characteristics of *in vitro* parasite–lymphocyte behaviour in invasions with *Theileria annulata* and *Theileria parva*. *Veterinary Parasitology* **12,** 115–134.

Kemp, D. J., Corcoran, L. M., Coppel, R. L., Stahl, H. D., Bianco, A. E., Brown, G. V. and Anders, R. F. (1985). Size variation in chromosomes from independent cultured isolates of *Plasmodium falciparum*. *Nature* **315,** 374–349.

Khayyat, S. M. and Gilder, A. A. (1947). Ovine piroplasmosis in Iraq. *Transactions of the Royal Society of Tropical Medicine and Hygiene* **41,** 119–126.

Kiltz, H. H., Uilenberg, G., Franssen, F. F. J. and Perié, N. M. (1986). *Theileria orientalis* occurs in central Africa (Burundi). *Research in Veterinary Science* **40,** 197–200.

Kimber, C. D. and Young, A. S. (1977). Serological studies on strains of *Theileria mutans* isolated in East Africa using the indirect fluorescent antibody technique. *Annals of Tropical Medicine and Parasitology* **71,** 1–10.

Knowles, G., Davidson, W. L., McBride, J. S. and Jolley, D. (1984). Antigenic diversity found in isolates of *Plasmodium falciparum* from Papua New Guinea by using monoclonal antibodies. *American Journal of Tropical Medicine and Hygiene* **33,** 204–211.

Koch, H. T., Ocama, J. G. R., Munatswa, F. C., Byrom, B., Norval, R. A. I., Spooner, P. R., Conrad, P. A. and Irvin, A. D. (in press). Isolation and characterisation of bovine *Theileria* parasites in Zimbabwe. *Veterinary Parasitology.*

Kohler, G. and Milstein, C. (1975). Continuous cultures of fused cells secreting antibody of predefined specificity. *Nature* **256,** 495–497.

Kurtti, T. J., Munderloh, U. G., Irvin, A. D. and Buscher, G. (1981). *Theileria parva*: early events in the development of bovine lymphoblastoid cell lines persistently infected with macroschizonts. *Experimental Parasitology* **52,** 280–290.

Lawrence, J. A. (1977). The serological relationship between *Theileria parva* (Muguga) and *Theileria lawrencei* from Rhodesia. *Veterinary Record* **100,** 470–472.

Lawrence, J. A. and Mackenzie, P. K. I. (1980). Isolation of a non-pathogenic *Theileria* of cattle transmitted by *Rhipicephalus appendiculatus. Zimbabwe Veterinary Journal* **11,** 27–35.

Lawrence, J. A. and Norval, R. A. I. (1979). A history of ticks and tick-borne diseases of cattle in Rhodesia. *Rhodesian Veterinary Journal* **10,** 28–40.

Lawrence, J. A., Norval, R. A. I. and Uilenberg, G. (1983). *Rhipicephalus zambeziensis* as a vector of bovine *Theileria. Tropical Animal Health and Production* **15,** 39–42.

Levine, N. D. (1971). Taxonomy of the piroplasms. *Transactions of the American Microscopical Society* **90,** 2–33.

Levine, N. D., Corliss, J. O., Cox, F. E. G., Deroux, G., Grain, J., Honigberg, B. M., Leedale, G. F., Loeblich, A. R., Lom, J., Lynn, D., Merinfield, E. G., Page, F. C., Poljansky, G., Sprague, V., Vavra. J. and Wallace, F. G. (1980). A newly revised classification of the Protozoa. *Journal of Protozoology* **27,** 37–58.

Lohr, K. F. (1978). A hypothesis on the role of *Theileria lawrencei* in the epizootiology of east coast fever and on its importance in attempting vaccination. *In* "Tick-borne Diseases and their Vectors" (J. K. H. Wilde, ed.), pp. 315–317. University of Edinburgh, Edinburgh, Scotland.

Lohr, K. F. and Ross, J. P. J. (1969). Serological response in cattle to east coast fever (*Theileria parva* infection) as measured by the indirect fluorescent antibody test. *Research in Veterinary Science* **10,** 453–460.

Majiwa, P. A. O., Masake, R. A., Nantulya, V. M., Hamers, R. and Matthyssens, G. (1985). *Trypansoma (Nannomonas) congolense*: identification of two karyotypic groups. *EMBO Journal* **4,** 3307–3313.

Martin, H. and Brocklesby, D. W. (1960). A new parasite of the eland. *Veterinary Record* **72,** 331.

Martins, M. I. (1978). Histochemical studies on the salivary glands of unfed and feeding *Rhipicephalus appendiculatus* during the development of *Theileria parva. In*

"Tick-borne Diseases and their Vectors" (J. K. H. Wilde, ed.), pp. 336–342. University of Edinburgh, Edinburgh, Scotland.

Massamba, N. N. and Williams, R. O. (1984). Distinction of African trypanosome species using nucleic acid hybridization. *Parasitology* **88,** 55–66.

Maxie, M. G., Dolan, T. T., Jura, W. G. Z. O., Tabel, H. and Flowers, M. J. (1982). A comparative study of the diseases in cattle caused by *Theileria parva* or *T. lawrencei.* II. Haematology, clinical chemistry, coagulation studies and complement. *Veterinary Parasitology* **10,** 1–9.

McBride, J. S., Walliker, D. and Morgan, G. (1982). Antigenic diversity in the human malaria parasite *Plasmodium falciparum. Science* **217,** 254–257.

McBride, J. S., Welsby, P. D. and Walliker, D. (1984). Serotyping *Plasmodium falciparum* from acute human infections using monoclonal antibodies. *Transactions of the Royal Society of Tropical Medicine and Hygiene* **78,** 32–34.

McCutchan, T. F., Dame, J. B., Miller, L. H. and Barnwell, J. (1984a). Evolutionary relatedness of *Plasmodium* species as determined by the structure of DNA. *Science* **225,** 808–811.

McCutchan, T. F., Hansen, J. L., Dame, J. B. and Mullins, J. A. (1984b). Mung bean nuclease cleaves *Plasmodium* genomic DNA at sites before and after genes. *Science* **225,** 625–628.

McHardy, N. (1984). Recent advances in the chemotherapy of theileriosis. *Preventive Veterinary Medicine* **2,** 179–192.

Melhorn, H. and Schein, E. (1977). Electron microscopic studies of the development of kinetes in *Theileria annulata* Dschunkowsky and Luhs, 1904 (Sporozoa, Piroplasmea). *Journal of Protozoology* **24,** 249–256.

Melhorn, H. and Schein, E. (1984). The piroplasms: life cycle and sexual stages. *Advances in Parasitology* **23,** 37–103.

Melhorn, H., Schein, E. and Warnecke, M. (1978). Electron microscopic studies on the development of kinetes of *Theileria parva* Theiler, 1904, in the gut of the vector ticks *Rhipicephalus appendiculatus* Neumann, 1901. *Acta Tropica* **35,** 123–136.

Melrose, T. R. and Brown, C. G. D. (1979). Isoenzyme variation in piroplasms isolated from bovine blood infected with *Theileria parva* and *T. annulata. Research in Veterinary Science* **27,** 379–381.

Melrose, T. R., Brown, C. G. D. and Sharma, R. D. (1980). Glucose phosphate isomerase isoenzyme patterns in bovine lymphoblastoid cell lines infected with *Theileria annulata* and *T. parva,* with an improved enzyme visualisation method using meldola blue. *Research in Veterinary Science* **29,** 298–304.

Melrose, T. R., Brown, C. G. D., Morzaria, S. P., Ocama, J. G. R. and Irvin, A. D. (1984). Glucose phosphate isomerase polymorphism in *Theileria annulata* and *T. parva. Tropical Animal Health and Production* **16,** 239–245.

Milstein, C. (1981). Monoclonal antibodies from hybrid myelomas. *Proceedings of the Royal Society of London B* **211,** 393–412.

Minami, T., Fujinaga, T., Furya, K. and Ishihara, T. (1980). Clinico-haematological and serological comparison of Japanese and Russian strains of *Theileria sergenti. National Institute of Animal Health Quarterly* **20,** 44–52.

Minami, T., Spooner, P. R., Irvin, A. D., Ocama, J. G. R., Dobbelaere, D. A. E. and Fujinaga, T. (1983). Characterization of stocks of *Theileria parva* by monoclonal antibody profiles. *Research in Veterinary Science* **35,** 334–340.

Moll, G., Lohding, A. and Young, A. S. (1981). The epidemiology of theileriosis in the Trans-Mara Division of Kenya. *In* "Advances in the Control of Theileriosis"

(A. D. Irvin, M. P. Cunningham and A. S. Young, eds), pp. 56–59. Martinus Nijhoff Publishers, The Hague.

Moll, G., Lohding, A., Young, A. S. and Leitch, B. L. (1986). Epidemiology of theileriosis in calves in an endemic area of Kenya. *Veterinary Parasitology* **19,** 255–273.

Moltmann, U. G., Mehlhorn, H., Schein, E., Rehbein, G., Voigt, W. P. and Zweygarth, E. (1983). Fine structure of *Babesia equi* within lymphocytes and erythrocytes of horses: an *in vivo* and *in vitro* study. *Journal of Parasitology* **69,** 111–120.

Morel, P. C. (1969). "Contribution à la connaissance de la distribution des tiques (Acariens, Ixodidae et Amblyommidae) en Afrique éthiopienne continentale." Thèse de Doctorat des Sciences Naturelles, Faculté des Sciences d'Orsay, Université de Paris.

Morel, P. C. and Uilenberg, G. (1981). The nomenclature of some *Theileria* species (Sporozoa, Babesioidea) of domestic ruminants. *Revue d'Élevage et de Médecine Vétérinaire des Pays Tropicaux* **34,** 139–143.

Morrison, W. I., Lalor, P. A., Goddeeris, B. M. and Teale, A. J. (1986a). Theileriosis: antigens and host–parasite interactions. *In* "Parasite Antigens, Towards New Strategies for Vaccines" (T. W. Pearson, ed.), pp. 167–231. Marcel Dekker Inc., New York.

Morrison, W. I., Goddeeris, B. M., Teale, A. J., Baldwin, C. L., Bensaid, A. and Ellis, J. (1986b). Cell-mediated immune responses of cattle *Theileria parva. Immunology Today* **7,** 211–216.

Morzaria, S. P., Brocklesby, D. W. and Harradine, D. I. (1977). Evaluation of the indirect fluorescent antibody test for *Babesia major* and *Theileria mutans* in Britain. *Veterinary Record* **100,** 484–487.

Morzaria, S. P., Naessens, J., Musoke, A. J., Voigt, W. P., Brown, W. C., Dobbelaere, D. A. E. and Irvin, A. D. (1985). Quantitation of *Theileria parva* sporozoites. *Proceedings of the VIIth International Congress of Protozoology*, abstract No. 167. Nairobi, Kenya.

Morzaria, S. P., Irvin, A. D., Taracha, E., Spooner, P. R., Voigt, W. P., Fujinaga, T. and Katende, J. (in press, a). Immunization against east coast fever: the use of selected stocks of *Theileria parva* for immunization of cattle exposed to field challenge. *Veterinary Parasitology.*

Morzaria, S. P., Irvin, A. D., Voigt, W. P., Taracha, E. L. N. and Kiarie, J. (in press, b). Immunization against east coast fever (*Theileria parva* infection of cattle): effect of timing and intensity of challenge on immunity. *Veterinary Parasitology.*

Mpangala, C., Uilenberg, G. and Schreuder, B. E. C. (1976). Studies on Theileriidae (Sporozoa) in Tanzania. II. Serological characterization of *Haematoxenus veliferus. Tropenmedizin und Parasitologie* **27,** 192–196.

Munderloh, U. G. and Kurtti, T. J. (1982). *Theileria parva*: cell culture analysis of clones of macroschizont-infected bovine lymphoblastoid cells. *Experimental Parasitology* **54,** 175–181.

Musisi, F. L., Bird, R. G., Brown, C. G. D. and Smith, M. (1981a). The fine structural relationship between *Theileria* schizonts and infected bovine lymphoblasts from culture. *Zeitschrift für Parasitenkunde* **65,** 31–41.

Musisi, F. L., Kilgour, V., Brown, C. G. D. and Morzaria, S. P. (1981b). Preliminary investigations on isoenzyme variants of lymphoblastoid cell lines infected with *Theileria* species. *Research in Veterinary Science* **30,** 38–43.

Musisi, F. L., Morgan, D. W. T. and Schels, H. F. (1985). Treatment of theileriosis with parvaquone in Zambia. *Veterinary Record* **117,** 338–339.

Musoke, A. J., Nantulya, V. M., Rurangirwa, F. R. and Buscher, G. (1984). Evidence for a common protective antigenic determinant on sporozoites of several *Theileria parva* species [sic]. *Immunology* **52,** 231–233.

Neitz, W. O. (1957). Theileriosis, gonderiosis and cytauxzoonosis: a review. *Onderstepoort Journal of Veterinary Research* **27**, 275–430.

Neitz, W. O. (1959). Theilerioses. *Advances in Veterinary Science* **5,** 241–297.

Neitz, W. O. and Thomas, A. D. (1948). *Cytauxzoon silvicaprae* gen. nov., spec. nov., a protozoan responsible for a hitherto undescribed disease in the duiker (*Sylvicapra grimmia*). *Onderstepoort Journal of Veterinary Science* **23,** 63–76.

Nelson, R. T. and Hirumi, H. (1981). *In vitro* cloning of *Theileria*-infected bovine lymphoblastoid cells: standardisation and characterization. *In* "Advances in the Control of Theileriosis" (A. D. Irvin, M. P. Cunningham and A. S. Young, eds), pp. 120–121. Martinus Nijhoff Publishers, The Hague.

Newson, J., Naessens, J., Stagg, D. A. and Black, S. J. (1986). A cell surface antigen associated with *Theileria parva lawrencei*-infected bovine lymphoid cells. *Parasite Immunology* **8**, 149–158.

Norval, R. A. I., Fivaz, B. H., Lawrence, J. A. and Brown, A. F. (1985). Epidemiology of tick-borne diseases of cattle in Zimbabwe. III. The *Theileria parva* group. *Tropical Animal Health and Production* **17,** 19–28.

Nussenzweig, V. and Nussenzweig, R. S. (1985). Circumsporozoite proteins of malaria parasites. *Cell* **42,** 401–403.

Nyormoi, O. and Bwayo, J. J. (1981). Isozyme patterns of *Theileria parva*-infected bovine lymphoblastoid cells and purified *Theileria* macroschizonts. *In* "Advances in the Control of Theileriosis" (A. D. Irvin, M. P. Cunningham and A. S. Young, eds), pp. 383–385. Martinus Nijhoff Publishers, The Hague.

Paling, R. W. and Geysen, D. (1981). Observations on Rwandan strains of *Theileria parva* and the value of *T. parva* Nyakizu as a possible vaccine strain. *In* "Advances in the Control of Theileriosis" (A. D. Irvin, M. P. Cunningham and A. S. Young, eds), pp. 238–241. Martinus Nijhoff Publishers, The Hague.

Pearson, T. W., Lundin, L. B., Dolan, T. T. and Stagg, D. A. (1979). Cell-mediated immunity to *Theileria*-transformed cell lines. *Nature* **281,** 678–680.

Pearson, T. W., Pinder, M., Roelants, G. E., Kar, S. K., Lundin, L. B., Mayor-Withey, K. S. and Hewett, R. S. (1980). Methods for derivation and detection of anti-parasite monoclonal antibodies. *Journal of Immunological Methods* **34,** 141–154.

Pearson, T. W., Hewett, R. S., Roelants, G. E., Stagg, D. A. and Dolan, T. T. (1982). Studies on the induction and specificity of cytotoxicity to *Theileria*-transformed cell lines. *Journal of Immunology* **128,** 2509–2513.

Perié, N. M., Uilenberg, G. and Schreuder, B. E. C. (1979). *Theileria mutans* in Nigeria. *Research in Veterinary Science* **26,** 359–362.

Pinder, M. and Hewett, R. S. (1980). Monoclonal antibodies detect antigenic diversity in *Theileria parva* parasites. *Journal of Immunology* **124,** 1000–1001.

Pipano, E. (1977). Basic principles of *Theileria annulata* control. *In* "Theileriosis" (J. B. Henson and M. Campbell, eds), pp. 55–65. International Development Research Centre, Ottawa, Canada.

Pipano, E. (1981). Schizonts and tick stages in immunization against *Theileria annulata* infection. *In* "Advances in the Control of Theileriosis" (A. D. Irvin, M.

P. Cunningham and A. S. Young, eds), pp. 242–252. Martinus Nijhoff Publishers, The Hague.

Pipano, E. and Cahana, M. (1969). Fluorescent antibody test for the serodiagnosis of *Theileria annulata*. *Journal of Parasitology* **55,** 765.

Pollack, Y., Katzen, A. L., Spira, D. T. and Golenser, J. (1982). The genome of *Plasmodium falciparum*. I. DNA base composition. *Nucleic Acids Research* **10,** 539–546.

Pollack, Y., Metzger, S., Shemer, R., Landau, D., Spira, D. T. and Golenser, J. (1985). Detection of *Plasmodium falciparum* in blood using DNA hybridization. *American Journal of Tropical Medicine and Hygiene* **34,** 663–667.

Post, R. J. (1985). DNA probes for vector identification. *Parasitology Today* **1,** 89–90.

Pratt, D. M. and David, J. R. (1981). Monoclonal antibodies that distinguish between New World species of *Leishmania*. *Nature* **291,** 581–583.

Pratt, D. M., Bennett, E. and David, J. R. (1982). Monoclonal antibodies that distinguish subspecies of *Leishmania braziliensis*. *Journal of Immunology* **129,** 926–927.

Preston, P. M., Brown, C. G. D. and Spooner, R. L. (1983). Cell-mediated cytotoxicity in *Theileria annulata* infection of cattle with evidence for BoLA restriction. *Clinical and Experimental Immunology* **53,** 88–100.

Purnell, R. E. (1977). East coast fever: some recent research in East Africa. *Advances in Parasitology* **15,** 83–132.

Purnell, R. E. and Joyner, L. P. (1968). The development of *Theileria parva* in the salivary glands of the tick *Rhipicephalus appendiculatus*. *Parasitology* **58,** 725–732.

Radley, D. E. (1978a). Immunization against east coast fever by chemoprophylaxis. *In* "Research on Tick-borne Diseases and Tick Control Kenya, Tanzania, Uganda". Technical Report 1, AG:DP/67/077, pp. 37–38. Food and Agriculture Organization, Rome.

Radley, D. E. (1978b). Chemoprophylactic immunization against east coast fever. *In* "Tick-borne Diseases and their Vectors" (J. K. H. Wilde, ed.), pp. 324–329. University of Edinburgh, Edinburgh, Scotland.

Radley, D. E. (1981). Infection and treatment method of immunization. *In* "Advances in the Control of Theileriosis" (A. D. Irvin, M. P. Cunningham and A. S. Young, eds), pp. 227–237. Martinus Nijhoff Publishers, The Hague.

Radley, D. E., Brown, C. G. D., Burridge, M. J., Cunningham, M. P., Peirce, M. A. and Purnell, R. E. (1974). East coast fever: quantitative studies of *Theileria parva* in cattle. *Experimental Parasitology* **36,** 278–287.

Radley, D. E., Brown, C. G. D., Burridge, M. J., Cunningham, M. P., Kirimi, I. M., Purnell, R. E. and Young, A. S. (1975a). East coast fever. 1. Chemoprophylactic immunization of cattle against *Theileria parva* (Muguga) and five theilerial strains. *Veterinary Parasitology* **1,** 35–42.

Radley, D. E., Young, A. S., Brown, C. G. D., Burridge, M. J., Cunningham, M. P., Musisi, F. L. and Purnell, R. E. (1975b). East coast fever. 2. Cross immunity trials with a Kenya strain of *Theileria lawrencei*. *Veterinary Parasitology* **1,** 43–50.

Radley, D. E., Brown, C. G. D., Cunningham, M. P., Kimber, C. D., Musisi, F. L., Payne, R. C., Purnell, R. E., Stagg, S. M. and Young, A. S. (1975c). East coast fever. 3. Chemoprophylactic immunization of cattle using oxytetracycline and a combination of theilerial strains. *Veterinary Parasitology* **1,** 51–60.

Radley, D. E., Young, A. S., Grootenhuis, J. G., Cunningham, M. P., Dolan, T. T. and Morzaria, S. P. (1979). Further studies on the immunization of cattle against

Theileria lawrencei by infection and chemoprophylaxis. *Veterinary Parasitology* **5,** 117–128.

Rafyi, A., Maghami, G. and Hooshmand-Rad, P. (1965). The virulence of *Theileria annulata* and premunition against bovine theileriosis in Iran. *Bulletin: Office International des Epizooties* **64,** 431–446.

Rehbein, G., Zweygarth, E., Voigt, W. P. and Schein, E. (1982). Establishment of *Babesia equi*-infected lymphoblastoid cell lines. *Zeitschrift für Parasitenkunde* **67,** 125–127.

Roberts, R. J. (1983). Restriction and modification enzymes and their recognition sequences. *Nucleic Acids Research* **11,** 135–167.

Robinson, P. M. (1982). Theileriosis annulata and its transmission—a review. *Tropical Animal Health and Production* **14,** 3–12.

Robson, J., Pedersen, V., Odeke, G. M., Kamya, E. P. and Brown, C. G. D. (1977). East coast fever immunization trials in Uganda; field exposure of zebu cattle immunized with three isolates of *Theileria parva. Tropical Animal Health and Production* **9,** 219–231.

Saidu, S. N. A. (1982). Bovine theileriosis due to *Theileria mutans*: a review. *Veterinary Bulletin* **52,** 451–460.

Schein, E. (1975). On the life cycle of *Theileria annulata* (Dschunkowsky and Luhs 1904) in the midgut and haemolymph of *Hyalomma anatolicum excavatum* (Koch 1844). *Zeitschrift für Parasitenkunde* **47,** 165–167.

Schein, E. and Voigt, W. P. (1979). Chemotherapy of bovine theileriosis with halofuginone. *Acta Tropica* **36,** 391–394.

Schein, E., Buscher, G. and Friedhoff, K. T. (1975). Light microscopic studies on the development of *Theileria annulata* (Dschunkowsky and Luhs 1904) in *Hyalomma anatolicum excavatum* (Koch 1844). 1. The development in gut of the engorged nymphs. *Zeitschrift für Parasitenkunde* **48,** 123–136.

Schein, E., Mehlhorn, H. and Warnecke, M. (1977). Fine structural study on the erythrocytic stages of *Theileria annulata* (Dschunkowsky and Luhs 1904). *Tropenmedizin und Parasitologie* **28,** 349–360.

Schein, E., Rehbein, G., Voigt, W. P. and Zweygarth, E. (1981). *Babesia equi* (Laveran 1901). 1. Development in horses and in lymphocyte culture. *Tropenmedizin und Parasitologie* **32,** 223–227.

Schindler, R. and Wokatsch, R. (1965). Attempts at differentiation of *Theileria* species from cattle by serological tests. *Zeitschrift für Parasitenkunde* **16,** 17–23.

Schwartz, D. C. and Cantor, C. R. (1984). Separation of yeast chromosome-sized DNAs by pulsed field gradient gel electrophoresis. *Cell* **37,** 67–75.

Sergent, E., Donatien, A., Parrot, L, and Lestoquard, F. (1945). "Études sur les piroplasmoses bovine." Institut Pasteur d'Algérie.

Shapiro, S. Z., Fujisaki, K., Morzaria, S. P., Webster, P., Fujinaga, T., Spooner, P. R. and Irvin, A. D. (in press). A life cycle stage specific antigen of *Theileria parva* recognised by anti-macroschizont monoclonal antibodies. *Parasitology*.

Shiels, B., McDougall, C., Tait, A. and Brown, C. G. D. (1986a) Antigenic diversity of *Theileria annulata* macroschizonts. *Veterinary Parasitology* **21**, 1–10.

Shiels, B., McDougall, C, Tait, A. and Brown, C. G. D. (1986b). Identification of infection-associated antigens in *Theileria annulata*-transformed cells. *Parasite Immunology* **8**, 69–77.

Shirley, M. W. and Millard, B. J. (1976). Some observations on the sexual differentiation of *Eimeria tenella* using single sporozoite infections in chicken embryos. *Parasitology* **73,** 337–341.

Shirley, M. W. and Rollinson, D. (1979). Coccidia: the recognition and characterization of populations of *Eimeria*. *Symposia of the British Society for Parasitology* **17**, 7–30.

Shortt, H. E. and Cooper, W. (1948). Staining of microscopical sections containing protozoal parasites by modification of McNamara's method. *Transactions of the Royal Society of Tropical Medicine and Hygiene* **41**, 427–428.

Simpson, L. (1979). Isolation of maxicircle components of kinetoplast DNA from hemoflagellate protozoa. *Proceedings of the National Academy of Sciences*, USA **76**, 1585–1588.

Sinden, R. E., Hartley, R. H. and Winger, L. (1985). The development of *Plasmodium berghei* ookinetes *in vitro*: an ultrastructural study including a description of meiotic division. *Parasitology* **91**, 227–244.

Southern, E. M. (1975). Detection of specific sequences among DNA fragments separated by gel electrophoresis. *Journal of Molecular Biology* **98**, 503–517.

Stagg, D. A., Chasey, D., Young, A. S., Morzaria, S. P. and Dolan, T. T. (1980). Synchronisation of the division of *Theileria* macroschizonts and their mammalian host cells. *Annals of Tropical Medicine and Parasitology* **74**, 263–265.

Stagg, D. A., Young, A. S., Leitch, B. L., Grootenhuis, J. G. and Dolan, T. T. (1983). Infection of mammalian cells with *Theileria* species. *Parasitology* **86**, 243–254.

Stagg, D. A., Fawcett, D. W., Young, A. S. and Leitch, B. L. (1984). Superinfection of established *Theileria*-infected bovid cell lines with *Theileria parva* sporozoites. *Annals of Tropical Medicine and Parasitology* **78**, 335–337.

Stobbs, T. H. (1966). The introduction of Boran cattle into an ECF endemic area. *East African Agriculture and Forestry Journal* **31**, 298–304.

Stone, W. H. (1981). The bovine lymphocyte antigen (BoLA) system. *In* "The Ruminant Immune System" (J. E. Butler, ed.), pp. 433–450. Plenum Press, New York.

Takahashi, K., Yamashita, S., Isayama, Y. and Shimizu, Y. (1976). Serological response to the indirect fluorescent antibody test of cattle infected with *Theileria sergenti*. *British Veterinary Journal* **132**, 112–117.

Taracha, E. L. N. (1985). "Lectin affinity chromatography studies on *Theileria annulata*-infected lymphoblastoid cell lines." MSc Thesis, University of Birmingham, U.K.

Teale, A. J., Kemp, S. J., Brown, C. G. D. and Spooner, R. L. (1981). Selection on the basis of major histocompatibility type of lymphoid cells from a bovine chimaera transformed by *Theileria* parasites. *In* "Advances in the Control of Theileriosis" (A. D. Irvin, M. P. Cunningham and A. S. Young, eds), pp. 365–367. Martinus Nijhoff Publishers, The Hague.

Theiler, A. (1912). The immunization of cattle against east coast fever. *Second Report of the Director of Veterinary Research of the Union of South Africa*, pp. 266–314.

Townsend, A. R. M. and McMichael, A. J. (1985). Specificity of cytotoxic T lymphocytes stimulated with influenza virus. *Progress in Allergy* **36**, 10–43.

Uilenberg, G. (1964). *Haematoxenus veliferus*, n.g., n.sp., parasite *incertae sedis* du sang de bovins á Madagascar. *Revue d'Élevage et de Médecine Vétérinaire des Pays Tropicaux* **17**, 655–662.

Uilenberg, G. (1976). Tick-borne livestock diseases and their vectors. 2. Epizootiology of tick-borne diseases. *World Animal Review* **17**, 8–15.

Uilenberg, G. (1981a). *Theileria* infections other than east coast fever. *In* "Diseases of Cattle in the Tropics" (M. Ristic and I. McIntyre, eds), pp. 411–427. Martinus Nijhoff Publishers, The Hague.

Uilenberg, G. (1981b). Theilerial species of domestic livestock. *In* "Advances in the Control of Theileriosis" (A. D. Irvin, M. P. Cunningham and A. S. Young, eds), pp. 4–37. Martinus Nijhoff Publishers, The Hague.

Uilenberg, G., Mpangala, C., McGregor, W. and Callow, L. L. (1977a). Biological differences between African *Theileria mutans* (Theiler, 1906) and two benign species of *Theileria* of cattle in Australia and Britain. *Australian Veterinary Journal* **53,** 271–273.

Uilenberg, G., Schreuder, B. E. C., Mpangala, C. and Tondeur, W. (1977b). Studies on Theileriidea (Sporozoa) in Tanzania. IX. Unidentified bovine *Theileria. Tropenmedizin und Parasitologie* **28,** 494–498.

Uilenberg, G., Silayo, R. S., Mpangala, C., Tondeur, W., Tatchell, R. J. and Sanga, H. J. N. (1977c). Studies on Theileriidae (Sporozoa) in Tanzania. X. A large-scale field trial on immunization against cattle theileriosis. *Tropenmedizin und Parasitologie* **28,** 499–506.

Uilenberg, G., Perié, N. M., Lawrence, J. A., de Vos, A. J., Paling, R. W. and Spanjer, A. A. M. (1982). Causal agents of bovine theileriosis in Southern Africa. *Tropical Animal Health and Production* **14,** 127–140.

Uilenberg, G., Camus, E. and Barré, N. (1983). Existence in Guadeloupe (French West Indies) of *Theileria mutans* and *Theileria velifera* (Sporozoa, Theileriidae). *Revue d'Élevage et de Médecine Vétérinaire des Pays Tropicaux* **36,** 261–264.

Uilenberg, G., Perié, N. M., Spanjer, A. A. M. and Franssen, F. F. J. (1985). *Theileria orientalis*, a cosmopolitan blood parasite of cattle—demonstration of the schizont stage. *Research in Veterinary Science* **38,** 352–360.

Van Dam, R. H. (1981). Definition and biological significance of the major histocompatibility system (MHS) in man and animals. *Veterinary Immunology and Immunopathology* **2,** 517–539.

Van der Meer, P., Uilenberg, G., Van der Bergh, S. G., Spanjer, A. A. M. and Perié, N. M. (1981). Isoenzyme studies on *Theileria* (Protozoa, Sporozoa). Enzyme activity associated with the erythrocytic stage. *Veterinary Quarterly* **3,** 61–65.

Van der Ploeg, L. H. T., Schwartz, D. C., Cantor, C. R. and Borst, P. (1984a). Antigenic variation in *Trypanosoma brucei* analysed by electrophoretic separation of chromosome-sized DNA molecules. *Cell* **37,** 77–84.

Van der Ploeg, L. H. T., Cornelissen, A. W. C. A., Barry, J. D. and Borst, P. (1984b). Chromosomes of Kinetoplastida. *EMBO Journal* **3,** 3109–3115.

Van der Ploeg, L. H. T., Smits, M., Ponnudurai, T., Vermeulen, A., Meuwissen, J. H. E. T. and Langsley, G. (1985). Chromosome-sized DNA molecules of *Plasmodium falciparum. Science* **229,** 658–661.

Van Vorstenbosch, C. J. A. H., Uilenberg, G. and Van Dijk, J. E. (1978). Erythrocytic forms of *Theileria velifera. Research in Veterinary Science* **24,** 214–221.

Vickerman, K. and Irvin, A. D.(1981). Association of the parasite of east coast fever (*Theileria parva*) with spindle microtubules of the bovine lymphoblast. *Transactions of the Royal Society of Tropical Medicine and Hygiene* **75,** 329.

Vincenzo, E., Ellis, J., Zavala, F., Arnot, D. E., Asavanish, A., Masuda, A., Quakyi, I. and Nussenzweig, R. S. (1984). DNA cloning of *Plasmodium falciparum* circumsporozoite gene: amino-acid sequence of repetitive epitope. *Science* **225,** 628–630.

Wagner, J. E.(1976). A fatal cytauxzoonosis-like disease in cats. *Journal of the American Veterinary Medical Association* **168,** 585–588.

Wagner, C. G., Brown, C. G. D., Duffus, W. P. H., Kimber, C. D., Crawford, J. G. and Lule, M. (1974a). Immunochemical studies on east coast fever. I. Partial segregation and characterisation of the *Theileria parva* schizont antigen. *Journal of Parasitology* **60,** 848–853.

Wagner, C. G., Brown, C. G. D., Duffus, W. P. H., Kimber, C. D. and Lule, M. (1974b). Immunochemical studies on east coast fever. III. Partial segregation and characterization of the *Theileria parva* piroplasm antigen. *Journal of Parasitology* **60,** 854–859.

Walker, A. R., McKellar, S. B., Bell, L. J. and Brown, C. G. D. (1979). Rapid quantitative assessment of *Theileria* infection in ticks by methyl green pyronin staining of whole salivary glands. *Tropical Animal Health and Production* **11,** 21–26.

Walker, A. R., Fletcher, J. D. and Gill, H. S. (1985). Structural and histochemical changes in the salivary glands of *Rhipicephalus appendiculatus* during feeding. *International Journal for Parasitology* **15,** 81–100.

Walker, J. B., Norval, R. A. I. and Corwin, M. D. (1981). *Rhipicephalus zambeziensis* sp. nov., a new tick from eastern and southern Africa, together with a redescription of *Rhipicephalus appendiculatus* Neumann, 1901 (Acarina, Ixodidae). *Onderstepoort Journal of Veterinary Research* **48,** 87–104.

Walliker, D. (1972). An infection of *Plasmodium berghei* derived from sporozoites of a single oocyst. *Transactions of the Royal Society of Tropical Medicine and Hygiene* **4,** 543.

Walliker, D. (1976). Genetic factors in malaria parasites and their effect on host–parasite relationships. *Symposia of the British Society for Parasitology* **14,** 25–44.

Walliker, D. (1983). The genetic basis of diversity in malaria parasites. *Advances in Parasitology* **22,** 217–259.

Walliker, D., Carter, R. and Morgan, S. (1971). Genetic recombination in malaria parasites. *Nature* **232,** 561–562.

Weber, J. L. and Hockmeyer, W. T. (1985). Structure of the circumsporozoite protein gene in 18 strains of *Plasmodium falciparum. Molecular and Biochemical Parasitology* **15,** 305–316.

Webster, P., Dobbelaere, D. A. E. and Fawcett, D. W. (1985). The entry of sporozoites of *Theileria parva* into bovine lymphocytes *in vitro*. Immunoelectron microscopic observations. *European Journal of Cell Biology* **36,** 157–162.

WHO (1978). Proposals for the nomenclature of salivarian trypanosomes and for the maintenance of reference collections. *Bulletin of the World Health Organization* **56,** 467–480.

Wilde, J. K. H. (1967). East coast fever. *Advances in Veterinary Science* **11,** 207–259.

Wilde, J. K. H., Brown, C. G. D., Hulliger, L., Gall, D. and Macleod, W. G. (1968). East coast fever: experiments with the tissues of infected ticks. *British Veterinary Journal* **124,** 196–208.

Wirth, D. F. and Pratt, D. M. (1982). Rapid identification of *Leishmania* species by specific hybridization of kinetoplast DNA in cutaneous lesions. *Proceedings of the National Academy of Sciences, USA* **79,** 6999–7003.

Young, A. S. and Morzaria, S. P. (1986). Biology of *Babesia*. *Parasitology Today* **2,** 211–219.

Young, A. S. and Purnell, R. E. (1973). Transmission of *Theileria lawrencei* (Serengeti) by the ixodid tick *Rhipicephalus appendiculatus*. *Tropical Animal Health and Production* **5,** 146–152.

Young, A. S., Branagan, D., Brown, C. G. D., Burridge, M. J., Cunningham, M. P. and Purnell, R. E. (1973a). Preliminary observations on a theilerial species pathogenic to cattle isolated from buffalo (*Syncerus caffer*) in Tanzania. *British Veterinary Journal* **129,** 382–389.

Young, A. S., Brown, C. G. D., Burridge, M. J., Cunningham, M. P., Kirimi, I. M. and Irvin, A. D. (1973b). Observations on the cross-immunity between *Theileria lawrencei* (Serengeti) and *Theileria parva* (Muguga) in cattle. *International Journal for Parasitology* **3,** 723–728.

Young, A. S., Grootenhuis, J. G., Kimber, C. D., Kanhai, G. K. and Stagg, D. A. (1977a). Isolation of a *Theileria* species from eland (*Taurotragus oryx*) infective for cattle. *Tropenmedizin und Parasitologie* **18,** 185–194.

Young, A. S., Radley, D. E., Cunningham, M. P., Musisi, F. L., Payne, R. C. and Purnell, R. E. (1977b). Exposure of immunized cattle to prolonged natural challenge of *Theileria lawrencei* derived from African buffalo (*Syncerus caffer*). *Veterinary Parasitology* **3,** 283–290.

Young, A. S., Brown, C. G. D., Burridge, M. J., Grootenhuis, J. G., Kanhai, G. K., Purnell, R. E. and Stagg, D. A. (1978a). The incidence of theilerial parasites in East African buffalo (*Syncerus caffer*). *Tropenmedizin und Parasitologie* **29,** 281–288.

Young, A. S., Brown, C. G. D., Cunningham, M. P. and Radley, D. E. (1978b). Evaluation of methods of immunizing cattle against *Theileria lawrencei*. *In* "Tick-borne Diseases and their Vectors" (J. K. H. Wilde, ed.), pp. 293–296. University of Edinburgh, Edinburgh, Scotland.

Young, A. S., Purnell, R. E., Payne, R. C., Brown, C. G. D. and Kanhai, G. K. (1978c). Studies on the transmission and course of infection of a Kenyan strain of *Theileria mutans*. *Parasitology* **76,** 99–115.

Young, A. S., Grootenhuis, J. G., Leitch, B. L. and Schein, E. (1980). The development of *Theileria*= *Cytauxzoon taurotragi* (Martin and Brocklesby, 1960) from eland in its tick vector *Rhipicephalus appendiculatus*. *Parasitology* **81,** 129–144.

Young, A. S., Leitch, B. L., Stagg, D. A. and Dolan, T. T. (1983). Identification of *Theileria* infections in living salivary glands of ticks. *Parasitology* **86,** 519–528.

Young, A. S., Leitch, B. L., Morzaria, S. P., Grootenhuis, J. G., Omwoyo, P. L. and Stagg, D. A. (in press). *In vivo* and *in vitro* infections with *Theileria parva* sporozoites derived from a single infected tick salivary acinar cell. *Parasitology*.

Zinkernagel, R. M. (1979). Cellular immune responses to intracellular parasites: role of the major histocompatibility gene complex and thymus in determining immune responsiveness and susceptibility to disease. *Parasite Immunology* **1,** 91–109.

Zinkernagel, R. M. and Doherty, P. C. (1979). MHC restricted cytotoxic T cells: studies on the biological role of polymorphic major transplantation antigens determining T-cell restriction-specificity, function and responsiveness. *Advances in Immunology* **27,** 51–177.

Cryptobia and Cryptobiosis in Fishes

P. T. K. WOO

Department of Zoology, College of Biological Science, University of Guelph, Guelph, Ontario, Canada N1G 2W1

I. Introduction

According to Foster (1965), Valentin in 1841 was the first to observe a haemoflagellate in the blood of a trout. At the beginning of the century there

ADVANCES IN PARASITOLOGY VOL. 26
ISBN 0-12-031726-5

Copyright © 1987 Academic Press Inc. (London) Ltd.
All rights of reproduction in any form reserved.

was considerable interest in the morphology and biology of piscine haemoflagellates (trypanosomes and trypanoplasms), partly because some mammalian trypanosomes had recently been found to cause disease in man and domestic animals in the tropics. The initial level of interest in piscine haemoflagellates was not sustained because of the fact that many of them were not pathogenic and because of the perceived need to study more urgently those parasites that were of medical and economic importance.

In the last 20 years there has been renewed interest in the parasitic protozoa of fishes; particular emphasis has been placed on the study of haemoflagellates and three reviews have been written (Becker, 1970, 1977; Lom, 1979). The first review (Becker, 1970) dealt with the haematozoa of fishes, with particular attention paid to North American work, while the second (Becker, 1977) was more general and included most of the parasitic protozoa of fishes. Lom (1979) concentrated on the haemoflagellates and summarized the pertinent work done in the last 80 years.

Cryptobia is a flagellate with two flagella (one being attached to the body), a prominent kinetoplast and a nucleus. The parasite has been reported on the body surface, in the digestive tract and in the blood of fishes. Some workers considered the location of the parasite (and consequently the mode of transmission) to be important enough to transfer the "digenetic" haematozoic species to the genus *Trypanoplasma* and retain the "monogenetic" species in the genus *Cryptobia*. This was a mistake because it tends to segregate workers and their thinking, which may lead to a lack of overall appreciation of this group as a whole. The taxonomic reasons for synonymizing *Trypanoplasma* and *Cryptobia* are discussed in Section III.

The aims of the present review are, firstly, to unify and clarify the relationship between the various groups of *Cryptobia* (those on the body surface, in the digestive tract and in the blood) and, as a result, to rekindle research interests in the often neglected ectoparasitic *Cryptobia* and those in the digestive tract; secondly to integrate what is known and thereby to point out the gaps in knowledge so as to stimulate further work; thirdly, to bring together studies that would otherwise not be available to a more general readership. The hope is to interest other specialists in working on this very challenging host–parasite system.

This review is meant to complement the earlier reviews; consequently much of the literature that was adequately dealt with (e.g. the list of haematozoic *Cryptobia* and their localities, transmission electron microscopic studies) are only referred to but not discussed. However, in trying to present a more complete and balanced review, some of the work cited briefly in earlier reviews is discussed more fully in light of recent advances. Also, specific suggestions for further work are indicated whenever it was felt necessary to help resolve a controversy, to bridge a gap in our understanding, or both.

II. Brief History of *Cryptobia* and *Trypanoplasma*

The genus *Cryptobia* was proposed by Leidy (1846) for a biflagellated organism from the reproductive system of *Helix* spp. Leidy (1847) changed the name to *Cryptoicus* when he thought it to be "preoccupied". Diesing (1850) named a biflagellated organism in snails *Bodo (Cercomonas) helicis*. However, subsequent workers felt the changes from *Cryptobia* to *Cryptoicus* and later to *Bodo* were not justified.

Laveran and Mesnil (1901) proposed the name *Trypanoplasma* for a biflagellated haemoflagellate of freshwater fish. Subsequently, numerous species (see Lom, 1979) were described from freshwater and marine fishes. Some species were proposed because they were from new hosts, while others were erected because of minor morphological differences (e.g. the relative lengths of the two flagella, the presence of cytoplasmic granules). Léger (1904a,b) indicated that *Cryptobia (= "Trypanoplasma") borreli* caused severe anaemia and death and that it was not host-specific. He (Léger, 1904c) also described *Cryptobia (= "Trypanoplasma") varium* and succeeded in transmitting it using the leech *Hemiclepsis marginata*. The lack of host specificity was confirmed by Laveran (1904).

Léger (1905) described *Cryptobia (= "Trypanoplasma") intestinalis* from the oesophagus and anterior region of the stomach of a marine fish, *Box boops*. This further complicated the situation because, until then, *Cryptobia* had been used for the parasites in the reproductive system of land snails and *Trypanoplasma* for those in the blood of fishes. Subsequently, other species were described from the alimentary tract and blood of marine fishes.

Cryptobia (= "Trypanoplasma") carassii was reported as an ectoparasite on the body surface of goldfish, *Carassius auratus*, by Swezy (1916), who later gave a detailed description (Swezy, 1919). Other species have since been reported from the body surface of fishes.

Numerous flagellates of invertebrates were also included in the genus *Trypanoplasma* (see Hesse, 1910; Fantham and Porter, 1910; Hovasse, 1924). Crawley (1909) synonymized *Trypanoplasma* from the blood of fish (vascular or haematozoic species) with *Cryptobia* from snails (non-vascular species), because of morphological similarities.

III. Further Discussion on Synonymizing *Trypanoplasma* with *Cryptobia*

It is generally agreed that there is no morphological feature, visible under the light microscope, that can be used to differentiate the vascular from the nonvascular species (see, e.g. Laveran and Mesnil, 1912; Becker, 1977; Bower and Woo, 1977a; Burreson, 1979; Paterson and Woo, 1983). Similarly, scanning electron microscope studies showed no gross difference in external morphology between vascular and nonvascular species (Brugerolle *et al.*, 1979; Current, 1980; Lom, 1980; Vickerman, 1977; Paterson and Woo, 1983).

Using the transmission electron microscope, Brugerolle *et al.* (1979) showed that *Cryptobia (= "Trypanoplasma") borreli* was similar to nonvascular species except for the absence of a contractile vacuole. Contractile vacuoles were found (Current, 1980; Lom, 1980; Vickerman, 1977) in nonvascular species (*Cryptobia* sp. from spermatheca of a snail, *Cryptobia branchialis* from the gills of a fish, and *Cryptobia vaginalis* from the reproductive system of a leech). Since *C. borreli* was from the blood, Brugerolle *et al.* (1979) suggested that a contractile vacuole was unnecessary and inferred that the absence of the organelle could be used to differentiate vascular from nonvascular species. However, ultrastructural study of the blood forms of a vascular species (Paterson and Woo, 1983) showed a functional contractile vacuole (see Figs 3 and 4, p. 211), and there was no ultrastructural difference between *C. salmositica* and nonvascular species.

Laveran and Mesnil (1912) pointed out that there must be distinct biological differences between the nonvascular and vascular species. The former, in the reproductive organs of snails, are transmitted directly during reproduction while the latter, in the blood, are transmitted indirectly by leeches. Consequently, most European workers (e.g. Martin, 1913; Nowicki, 1940; Lom and Nohynkova, 1977; Lom, 1979) retained *Trypanoplasma* for vascular species while North American workers (e.g. Katz, 1951; Becker and Katz, 1965a,b, 1966; Strout, 1965; Putz, 1972a,b; Bower and Woo, 1977a,b,c), for a time, accepted Crawley's (1909) proposal and placed them in *Cryptobia*. Becker (1977) and Lom (1979) agreed that the vascular species should be placed in the genus *Trypanoplasma* while those from the gills, skin or digestive tract should be retained in the genus *Cryptobia*; they believed the differences in life cycles were distinct enough for this separation.

Recent transmission studies (Woo and Wehnert, 1983; Bower and Margolis, 1983) on a haematozoic species in salmonids, *C. salmositica*, showed that it could be transmitted directly between fish, and that the parasite also occurred on the body surface. An ectoparasitic phase was also demonstrated in another haematozoic species, *Cryptobia bullocki* (E. M. Burreson, personal communication).

These recent studies clearly show that Crawley (1909) was right when he synonymized *Trypanoplasma* with *Cryptobia*. All species originally described as *Trypanoplasma* are placed in the genus *Cryptobia* in subsequent Sections in this review.

IV. *Cryptobia* Parastic on Body Surface and Gills

As indicated earlier, *C. carassii* was described from mucus on the body surface of goldfish (Swezy, 1916, 1919). Wenrich (1931) found an ectoparasitic cryptobiid on the gills of carp that were dying in the Schuylkill River, Pennsylvania, U.S.A. As the parasitemia was low, he did not consider the parasite to be the cause of mortality. Since then, five other species (*Cryptobia agitans* (Davis, 1947), *Cryptobia agitata* Chen, 1956, *C. branchialis* Nie in Chen, 1956, *Cryptobia concava* (Davis, 1947), *Cryptobia rebae* (Tripathi, 1954) and *Cryptobia indica* Jayasri and Parvateesam, 1982 have been reported from freshwater fishes in Asia, Eastern Europe and North America. There was also a report of a *Cryptobia* on the gills of marine fishes in North America (Burreson and Sypek, 1981).

Davis (1947) proposed the genus *Bodomonas* for a parasite from the gills of *Pomoxis annularis* and *Pomoxis sparoides*. Since *Bodomonas concava* and *Colponema agitans*, described by Davis (1947), and *Bodomonas rebae*, described by Tripathi (1954), are all morphologically *Cryptobia*, I agree with Lom (1980), who transferred them to the genus *Cryptobia*. *Cryptobia indica*, described from the gills of *Puntius sarana*, was differentiated from the other species morphometrically (Jayasri and Parvateesam, 1982).

A *Cryptobia* sp. was recently found on the gills of fishes (*Paralichthys dentatus*, *Trinectes maculatus* and *Morone americana*) from York River near Chesapeake Bay, U.S.A. (Burreson and Sypek, 1981). Although the parasitemia was high in some fish, the gill epithelium was unaffected. The fish were also infected with *C. bullocki*. The possibility that the ectoparasitic flagellate was actually an ectoparasitic form of *C. bullocki* should be considered, especially as Burreson (personal communication) has shown that this species does have an ectoparasitic phase.

Little is known about the biology of the ectoparasitic species of *Cryptobia*. However, it was shown (Woo and Wehnert, 1983; Bower and Margolis, 1983; E. M. Burreson, personal communication) that an ectoparasitic phase occurs in two vascular species. Woo and Wehnert (1983) suggested that some ectoparasitic *Cryptobia* spp. may actually be ectoparasitic forms of vascular *Cryptobia* spp., or vice versa. It is recommended that this possibility be examined experimentally with the described species before their biology is studied further. It is likely that many, if not all, are "good" species; the recommendation is precautionary and merely to avoid future confusion.

A. DETECTION OF INFECTION

Mucus is gently scraped from the body surface and examined using a compound microscope. Freshly excised gill filaments, mucus from the body surface, or both, are best examined with an inverted microscope (Woo and Wehnert, 1983). The material can later be fixed with absolute ethanol and then with buffered formalin before staining with Giemsa's stain for confirmation.

B. HOST-PARASITE RELATIONSHIP

Most species have not been shown to be pathogenic. However, *C. branchialis* was implicated in mortality of cultured carp in Asia and eastern Europe (Chen, 1956; Naumova, 1969; Bauer *et al.*, 1969) and goldfish and catfish in the U.S.A. (Hoffman, 1978). According to Bauer *et al.* (1969), Chinese workers studying grass carp (*Ctenopharyngdom idella*) reported high mortality in infected fingerlings and young fish less than one year old, while older fish usually recovered. The gills of infected fish were abnormally red and the body produced a copious amount of mucus. In heavy infestations, the epithelium of the gill filaments was destroyed, with the formation of thrombi (Chen, 1956). Bighead carp (*Aristichthys nobilis*) and silver carp (*Hypophthalmichthys molitrix*) may also be infected but normally do not die and are considered to be reservoir hosts.

Lom (1980), in an ultrastructural study, found no evidence that *C. branchialis* damaged the gills of the common carp (*Cyprinus carpio*) from Czechoslovakia or the fantail darter (*Etheostoma flabellare*) from U.S.A. He concluded that the parasite was not pathogenic and suggested that other pathogens were probably responsible for the mortality of these fish. The study should be repeated with experimentally infected young grass carp, because the disease was shown not to be severe in older fish of other species of carp (Chen, 1956).

C. CONTROL MEASURES

According to Bauer *et al.* (1969), Chinese workers immersed bighead and silver carp for 15–30 minutes in 0.001% chloride of lime (10 g/1000 litres of water) and 0.0008% copper sulfate (8 g/1000 litres) before the fish were introduced into ponds. Ponds were treated by suspending a mixture of iron sulfate and copper sulfate in bags or baskets in them for 4–5 hours; the number of bags depended on the volume of water. This process was very effective.

V. *Cryptobia* in the Digestive Tract

Seven species of *Cryptobia* have been described from the digestive system. Those from marine fishes were *Cryptobia congeri* (Elmhirst and Martin, 1910), *Cryptobia coryphaenoideana* Noble, 1968, *Cryptobia dahlii* (Möbius, 1888), *Cryptobia intestinalis* (Léger, 1905), *Cryptobia stilbia* Noble, 1968 and *Cryptobia trematomi* Woodcock and Lodge, 1921. *Cryptobia iubilans* Nohynkova, 1984 was reported from freshwater fish.

Most species were differentiated by morphology, morphometrics, or both; however, these features are quite variable. Consequently, it is suggested that other biological criteria (e.g. host specificity as determined by careful cross transmission experiments) be included in species descriptions (Section VI A).

Since it is virtually impossible to remove and cut open the digestive tract of a freshly killed fish without blood contamination (and consequently contamination of gut contents with haematozoic protozoa if the fish is infected), it is recommended that blood should also be examined for haematozoic *Cryptobia* (Section VI F). This precautionary procedure helps to ensure that a *Cryptobia* described from the digestive tract (or from other organs) is not a haematozoic species.

A. Detection of Infection

Species in the digestive tract are detected by examination of wet preparations of fluid or scrapings from the stomach or intestine. Regurgitated food or faeces may also contain flagellates. Diagnosis is confirmed by examination of stained preparations.

B. Transmission and Host Specificity

There has been little experimental study of transmission and host specificity in these intestinal flagellates. Noble (1968) suggested that *C. stilbia* and *C. coryphanoideana* were transmitted directly via sea water. Khan and Noble (1972) transmitted *C. dahli* from lumpfish (*Cyclopterus lumpus*) to lumpfish, but not to four other fishes (*Myoxocephalus octodecemspinosus*, *Mallotus villosus*, *Pseudopleuronectes americanus* and *Tautogolabrus adspersus*), by feeding stomach fluid containing the parasite. *Cryptobia dahli* was found in material regurgitated by captive lumpfish and remained alive for up to 2 days. Khan and Noble (1972) also suggested that lumpfish acquired the infection by ingesting "... intermediate hosts" which may be "... pelagic crustacea, annelids, jellyfish, and small fish which serve as food for lumpfish".

It is suggested that future work on transmission (including cross transmission to determine host specificity) be conducted with fish (preferably laboratory raised) of known history. *Cryptobia iubilans*, unlike *C. dahli*, is not host-specific. Transmission to cichlids (*Cichlasoma nigrofasciatum*) was accomplished by feeding organs from infected *Herichthys cyanoguttatum* to uninfected cichlids (Nohynkova, 1984). The parasite survived at least 4 hours in water at 20 °C. This study suggested that cannibalism may be important in transmission.

C. HOST–PARASITE RELATIONSHIP

Cryptobia iubilans is the only pathogenic intestinal *Cryptobia*. Nohynkova (1984) found *Cryptobia* free in the stomach, intestine, fat, liver, spleen, ovary and gall bladder of moribund fish. There was no indication that the blood was examined nor was there mention of obvious perforation of the digestive tract. Consequently, it is not known how the parasite spreads to organs (spleen, ovary, etc.) not continuous with the gut. Active parasites (usually one to four) were also found in macrophage-like cells and it was concluded that they were multiplication stages. *Cryptobia salmositica* and *C. bullocki* have also been found in mononuclear macrophages (Woo, 1979; Sypek and Burreson, 1983), but these had been ingested by the macrophages (see Fig. 9, p. 223) and the phenomenon was considered to be part of protective immunity (Section VI H). *In vitro* culture of *C. iubilans* with these macrophage-like cells (from a naive fish) may help to confirm that the parasite has an intracellular phase.

VI. *CRYPTOBIA* IN THE VASCULAR SYSTEM

Lom (1979) listed 33 species of *Cryptobia* from the blood of fishes. Seven more species have since been described. Shul'man (1984) proposed three new species from freshwater fishes in the U.S.S.R.: *Cryptobia C. indistincta cyprini* pro parte to *Cryptobia guerneyorum* pro parte to *C. humilis*, and *Cryptobia keysselitzi* pro parte to *C. minuta*. Four new species were described from the freshwater fish *Mystus* spp. in India (Wahul, 1985): *Cryptobia krishnamurthyi* and *Cryptobia cavacii* were reported from *Mystus cavacius*, the major difference between them being that *C. krishnamurthyi* "... lacks a kinetoplast"; *Cryptobia vidyai* and *Cryptobia seenghali* were described from *Mystus seenghala*, *C. seenghali* being differentiated from *C. vidyai* by its size,

"... elongated kinetoplast and patterns of undulations of the posterior flagellum".

More careful studies (Section VI A) will probably show that many of the nominal species are invalid. For example, I can find no valid morphometric difference between the four *Cryptobia* species from *Mystus* (Wahul, 1985). Since these haemoflagellates are normally not host-specific (e.g. Putz, 1972b; Bower and Woo, 1977a), careful cross transmission experiments using cloned strains will probably show that there is only a single species of *Cryptobia* in *Mystus* spp.

A. CRITERIA FOR SPECIES DEFINITION IN HAEMATOZOIC *CRYPTOBIA*

Bower and Woo (1977a), after careful study of *Cryptobia catostomi* and of the literature, concluded that many of the morphological features (e.g. length of flagella, cytoplasmic granules, size) are of limited value for species identification. Similarly, morphology and morphometrics were considered to be insufficient for identification of many species of *Trypanosoma*. Identifications of some trypanosomes of amphibia (Woo and Bogart, 1984, 1986), birds (Woo and Bartlett, 1982) and mammals (Woo *et al.*, 1980) were considered tentative unless other biological characters were included. In a recent experimental study (Woo and Black, 1984), it was shown that the fish host affects the morphometrics of *Trypanosoma danilewskyi*. Since many species of *Cryptobia* (e.g. *C. salmositica*, *C. bullocki*) are not host-specific, the effects of the host on morphometrics should be considered.

The inclusion of biological characters (e.g. the results of experimental cross transmission experiments) in the description of species of trypanosomes was recommended (Woo and Black, 1984) because there are morphologically similar trypanosomes which are distinct physiological species. For example, two morphologically similar mammalian trypanosomes, *Trypanosoma (Schizotrypanum) hedricki* and *T. (S.) myoti* from *Eptesicus fuscus* and *Myotis lucifugus* respectively (Bower and Woo, 1981a), with similar cultural characteristics (Bower and Woo, 1981b), could be differentiated by experimental cross transmission experiments (Bower and Woo, 1981a), antigenic differences (Bower and Woo, 1982), polypeptide profiles (Taylor *et al.*, 1982) and buoyant density of nuclear and kinetoplast deoxyribonucleic acid (DNA) (Woo *et al.*, 1984).

It is recommended that a similar approach be taken in the study of *Cryptobia*, because there may be physiologically distinct species (separated by careful cross transmission studies) that are morphologically similar and there may be species whose morphology and morphometrics are affected by the fish host.

B. REVIEW OF TAXONOMIC STUDIES IN NORTH AMERICA

Early work on vascular *Cryptobia* has been adequately summarized (Lom, 1979); consequently, much of it is not repeated here. However, for completeness, a brief summary of taxonomic studies carried out in North America is included.

In North America, Mavor (1915) was the first to report *Cryptobia* from the blood of a white sucker (*Catostomus commersoni*), near Georgian Bay in Lake Huron. He tentatively identified it as *C. borreli* because he thought Plehn (1903) had described *C. borreli* from carp, and that the parasite had been introduced with German carp to North America. However, Plehn (1903) had described *Cryptobia cyprini*, but not *C. borreli*, from carp and goldfish. More recently, Bower and Woo (1977a) described *C. catostomi* from white sucker from southern Lake Huron. After morphological and cross transmission studies, they concluded that Mavor's identification was incorrect.

Katz (1951) described *C. salmositica* from coho salmon (*Oncorhynchus kisutch*) and *Cryptobia lynchi* from sculpins (*Cottus rhotheus* and *Cottus aleuticus*) in Washington State. Becker and Katz (1965a) later concluded that *C. lynchi* was a synonym of *C. salmositica*. Wales and Wolf (1955) reported *Cryptobia* in rainbow trout (*Salmo gairdneri*), steelhead (*Salmo gairdneri gairdneri*), brown trout (*Salmo trutta*), coho salmon (*O. kisutch*), large-scaled sucker (*Catostomus snyderi*), and sculpin (*Cottus* sp.) in California.

Bullock (1952, 1953) found *Cryptobia* in a winter flounder (*Pseudopleuronectes americanus*) taken through the ice in Great Bay, New Hampshire. He proposed the name *Cryptobia newingtoniensis* for it "... when adequately described ...". Strout (1965) considered this provisional name to be a *nomen nudum* and redescribed the parasite as *C. bullocki*. *Cryptobia gurneyorum* was recorded by Laird (1961) in northern pike (*Esox lucius*) and salmonids (*Coregonus clupeaformis* and *Salvelinus namaycush*) from the Northwest Territories. Putz (1972a) described *Cryptobia cataractae* from the longnose dace (*Rhinichthys cataractae*) in Jefferson County, West Virginia. Recently *Cryptobia beckeri* was proposed for a very long and slender organism from the blood of a cabezon (*Scorpaenichthys marmoratus*) collected from Yaquina Bay, Oregon (Burresson, 1979).

Cryptobia was reported from the blood of the toadfish (*Opsanus tau*) in Long Island Sound (Nigrelli *et al.*, 1975). This parasite was transmitted by the leech *Piscicola funduli*. Sloan *et al.* (1984) found *Cryptobia* in the blood of

Limanda aspera in fjords in British Columbia and suggested that the leech *Notostomum cyclostoma* was the vector.

C. MORPHOLOGY

1. *Light microscopy*

Most species of *Cryptobia* (Fig. 1) from the blood are elongated flagellates (ranging from the oval shape of newly divided *C. catostomi* to the long ribbon-like *C. beckeri*) with a rounded anterior and a more pointed posterior end. Two flagella arise at the anterior end; the anterior flagellum is free while the recurrent flagellum is attached to the body and extends beyond it as a free flagellum. The prominent kinetoplast is oval to elongated and is anterior to, or beside, the round nucleus.

3. *Electron microscopy*

Scanning electron microscopy study of *C. salmositica* (Fig. 2) indicates that it has a cytostome and two flagella arising from a flagellar pocket (Paterson and Woo, 1983). The recurrent flagellum is attached to the body surface and, as it beats, it draws out the pellicle, thus giving the appearance of an

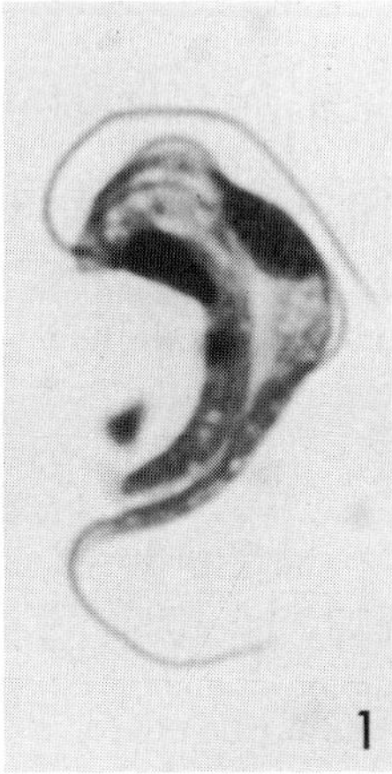

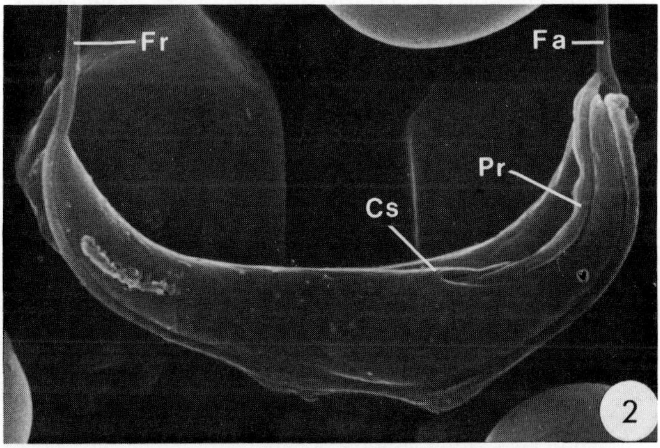

FIG. 1. Photomicrograph of *Cryptobia salmositica*. (Original, × 1150.)
FIG. 2. Scanning electron micrograph of blood stream form of *Cryptobia salmositica*; anterior free flagellum (Fa), recurrent flagellum (Fr), preoral ridge (Pr) and lipped cytostome (Cs). (× 6300.) (From Paterson and Woo, 1983; by courtesy of *Journal of Protozoology*.)

undulating membrane. The preoral ridge arises from the right side of the flagellar pocket and is reflected posteriorly along the cell surface. The gross external morphology is similar to that of *C. boreli* from the blood of fish (Brugerolle *et al.*, 1979), *C. dahli* from the stomach of fish (Khan *et al.*, 1980), *C.* sp. indet. from the snail (Current, 1980) and *C. vaginalis* from the leech (Vickerman, 1977).

Transmission electron microscopic studies have been adequately reviewed (Lom, 1979) and consequently the present discussion will mainly be confined to studies published after the previous review. Studies of nonvascular species (Vickerman, 1977; Current, 1980; Lom, 1980; Khan *et al.*, 1980; Nohynkova, 1984) showed that they are essentially similar to the vascular species (Vickerman, 1971; Brugerolle *et al.*, 1979; Paterson and Woo, 1983). According to Brugerolle *et al.* (1979) the major difference between the vascular and nonvascular species of *Cryptobia* is the absence of contractile vacuoles in the vascular species. They did not find a contractile (pulsatile) vacuole in *C. borreli*; however, Paterson and Woo (1983) found a pulsatile vacuole (Figs 3 and 4) in *C. salmositica* from the blood. The organelle was functional in the blood form and could be seen in both systole and diastole stages.

D. LIFE CYCLE

1. *Development in and transmission by the leech vector*

Transmission of haematozoic *Cryptobia* normally occurs through the bite of infected aquatic leeches (Léger, 1904c; Keysselitz, 1906; Brumpt, 1906; Robertson, 1911; Becker and Katz, 1965a; Burreson, 1979, 1982a). The only morphological changes which occur in the vector are in size; the organisms become more slender or rounded and smaller. Similar forms are seen in the vertebrate host during multiplication (Section VI D). The development of *Cryptobia* in the leech does not resemble the sequential development,

FIG. 3. Transmission electron micrographs of blood form of *Cryptobia salmositica*. The vesicles of the spongiome (Sp) are continuous with the pulsatile vacuole (Pv); also visible are the recurrent flagellum (Fr), flagellar pocket (Fp), lead contaminant (Lc) and preoral ridge (Pr). Small vesicles with an electron-dense outer bristle coat are found in association with the membrane of the flagellar pocket (arrows). (× 34 000.) (From Paterson and Woo, 1983; courtesy of *Journal of Protozoology*.)
FIG. 4. Transmission electron micrographs of blood form of *Cryptobia salmositica*. A cross-section through the pulsatile vacuole (Pv) during diastole, also showing flagellar pocket (Fp), electron-dense plaque (Pk) and kinetoplast (Kp) and preoral ridge (Pr). (× 34 000.) (From Paterson and Woo, 1983; courtesy of *Journal of Protozoology*.)

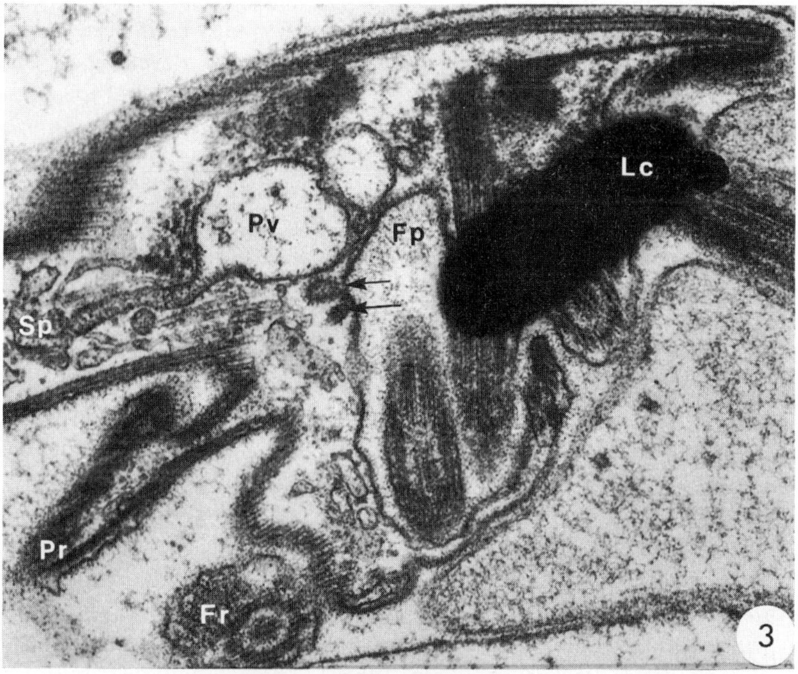
Lc
Pv
Fp
Sp
Pr
Fr
3

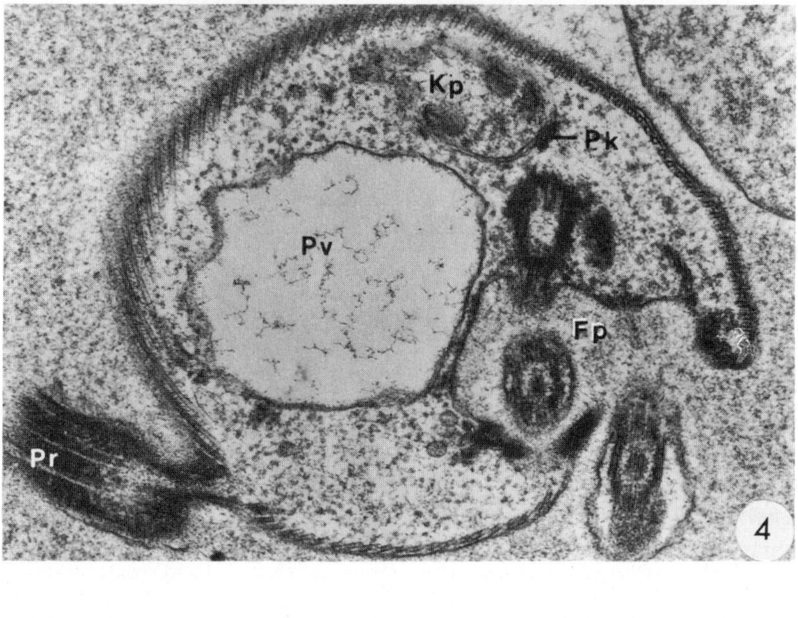
Kp
Pk
Pv
Fp
Pr
4

through different distinct stages, found in *Trypanosoma*. Consequently some workers (e.g. Becker and Katz, 1965b; Lom, 1979) may have been incorrect in calling the slender infective form "metacyclic". The development in the vector needs further clarification.

Cryptobia beckeri, from the marine fish *Scorpaenichthys marmoratus*, became rounded after ingestion by the leech (*Malmiana diminuta*) and this was followed by binary fission (Burreson, 1979); these forms were thought to be "non-infective", but this was not proven experimentally. The small, infective stages migrated to the proboscis sheath within 72 hours. The development of *C. beckeri* in the marine leech was similar to that of *C. cyprini* and *C. borelli* in freshwater leeches (Robertson, 1911; Lom, 1979). The appearance of infective "metacyclic" forms was rapid and, as with trypanosomes, development was affected by the rate the blood meal was digested.

The development of *C. bullocki* in the marine leech *Calliobdella vivida* was similar to that of other *Cryptobia*. The infective stage was in the proboscis sheath by the fifth day at 10° C (Burreson, 1982a). Development took longer at lower temperature (10 days at 5° C) and was quicker at higher temperature (24 hours at 20° C). The development of *C. salmositica* in, and its transmission by, *Piscicola salmositica* was demonstrated by Becker and Katz (1965a). *Cryptobia* was not transferred transovarially from infected leeches to their offspring and infection did not occur by ingestion of infected leeches (Robertson, 1911; Becker and Katz, 1965a). The ecology, distribution and biology of *P. salmositica* has been extensively studied (Becker and Katz, 1965c).

2. *Direct transmission between fishes*

Haemoflagellates of fishes are certainly transmitted by blood-sucking leeches. However, recent studies (Woo and Wehnert, 1983; Bower and Margolis, 1983) demonstrated direct transmission of *C. salmositica* if infected and uninfected fish were kept in the same tank. When infected and uninfected rainbrow trout were allowed to mix, 67–80% of the uninoculated trout acquired detectable infections by 27 weeks (Woo and Wehnert, 1983). If infected and uninfected trout were separated by a wire screen about 50% of the uninoculated fish acquired detectable infections. *Cryptobia salmositica* was found in the mucus on the body surface 6 weeks after infection (Figs 5 and 6) and some were morphologically similar to the "rounded forms" of *C. beckeri* in the leech (Section VI D). Some of the ectoparasitic forms were similar to those in the blood and were infective when inoculated into fish. It was assumed that the parasite was carried in the mucus to the recipient fish and either entered the vascular system through lesions on the body or actively penetrated the mucous membrane in the oral cavity or gills.

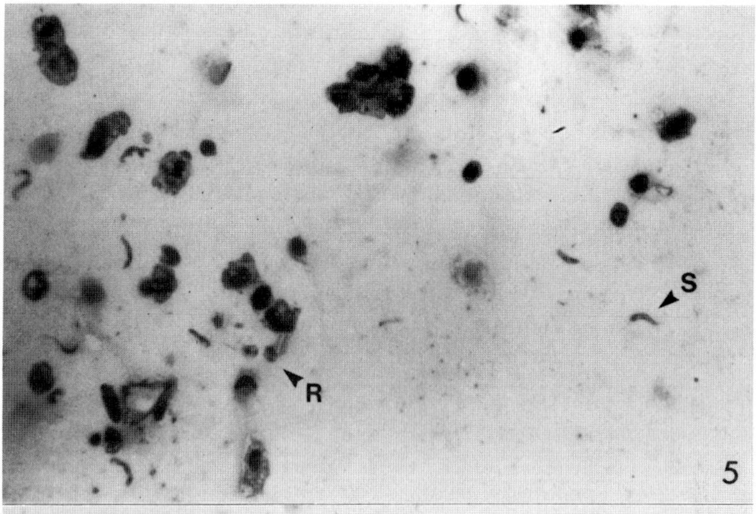

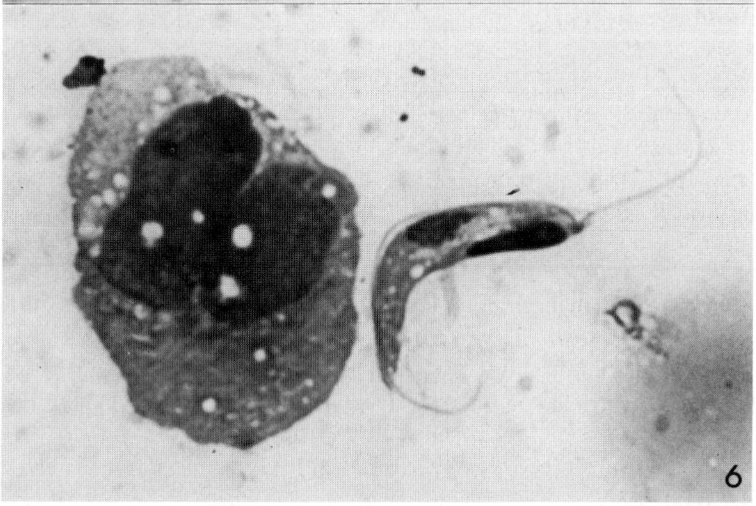

FIG. 5. *Cryptobia salmositica* in mucus from body surface of a fish 6 weeks after infection. Low power photomicrograph; note the numerous slender (S) and round (R) forms among the epithelial cells (× 110). (From Woo and Wehnert, 1983; courtesy of *Journal of Protozoology*.)

FIG. 6. *Cryptobia salmositica* in mucus from body surface of a fish 6 weeks after infection. High power photomicrograph; slender form next to epithelial cell (× 1150). (From Woo and Wehnert, 1983; courtesy of *Journal of Protozoology*.)

In fish infected with *C. salmositica* there was dissociation of the connective tissues near the abdominal pore, with infiltration of the parasite (Bower and Margolis, 1983). Eventually the parasite was released through a blister on the body surface. Juvenile sockeye were held in a dip net with "brief out-of-water" contact with heavily infected fish; deaths were first observed 27 days later. Transmission was lower (64–89%) in fresh water than in sea water (94%). There was some evidence of direct transmission when fish were transferred in a hatchery. The prevalence in coho salmon rose from 29% to 74% 1.5 months after they were transferred, while that in fish in another channel (not transferred) remained the same. The authors suggested that direct transmission might be an important mode of transmission in hatcheries. However, they indicated that the increase in prevalence might have been due to undetectable infections becoming patent because of stress associated with the transfer.

3. *Multiplication in the fish*

Laveran and Mesnil (1902a,b) observed several dividing forms of *C. borreli* in experimentally infected *Scardinius erythrophthalmus*. Keysselitz (1906) suggested a sexual process with male and female gametes conjugating in the vector. Most early workers (Plehn, 1903; Minchin, 1909; Tanabe, 1924; Wenyon, 1926; Becker and Katz, 1965b) did not see dividing stages. Recent studies (Bower and Woo, 1977b; Woo, 1978) showed that the parasite multiplied by binary fission. Two basic types of division were described. In type I the organism became rounded before cytokinesis and division was equal (e.g. in *C. catostomi*), while in type II the parasite retained its elongated form and division was unequal (e.g. in *C. salmositica*). Another major difference was that in type I each progeny inherited one new flagellum, while in type II the more slender progeny retained both new flagella. The two types of multiplication were described using cloned strains (Bower and Woo, 1977b; Woo, 1978).

The first indication of type I division (in *C. catostomi*) was the production of two new short and equal flagella (Bower and Woo, 1977b). The organism became rounded and this was followed by nuclear division. The two nuclei were connected by a "chromatin" strand. The two basal bodies, each with a new flagellum, migrated away from each other so that they became located at either end of the kinetoplast (Fig. 7a). Kinetoplast division was unequal and was followed by cytokinesis, resulting in two round progeny of equal size. Woo (1981) also reported a similar "chromatin" strand in dividing *T. danilewskyi*; however, electron microscopic study (Paterson and Woo, 1984) showed that it was a microtubular bridge with no detectable chromatin.

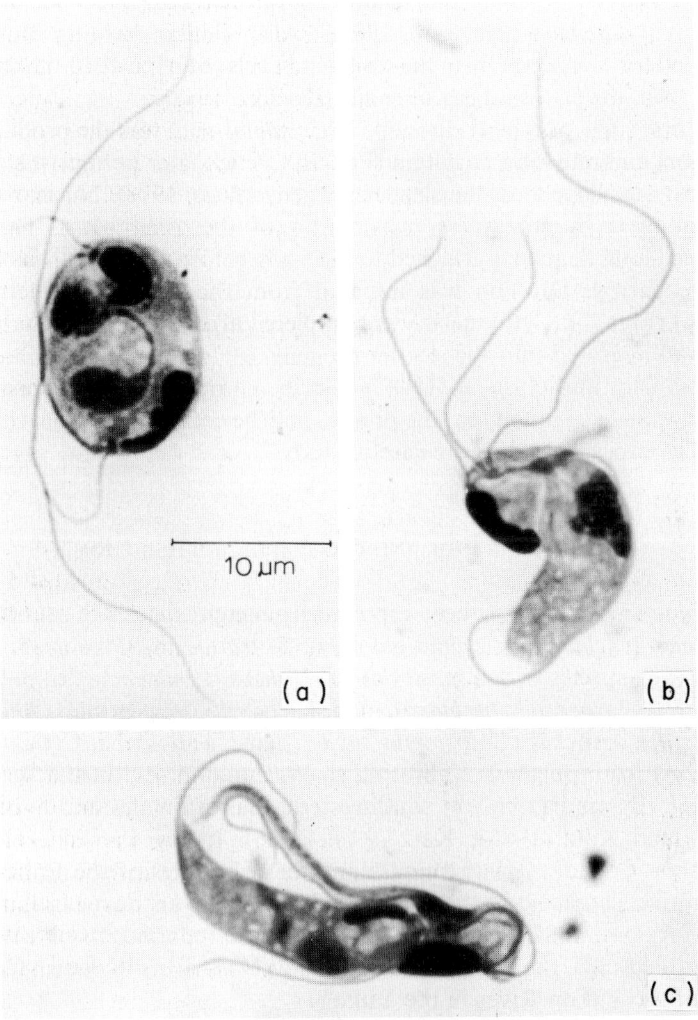

FIG. 7. Photomicrographs of dividing *Cryptobia* spp. in the blood of fishes. (a) *Cryptobia catostomi* in the blood of white sucker. (From Bower and Woo, 1977b; courtesy of *Canadian Journal of Zoology*.) (b) *Cryptobia salmositica*, with a new set of flagella, in the blood of rainbow trout. (From Woo, 1978; courtesy of *Canadian Journal of Zoology*.) (c) *Cryptobia salmositica*, unequal division in the blood of rainbow trout. (From Woo, 1978; courtesy of *Canadian Journal of Zoology*.)

The division of *C. bullocki* in a naturally infected hogchoker was similar to that of *C. catostomi* (Burreson, 1982a). Also, similar dividing stages were described for *C. congeri* from the stomach of eels (Martin, 1910, 1913) and *C. helicis* from the spermatheca of snails (Kozloff, 1948).

The first stage of type II division (in *C. salmositica*) was the production of one short and one long flagellum (Fig. 7b), which later became the anterior and posterior flagella of the slender progeny (Woo, 1978). Nuclear division was followed by transverse constriction of the kinetoplast. The newly produced long flagellum attached to the body before obvious division of the latter occurred. Division was initiated from the posterior end and was unequal (Fig. 7c). Cytokinesis was completed after the nucleus and kinetoplast had migrated into the slender progeny.

Khaibulaev and Guseinov (1982) described a novel type of schizogony in *C. cyprini* and suggested that the process may be considered sexual reproduction. The process needs more careful study.

E. HOST RANGE AND GEOGRAPHIC DISTRIBUTION

Cryptobia salmositica has been reported from eight species of salmonids (all five *Oncorhynchus* spp., *Salmo gairdneri*, *S. trutta*, and *Prosopium williamsoni*), seven species of sculpins (*Cottus rhotheus*, *C. aleuticus*, *C. gulosus*, *C. beldingi*, *C. asper*, *C. perplexus*, and *C. bairdi*), a cyprinid (*Rhinichthys cataractae*), a sucker (*Catostomus snyderi*), and a stickleback (*Gasterosteus aculeatus*) from northern California to Washington and in the Bering Sea drainage (Iliamna Lakes) in southwestern Alaska (Wales and Wolf, 1955; Becker and Katz, 1965a; Katz *et al.*, 1966). In the Province of British Columbia, Canada, it was found along the tributaries of the Fraser River, coastal rivers adjacent to the Fraser, and rivers on Vancouver Island (Bower and Margolis, 1984b). The parasite was not reported from the Queen Charlotte Islands, the Bella Coola, Skeena or Nass rivers in British Columbia or from the Yukon River in the Yukon.

To explain this disjunct distribution of *C. salmositica*, Bower and Margolis (1984b) suggested that the parasite and its leech vector survived the last glacial period (Wisconsin) in refuges in parts of Alaska (Bering Sea drainages and the Yukon River basin) and the Columbia River basin in the south. After the glacial period, infected fish and leeches spread north from the Columbia River basin and coastal rivers in Washington into southern British Columbia. From the Fraser River the parasite and its vector spread north throughout the entire system. Since the leech is sensitive to sea water its dispersal northwards to coastal rivers was slow; as a result, the parasite and its vector were not found in more northern rivers in British Columbia.

The other important cryptobiid pathogen of fish in North America is *C. bullocki*. It is found in estuarine and inshore marine fish on the east coast of North America and in the Gulf of Mexico (Strout, 1965; Laird and Bullock, 1969; Daily, 1978; Becker and Overstreet, 1979; Burreson and Zwerner, 1982). It was initially reported in smooth flounder (*Liopsetta putnami*), winter flounder (*Pseudopleuronectes americanus*) and mummichog (*Fundulus majalis*) in Great Bay, New Hampshire, U.S.A. (Strout, 1965). Subsequently, the parasite was found in smooth and winter flounders in New Brunswick, Canada (Laird and Bullock, 1969), in American plaice (*Hippoglossoides platessoides*) in Maine, U.S.A., in summer flounder (*Paralichthys dentatus*) in Chesapeake Bay, U.S.A. (Newman, 1978), and in southern flounder (*Paralichthys lethostigma*), hogchoker (*Trinectes maculatus*) and croaker (*Micropongonias undulatus*) in Mississippi Sound in the Gulf of Mexico (Becker and Overstreet, 1979). Commercially important flounders (*P. americanus, P. dentatus* along the Atlantic coast, and *P. lethostigma* along the south Atlantic coast and the Gulf of Mexico) are commonly infected. Since the leech *Calliobdella vivida* has the same geographical distribution (Sawyer *et al.*, 1975; Appy and Dadswell, 1981) as the hosts, it is probably the natural vector.

Less is known about the host range and distribution of the other species of *Cryptobia*. Laird (1961) reported *C. gurneyorum* from lake trout (*S. namaycush*), lake whitefish (*Coregonus clupeaformis*) and pike (*Esox lucius*) from the Northwest Territories, Canada. Identification was based on morphometrics and chromophilic granules. The parasite was initially described by Minchin (1909) from *E. lucius* in England.

Putz (1972a) described *C. cataractae* from the longnose dace (*Rhinichthys cataractae*) in Jefferson County, West Virginia, U.S.A. Natural infections were also detected in blacknose dace (*Rhinichthys atratulus*), cutlips minnow (*Exoglossum maxillingua*), and stoneroller (*Campostoma anomalum*). The parasite's natural host range was confined to the family Cyprinidae; no natural infection was observed in members of the families Cyprinidontidae, Cottidae, Centrarchidae or Ictaluridae. *Cryptobia catostomi* was described from the common white sucker (*C. commersoni*) in southern Lake Huron, Ontario, Canada (Bower and Woo, 1977a) and from longnose sucker (*Catostomus catostomus*). The prevalence and distribution of the parasite were studied in southern Ontario only, and it was found in every adult population of suckers examined.

Guseinov (1982) noted seven species of trypanosomes and three species of *Cryptobia* in nine species of fish in the Caspian Sea off Azerbaidzhan coast. The most heavily infected fish were *Esox lucius*, *Tinca tinca*, and *Perca fluviatilis*.

A species of *Cryptobia* was found in the blood of *Limanda aspera* in northern British Columbia (Sloan *et al.*, 1984). It was suggested that the leech *Notostomum cyclostoma* was the vector, because the haemoflagellate was found in the gut and proboscis area of 90% of *N. cyclostoma* from fjords in the Portland Inlet system, British Columbia.

F. DETECTION OF INFECTION

In heavy infections, *Cryptobia* may be detected by microscopic examination of blood and ascitic fluid. Low parasitemia is more readily detected after concentration of parasites by centrifugation (Woo, 1969) or clotting (Strout, 1962).

The haematocrit centrifuge technique (Woo, 1969) at room temperature was more sensitive than wet mount examination for detection of *C. catostomi* (Bower and Woo, 1977a); however, it was less sensitive for *C. salmositica* at 20° C. Later studies (Woo and Wehnert, 1983; Bower and Margolis, 1984a) showed that the sensitivity was increased if the centrifuge was kept cold (1–10° C), as *C. salmositica* became sluggish and died at about 21° C. The technique detected *C. salmositica* if there were about 75 organisms/ml of blood (Bower and Margolis, 1984a). The sensitivity was increased if more than one capilliary tube of blood was examined, as shown for mammalian trypanosomes (Woo and Rogers, 1974).

G. *IN VITRO* CULTURE AND CRYOPRESERVATION

1. In vitro *culture*

Ponselle (1913a,b) cultured *Cryptobia varium* from the loach (*Cobitus barbatula*) in blood agar medium. The culture forms resembled blood forms but infectivity was not tested. Other early work (by Tanabe, 1924; Nowicki, 1940; Quadri, 1962) was summarized by Lom (1979). More recently, Putz (1972b) maintained *C. cataractae* in three diphasic media (developed for mammalian trypanosomes) for 7–9 days.

Woo (1979) cultured *C. salmositica* in Hanks's solution with 10% heat-inactivated fetal calf serum. Initial cultures were at 5° C, subcultured every 15 days for the first 45 days. Subsequently, the cultures were maintained at 10°C. The culture forms and dividing stages were similar to those in the blood and they were infective. *Cryptobia bullocki* was still infective after being cultured continuously for about 4 years at 15°C, in MEM medium with Hanks's salts, 25 mM HEPES buffer, 20% fetal calf serum, L-glutamine and 0.33% dextrose (E. M. Burreson, personal communication).

2. *Cryopreservation*

Putz (1972b) cryopreserved *C. cataractae* and *C. salmositica* at − 120° C for over 36 months. The parasites were in Hanks's balanced salt solution and fetal bovine serum with 10% glycerol before they were frozen to − 120° C. The survival of *C. cataractae* was 72% after the first 12 months, 50% after 24 months and 25% after 36 months; it was similar for *C. salmositica*. Survival in glycerol or dimethylsulfoxide was lower.

H. HOST–PARASITE RELATIONSHIP

1. *Innate immunity*

Many *Cryptobia* are considered not to be host-specific. However, *C. catostomi* had a narrow host range (Bower and Woo, 1977a); it would not infect 16 other species of freshwater fishes (other than *Catostomus commersoni*) and was eliminated from the blood of refractory fishes within 3 hours of inoculation. Using an *in vitro* technique, Bower and Woo (1977c) showed that the plasma of refractory fish lysed *C. catostomi* within 3 hours. Cryptobicidal titres ranged from 1:2 to greater than 1:16, but were constant for any one fish species. Heat inactivation of plasma reduced the titre, as did selective removal of magnesium and calcium ions using EGTA and EDTA; the original titre was restored when the chelated plasma was resupplemented with the ions. The titre of serum was lower than that of plasma because some of the free ions were lost during coagulation of blood. Addition of zymosan to the plasma also reduced the titre; zymosan binds properdin which initiates the complement cascade. The alternative pathway of complement activation was proposed as one of the mechanisms of innate immunity (Bower and Woo, 1977c).

Wehnert and Woo (1980) showed that *C. salmositica* was more host-specific than originally reported. Plasma of refractory fish lysed *Cryptobia* and the titre ranged from 1:4 to 1:8. Undiluted fresh plasma lysed about 500 parasites in 30–60 minutes at 4° C; no lysis occurred in heat-inactivated plasma.

2. *Acquired immunity*

The parasitemia fluctuated during *C. salmositica* infection in trout (Woo, 1979), suggesting the occurrence of antigenic variation and immune lysis, phagocytosis, or both (see Fig. 9, p. 223). Trout that had recovered from an infection 4 months earlier were resistant to homologous challenge (Wehnert and Woo, 1981). Protective antibody was detected 56 days after infection. The protection in recovered trout was confirmed in a recent study by Jones and Woo (1986), who suggested that the immunity was nonsterile. Agglutinating and neutralizing antibodies were detected during the first 4 months. Complement fixing antibody was detected in recovered trout using the *in vitro* lysis test. Adoptive transfer of lymphocytes and plasma from immune fish conferred partial protection on naive fish.

Woo *et al.* (1986) showed that infected fish injected intraperitoneally with cortisol in coconut oil had significantly higher parasitemias and little or no humoral response against *C. salmositica*. This confirmed the immunodepressive effects of cortisol and showed that humoral antibody was important in protective immunity. The prepatent periods were shorter, more fish became infected, and parasitemias were higher in cortisol-treated fish than in infected control fish given coconut oil only. Furthermore, mortality in the infected cortisol-treated fish was higher than in the infected controls or in fish given cortisol but not infected.

Complement fixing antibody against *C. bullocki* was detected in infected summer flounder and the titre was related to temperature (Sypek and Burreson, 1983); it was concluded that humoral antibody was responsible for the annual spring decline in prevalence and eventual recovery. In a more recent study on naturally infected winter flounder (Sypek and Howe, 1985), it was suggested that temperature was not the only regulating factor. No antibody was detected in a fish that had been recovered for at least a year; however it was immune to homologous challenge (Burreson and Frizzell, 1986). The antibody titre rapidly increased to 1:3200 6 weeks after challenge. Burreson and Frizzell (1986) concluded that the immunity was sterile and that the challenged fish showed a classic secondary response. This experiment should be repeated, as it was based on a single fish, the history of which was not adequately documented. Fish that were inoculated with formalin-killed parasites produced antibody but were not protected from challenge.

3. *Immunodepression*

Although a great deal of work has been done on immunodepression in mammals infected with protozoa (see Krettli and Pereira, 1981), virtually nothing is known concerning its occurrence in fishes. Laudan *et al.* (1985) showed that *Glugea stephani* reduced IgM levels in winter flounder. The immune system in the fish is affected by heavy metals (Knittel, 1981), antibiotics (Rijkers *et al.*, 1980) and temperature (Avitalion *et al.*, 1973). Parenteral injection of corticosteroids also depresses the piscine immune system (Anderson *et al.*, 1982; Houghton and Matthews, 1985; Woo *et al.*, 1986).

There was depression of humoral response to sheep red blood cells during a *C. salmositica* infection (Wehnert and Woo, 1981). This depressed response to sheep erythrocytes was confirmed by Jones *et al.* (1986). Furthermore trout infected with *C. salmositica* and subsequently exposed to *Yersinia ruckeri* suffered higher mortality than those infected with either pathogen alone. The depressive effect was detected 7 days after *C. salmositica* infection. There was evidence that cellular immunity was also depressed by the parasite. Fish infected at the time of initial exposure to bacteria were as susceptible to *Yersinia* challenge as were naive trout. It was postulated that antigenic competition caused the immunodepression in infected fish. The immunodepressive effects (humoral and cellular) of the parasite should be borne in mind when considering the immunization of salmonids against other pathogens.

4. *Clinical signs and pathogenesis*

According to Lom (1979) many earlier workers (e.g. Plehn, 1903, 1924; Keysselitz, 1906) reported high mortality in naturally acquired cryptobiosis; the clinical signs were anemia, lethargic condition, loss of normal reactions and anorexia. However, Nowicki (1940) questioned the pathogenicity of *C. cyprini* because splenectomized carp did not develop the disease when infected with the parasite.

Recent reports of heavy losses of salmonids (e.g. by Wales and Wolf, 1955; Makeyeva, 1956; Bower and Margolis, 1983), grass carp (Britchuk, 1969; Migala, 1967, 1971) and tench (Kipp, 1968) were related to *Cryptobia* infection. Woo (1979) used three substrains (field, cultured and cloned) of *C. salmositica* to satisfy Koch's postulates and to characterize the disease in trout. The clinical signs produced by all three substrains were similar: anemia (Fig. 8a, p. 222), exophthalmia (Fig. 8b), splenomegaly (Fig. 8c) and abdominal distension with ascites fluid (Fig. 8d). The anemia was microcytic and hypochromic and developed with increasing parasitemia, becoming severe at high parasitemia; as the parasite number declined there was slight recovery until the next parasite peak. The spleens were enlarged five to ten times (by volume). Exophthalmia and abdominal distension with ascites were evident about 7 weeks after infection and became progressively more obvious with time. The ascitic fluid (about 5 ml from some fish) contained large numbers of parasites and mononuclear phagocytic cells. Peritoneal macrophages had engulfed, or were in the process of engulfing, parasites (Figs 9a and b, p. 223). Some of these clinical signs had earlier been observed in naturally and experimentally infected salmonids (Wales and Wolf, 1955 and Putz, 1972b, respectively).

All coho salmon infected with *C. salmositica* were dead within 15 days

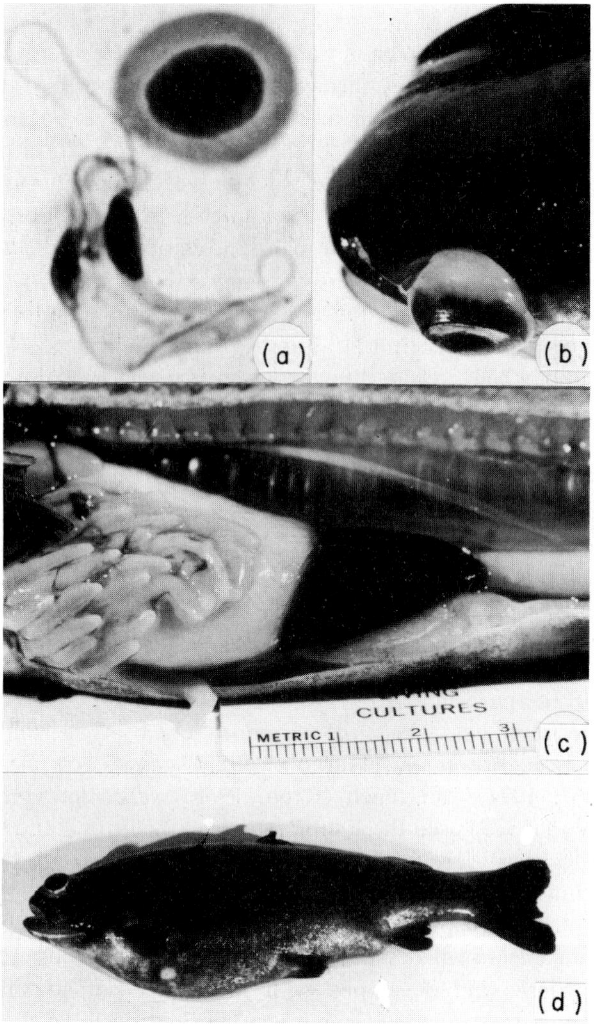

FIG. 8. Clinical signs of cryptobiosis due to *Cryptobia salmositica* in rainbow trout. (a) *Cryptobia* with red cell from an anemic fish; the anemia is microcytic and hypochromic; note the red cell is not oval and there is reduced haemoglobin. (Original, × 1150.) (b) Dorsal view of an infected rainbow trout showing obvious exophthalmia. (From Woo, 1979; courtesy of *Experimental Parasitology*.) (c) Splenomegaly in the same fish. (From Woo, 1979; courtesy of *Experimental Parasitology*.) (d) Abdominal distension and ascites. (From Woo, 1979; courtesy of *Experimental Parasitology*.)

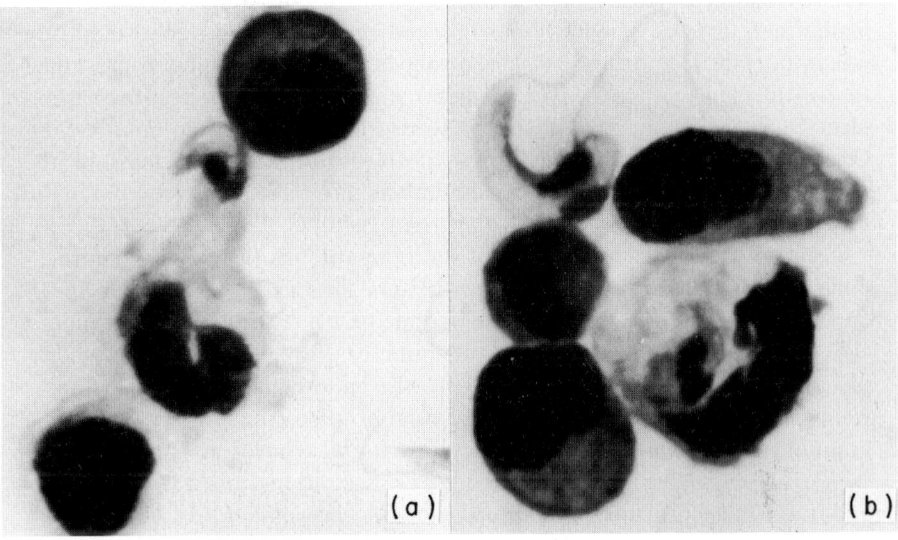

FIG. 9. Stained smears of ascites from rainbow trout infected with *Cryptobia salmositica*. (a) Macrophage in the process of engulfing the parasite. (b) *Cryptobia salmositica* in macrophage after being engulfed. (From Woo, 1979; courtesy of *Experimental Parasitology*.) (× 1000.)

(Putz, 1972b). There were focal haemorrhages, congestion of blood vessels and capillaries were occluded with parasites. Oedematous changes were especially marked in kidney glomeruli. Similar lesions were described in tench (Kipp, 1968). Putz (1972b) could not correlate mortality with histopathology. He concluded that mortality was probably due to loss of osmoregulatory control. The glucose and plasma protein levels in infected trout were low at the first parasitemia (Lowe-Jinde, 1979) and returned to near normal later. The blood lactic acid and lactic dehydrogenase levels were similar in infected and uninfected fish (Lowe-Jinde, 1980); however, the glycogen levels in the liver, heart and epaxial muscle were low. This was most evident in the liver, where the glycogen level was about 20% of that in uninfected fish. All these quantities returned to near normal towards the end of the infection.

There was progressive anemia, splenomegaly and abdominal distension in summer flounder infected with *C. bullocki*; however, exophthalmia was not seen (Burreson, 1982b; Burreson and Zwerner, 1984). Morbidity and mortality were 100% in experimentally infected summer flounder at low water temperature (0.5–1.5° C). Naturally infected fish with ascites at the time of collection survived for up to 6 weeks at 5° C; however, ascitic fish displayed no ascites after 2 weeks at 10° C. Infected fish with no ascites survived when maintained at 5° C. The authors suggested that the low water temperature was important in mortality. A laboratory-held summer flounder, presumed to be infected with *C. bullocki*, became moribund. At necropsy gross ulcerative and haemorrhagic lesions were found in the abdominal cavity. Oedema, haemorrhage and necrosis of the intestine and oedema of the stomach wall were also noted. Large numbers of *Cryptobia* were found in the submucosa of the gut and liver. (Newman, 1978).

Cryptobia borelli caused heavy mortality in goldfish (Lom, 1971); intracapillary glomerulitis and tubulonephritis were observed in the kidney 16–18 days after infection (Dykova and Lom, 1979). There was pronounced activation of the pulp in the spleen with increased plasma-like cells, macrophages and red cell phagocytosis. Also, the endothelial cells of the sinuses were swollen. There was focal necrosis in the liver and post-necrotic granulomatous inflammatory changes were found. The intercellular spaces in the fat tissues of the abdominal cavity were dilated and filled with parasites and mononuclear cells. The blood vessels showed endovasculitis, with marked endothelial hyperplasia.

Not all haematozoic *Cryptobia* are pathogenic (Putz, 1972a; Bower and Woo, 1977a). Putz experimentally infected blacknose dace with *C. cataractae* and no clinical sign or mortality was observed. *Cryptobia catostomi* did not produce disease in experimentally infected white suckers (Bower and Woo, 1977a), although the parasitemia was high in some fish (one parasite for every two red cells). Also, Burreson (1979) did not indicate that *C. beckeri* was pathogenic to cabezon.

5. *Mortality in susceptible fishes*

The two pathogenic *Cryptobia* species in North America infect a large number of fishes; however, not all susceptible hosts die from the infection. The sculpins (*Cottus* spp.) are the principal reservoirs of *C. salmositica* because the prevalence is high and there is no indication of disease in the infected fish (Becker and Katz, 1965a, 1966).

Cryptobia salmositica seemed to be more pathogenic to coho salmon (*Oncorhynchus nerka*), causing 100% mortality, than to chinook salmon—about 30% mortality (Putz, 1972b). Recent experimental studies indicated that mortality of infected sockeye salmon was consistent (56-74%) within a fish stock (Bower and Margolis, 1985). Also, the mortality due to different isolates of parasite was similar for the same fish stock. However, chinook salmon were most susceptible (100% mortality), while coho salmon were resistant (0% mortality). Currently, Bower and Riddell (S. M. Bower, personal communication) are examining the inheritance of the innate resistance of coho salmon to *Cryptobia*. Rainbow trout appeared to be intermediate between coho and sockeye salmon.

Although the susceptibility was consistent within a fish stock, there were differences between stocks. It was suggested that these differences were due to genetic factors (Bower and Margolis, 1984a). For example, chum and chinook salmon (Big Qualicum River stocks) and coho salmon (Skeena River stock) were equally susceptible and suffered high mortality when each fish was inoculated with about 10^2 parasites. However, sockeye salmon from the Weaver Creek stock were very resistant; there was no mortality, even though each fish was inoculated with 10^6 parasites.

I. ENVIRONMENTAL EFFECTS

1. *Temperature*

Rainbow trout acclimated to 20°C were not susceptible to *C. salmositica* (Woo *et al.*, 1983). Fish at 5°C had longer prepatent periods and lower parasitemias than those at 10°C. The parasitemia in fish at 10° C fluctuated, but this was not observed at 5°C. *In vitro* incubation of *Cryptobia* at 6°C in plasma from fish kept at 20°C did not affect the motility or infectivity of the parasite, i.e., the plasma from 20°C fish was not cryptobicidal. Parasites left in blood at 20°C died within an hour. Fish with low parasitemias lost their infections when the ambient temperature was raised to 20°C; in acute infections the parasitemia was significantly reduced. This study was confirmed by Bower and Margolis (1985), using sockeye salmon. Over 90% of the infected fish died when they were kept at 9°C. However, mortality was reduced to about 75% and 0% when the water temperatures after infection were raised to 13° and 20°C, respectively. The infection progressed more slowly when infected fish were maintained at 5° C.

Cryptobia bullocki occurred in low numbers in experimentally infected hogchoker, and were not seen in flounder at 25° C during the first 9 weeks after infection (Burreson and Zwerner, 1982); however, if the temperature was lowered to 15° C, the fish developed acute infections. The authors concluded that this phenomenon was host-mediated rather than due to the effect of temperature on the parasite. However, as the parasite is normally found in fish at low temperatures, another possible explanation is that the high temperature killed the parasites directly, as occurs with *C. salmositica* (Woo *et al.*, 1983).

All juvenile summer flounder experimentally infected with *C. bullocki* died within 11 weeks; the highest mortality occurred at 0.5–1.5° C (Burreson and Zwerner, 1984). Naturally infected fish with ascites survived better at about

10° C than at 5° C. However, the authors did not indicate whether the fish (two at 10° C and one at 13.5° C) that survived at the higher temperatures were still infected; they suggested that the low temperature was a contributing factor to mortality.

2. *Hypoxia*

Trout infected with *C. salmositica* were more susceptible to hypoxia than were uninfected fish (Woo and Wehnert, 1986). Susceptibility increased with time, as did the severity of the anemia and parasitemia. The parasitemia could affect susceptibility directly or indirectly by causing anemia, since the anemia was coincident with increasing parasitemia. Fish showed moderate recovery from anemia when the parasitemia decreased (Woo, 1979; Woo and Wehnert, 1986), and these fish were then less susceptible. It was assumed that oxygen uptake at the gills was reduced in anemic fish, especially when dissolved oxygen in the water was low. Heavy parasitemia also had a direct effect by occluding capillaries in the gills and thus interfering with unloading of carbon dioxide and loading of oxygen. Oxygen requirements of fish would be higher, especially when the immune system was responding to the infection and thus increasing the metabolic rate.

In fish infected with *Trypanosoma* and *Cryptobia* the parasitemia decreased in well-aerated tanks at 4–12° C; however, it remained unchanged in nonaerated tanks under similar conditions (Khaibulaev and Guseinov, 1982). One infected carp which died from massive infection was very anemic.

3. *Salinity*

There was no difference in mortality between infected pre-smolt salmon (at 9° or 13° C) that were retained in fresh water or slowly transferred to sea water over a period of 6–8 days (Bower and Margolis, 1985). Similarly, quick transfer over 1–2 days of infected smolts did not affect the number of fish surviving.

J. TREATMENT

Although there have been extensive studies on the chemotherapy of pathogenic mammalian trypanosomes, nothing is known about the effectiveness of drugs on pathogenic *Cryptobia*. Havelka *et al.* (1965) indicated that *C. cyprini* was killed by exposure *in vitro* to methylene blue, gentian violet and malachite green at concentrations of 1:2000–1:20 000. The parasite disappeared from the peripheral blood when infected carp fingerlings were exposed to the dyes (1:2000–1:5000), and in field experiments the dyes increased the survival rate of heavily infected fish and reduced their parasitemia. However, in a more recent study, methylene blue or "pirovet" were not effective against *Cryptobia* in young carp (Obradovic and Fijan, 1979).

Some of the mammalian trypanosomicidal drugs (suramin, berenil and antrycide) were not effective against *C. salmositica* in trout at 10° C (Thomas and Woo, unpublished data). Temperature therapy is a possibility; Woo *et al.* (1983) found that trout with low *C. salmositica* infections lost their infection when the water temperature was raised to 20° C. Similarly, there was no mortality in sockeye salmon when the temperature was raised to 20° C after infection (Bower and Margolis, 1985). This approach seems promising and should be explored further.

VII. Origin of the Haematozoic *Cryptobia*

Two hypotheses have been advanced to account for the origin of the haematozoic *Cryptobia*: the parasites either arose from free-living flagellates via ectoparasitic species, or their origin was linked to intestinal flagellates. Both hypotheses merit further careful consideration and experimental testing.

A. Origin from Free Living *Procryptobia* via the Ectoparasitic *Cryptobia*

Procryptobia vorax is a free-living flagellate (Vickerman, 1978). It is morphologically similar to the parasitic species, ingests bacteria through a cytostome and has a well-developed contractile vacuole. According to Woo and Wehnert (1983), *Procryptobia* could have initially become ectoparasitic on the body surface of fishes and fed on bacteria in the mucus or on the mucus itself. These ectoparasites could have entered the blood system through lesions on the body surface, or they may have actively penetrated mucous membranes.

Ectoparasitic forms of *C. salmositica* and *C. bullocki* have been described (Woo and Wehnert, 1983; E. M. Burreson, personal communication) and direct transmission between fish has been shown for *C. salmositica*. The blood form of *C. salmositica* has a functional contractile vacuole and a cytopharynx similar to these of nonvascular species (Paterson and Woo, 1983). Consequently, it was suggested (Woo and Wehnert, 1983) that the vascular species (e.g. *C. salmositica*) originated from ectoparasitic *Cryptobia* and that the latter were derived from free-living *Procryptobia*.

B. EVOLUTIONARY LINK WITH INTESTINAL *CRYPTOBIA*

Cryptobia iubilans was found throughout the digestive tract (including the liver) and the spleen and ovaries of aquarium fish in Czechoslovakia. Nohynkova (1984) believed that the original habitat of the flagellate was the stomach. Since the parasite was found in other organs, she suggested that migration to these organs represented an evolutionary link between the intestinal parasites and parasites in the blood.

VIII. CONCLUSIONS

It is clear from this review that there are tremendous gaps in our knowledge of the biology of *Cryptobia*, especially of those species found on the body surface and in the digestive tract of fishes. The information on these nonvascular species is not only incomplete and confusing, it is in some instances contradictory. Various suggestions for future work have been included to help clarify and, perhaps, resolve some of the confusion.

Our understanding of the haematozoic *Cryptobia* is better; however, there are some obvious deficiencies, e.g. nothing is known about the nutritional requirements or metabolism of the parasites. Such knowledge might help in understanding the pathogenicity (or lack of pathogenicity) of some species. It should also lead to a more rational approach to the study of chemotherapy. Since some species are pathogenic to commercially valuable fishes, it is likely that they will become increasingly more important as disease agents in aquaculture and new control measures will have to be found.

For purely scientific study *Cryptobia* is a very challenging and exciting genus to investigate. Some recent findings (e.g. a functional pulsatile vacuole in the blood forms of a haematozoic *Cryptobia*, an ectoparasitic phase in the life cycle and direct transmission in an aquatic system) are perhaps good indications that there are more exciting discoveries waiting to be unravelled. Further new insights into the biology of flagellates may emerge when we start to understand the metabolism and mechanisms which allow this organism to live both on and inside the host, in the blood or digestive tract.

ACKNOWLEDGEMENTS

I am very grateful to Drs Susan Bower, Eugene Burreson and Joseph Sypek for sending their unpublished data and preprints of papers for inclusion in this review. Ms S. Wehnert reprinted most of the micrographs.

References

Anderson, D. P., Robertson, B. S. and Dixon, O. W. (1982). Immunosuppression induced by a corticosteriod or an alkylating agent in rainbow trout (*Salmo gairdneri*) administered a *Yersina ruckeri* bacterin. *Developmental and Comparative Immunology*, supplement, **2,** 197–204.

Appy, R. G. and Dadswell, M. J. (1981). Marine and estuarine piscicolid leeches (Hirudinea) of the Bay of Fundy and adjacent waters with a key to species. *Canadian Journal of Zoology* **59,** 183–192.

Avtalion, R. R., Wojdani, A., Malik, Z., Shahrabani, R. and Duczyminer, M. (1973). Influence of environmental temperature on the immune response in fish. *Current Topics in Microbiology and Immunology* **61,** 1–35.

Bauer, O. N., Musselius, V. A. and Strelikov, Yu. A. (1969). "Diseases of Pond Fishes". Israel Program for Scientific Translation, Jerusalem (1973); U.S. Department of the Interior and the National Science Foundation, Washington, D.C.

Becker, C. D. (1970). Haematozoa of fishes, with emphasis on North American records. *In* "A Symposium on Diseases of Fishes and Shellfishes" (S. F. Sniezsko, ed.), Special Publication No. 5, pp. 82–100. American Fisheries Society, Washington.

Becker, C. D. (1977). Flagellate parasites of fish. *In* "Parasitic Protozoa" (J. P. Kreier, ed.), Vol. 1, pp. 357–416. Academic Press, New York.

Becker, C. D. and Katz, M. (1965a). Transmission of the hemoflagellate *Cryptobia salmositica* Katz 1951, by a rhynchobdellid vector. *Journal of Parasitology* **51,** 95–99.

Becker, C. D. and Katz, M. (1965b). Infections of the hemoflagellate *Cryptobia salmositica* Katz 1951, in freshwater teleosts of the Pacific coast. *Transactions of the American Fisheries Society* **94,** 327–333.

Becker, C. D. and Katz, M. (1965c). Distribution, ecology, and biology of the salmonid leech, *Piscicola salmositica* Meyer 1946 (Rhynchobdella: Piscicolidae). *Journal of the Fisheries Research Board of Canada* **22,** 1175–1195.

Becker, C. D. and Katz, M. (1966). Host relationships of *Cryptobia salmositica* (Protozoa: Mastigophora) in a Washington hatchery stream. *Transactions of the American Fisheries Society* **95,** 196–202.

Becker, C. D. and Overstreet, R. M. (1979). Haematozoa of marine fishes from the northern Gulf of Mexico. *Journal of Fish Disease* **2,** 469–479.

Bower, S. M. and Margolis, L. (1983). Direct transmission of the haemoflagellate *Cryptobia salmositica* among Pacific salmon (*Oncorhynchus* spp.). *Canadian Journal of Zoology* **61,** 1242–1250.

Bower, S. M. and Margolis, L. (1984a). Detection of infection and susceptibility of different Pacific salmon stocks (*Oncorhynchus* spp.) to the haemoflagellate *Cryptobia salmositica. Journal of Parasitology* **70,** 273–278.

Bower, S. M. and Margolis, L. (1984b). Distribution of *Cryptobia salmositica*, a haemoflagellate of fishes, in British Columbia and the seasonal pattern of infection in a coastal river. *Canadian Journal of Zoology* **62,** 2512–2518.

Bower, S. M. and Margolis, L. (1985). Effects of temperature and salinity on the course of infection with the haemoflagellate *Cryptobia salmositica* in juvenile Pacific salmon (*Oncorhynchus* spp.). *Journal of Fish Disease* **8,** 25–33.

Bower, S. M. and Woo, P. T. K. (1977a). Morphology and host specificity of *Cryptobia catostomi* n.sp. (Protozoa: Kinetoplastida) from white sucker (*Catostomus commersoni*) in southern Ontario. *Canadian Journal of Zoology* **55,** 1082–1092.

Bower, S. M. and Woo, P. T. K. (1977b). Division and morphogenesis of *Cryptobia catostomi* (Protozoa: Kinetoplastida) in the blood of white sucker (*Catostomus commersoni*). *Canadian Journal of Zoology* **55,** 1093–1099.

Bower, S. M. and Woo, P. T. K. (1977c). *Cryptobia catostomi*: incubation in plasma of susceptible and refractory fishes. *Experimental Parasitology* **43,** 63–68.

Bower, S. M. and Woo, P. T. K. (1981a). Two new species of trypanosomes (subgenus *Schizotrypanum*) in bats from southern Ontario. *Canadian Journal of Zoology* **59,** 530–545.

Bower, S. M. and Woo, P. T. K. (1981b). An *in vitro* comparison of *Trypanosoma* spp. (subgenus *Schizotrypanum*) from bats. *Systematic Parasitology* **3,** 217–235.

Bower, S. M. and Woo, P. T. K. (1982). Immunological comparison of four *Trypanosoma* spp. (subgenus *Schizotrypanum*) from bats. *Parasitology* **85,** 111–114.

Britchuk, P. F. (1969). [*Cryptobia cyprini* Plehn, 1903 (Flagellata, Bodonidae) as a cause of mortality of *Ctenopharyngodon idella* Val.] *Parazitologiya* **3,** 574–576.

Brugerolle, G., Lom. J., Nohynkova, E. and Joyon, L. (1979). Comparison et évolution des structures cellulaires chez plusieurs espèces de bodonides et cryptobiides appartenant aux genres *Bodo*, *Cryptobia* et *Trypanoplasma* (Kinetoplastida, Mastigophora). *Protistologica* **15,** 197–221.

Brumpt, E. (1906). Expériences relatives au mode de transmission des trypanosomes et trypanoplasmes par les Hirudinées. *Comptes Rendus des Séances de la Société de Biologie* **61,** 11–19.

Bullock, W. (1952). The occurrence of a species of *Cryptobia* (Protomonadina) in the blood of a marine fish. *Journal of Parasitology* **38,** 26.

Bullock, W. (1953). An interesting blood parasite of a New Hampshire fish. *Proceedings of the New Hampshire Academy of Science* **2,** 7–8.

Burreson, E. M. (1979). Structure and life cycle of *Trypanoplasma beckeri* sp.n. (Kinetoplastida), a parasite of the cabezon, *Scorpaenichthys marmoratus*, in Oregon coastal waters. *Journal of Protozoology* **26,** 343–347.

Burreson, E. M. (1982a). The life cycle of *Trypanoplasma bullocki* (Zoomastigophorea: Kinetoplastida). *Journal of Protozoology* **29,** 72–77.

Burreson, E. M. (1982b). Trypanoplasmiasis in flounder along the Atlantic coast of the United States. *In* "Les antigènes des micro-organismes pathogènes des poissons" (D. P. Anderson, M. Dorson and Ph. Dubourget, eds), pp. 251–260. Collection Fondation Marcel Merieux.

Burreson, E. M. and Frizzell, L. J. (1986). The seasonal antibody response in juvenile summer flounder (*Paralichthys dentatus*) to the hemoflagellate *Trypanoplasma bullocki. Veterinary Immunology and Immunopathology* **12**, 395–402.

Burreson, E. M. and Sypek, J. P. (1981). *Cryptobia* sp. (Mastigophorea: Kinetoplastida) from the gills of marine fishes in the Chesapeake Bay. *Journal of Fish Disease* **4,** 519–522.

Burreson, E. M. and Zwerner, D. E. (1982). The role of host biology, vector biology, and temperature in the distribution of *Trypanoplasma bullocki* infections in the lower Chesapeake Bay. *Journal of Parasitology* **68,** 306–313.

Burreson, E. M. and Zwerner, D. E. (1984). Juvenile summer flounder, *Paralichthys dentatus*, mortalities in western Atlantic Ocean caused by the hemoflagellate *Trypanoplasma bullocki*: evidence from field and experimental studies. *Heligolander Meeresunters* **37,** 343–352.

Chen, C. L. (1956). The protozoan parasites from four species of Chinese pond fishes: *Ctenopharyngodon idellus*, *Mylopharyngodon piceus*, *Aristhictys nobillis* and *Hypophthalmichthys molithrix*. II. The protozoan parasites of *Mylopharyngodon piceus*. *Acta Hydrobiology Sinica* **1,** 19–42.

Crawley, H. (1909). Studies on blood parasites: II. The priority of *Cryptobia* Leidy 1846 over *Trypanoplasma* Laveran and Mesnil, 1901. *Bulletin of the US Bureau of Animal Industry* **119,** 16–20.

Current, W. L (1980). *Cryptobia* sp. in the snail *Triadopsis multilineata* (Say): fine structure of attached flagellates and their mode of attachment to the spermatheca. *Journal of Protozoology* **27,** 278–287.

Daily, D. D. (1978). Marine fish hematozoa from Maine. *Journal of Parasitology* **64,** 361–362.

Davis, H. S. (1947). Studies of the protozoan parasites of freshwater fishes. *United States Department of the Interior Fishery Bulletin* **51,** 1–29.

Diesing, K. M. (1850). "Systema helminthum". Vol. 1, XIII, Vindobonae.

Dykova, I. and Lom, J. (1979). Histopathological changes in *Trypanosoma danilewskyi* Laveran and Mesnil, 1904 and *Trypanoplasma borelli* Laveran & Mesnil 1902 infections of goldfish, *Carassius aurata* (L.). *Journal of Fish Diseases* **2,** 381–390.

Elmhirst, R. and Martin, C. H. (1910). On a *Trypanoplasma* from the stomach of the conger eel (*Conger niger*). *Zoologische Anzeiger* **35,** 475–477.

Fantham, H. B., and Porter, A. (1910). On a new trypanoplasm, *T. dendrocoeli* sp.n. from *Dendrocoelum lacteum*. *Proceedings of the Zoological Society of London* **2,** 670–671.

Foster, W. D. (1965). "A History of Parasitology". Livingstone, Edinburgh and London.

Guseinov, M. A. (1982). [Blood parasites of fish in the Divichin Bay of the Caspian Sea and their ecology.] *Izvestiya Akademii Nauk Azerbaidzhanskoi SSSR, Biologicheskie Nauki* No. 1, 60–63.

Havelka, J., Tesarcik, J. and Volf, F. (1965). [Research of antiparasitic and antifungal control measurements. I. Investigation of the action of new antiparasitic medicaments on *Cryptobia cyprini* Plehn, 1903 (syn. *Trypanoplasma cyprini* Plehn, 1903)]. *Vyzkumny Ustav Rybarsky a Hydrobiologicky, Vodnany* **5,** 67–87.

Hesse, E. (1910). *Trypanoplasma vaginalis* n.sp., parasite du vagin de la sangsue. *Comptes Rendus Hebdomadaires des Séances de l'Académie des Sciences, Paris* **151,** 504–505.

Hoffman, G. L. (1978). *Bodomonas concava*, a cryptic cryptogram for crippling *Cryptobia branchialis*. *American Fisheries Society, Fish Health Section Newsletter* **6,** 9.

Houghton, G. and Matthews, R. A. (1985). Immunosuppression of juvenile carp (*Cyprinus carpio* L.) to the parasite *Ichthyophthirius multifiliis* induced by a corticosteriod. *Abstracts, International Meeting on Fish Immunology, Sandy Hook, New Jersey*, p. 53.

Hovasse, R. (1924). *Trypanoplasma sagittae* sp. nov. *Comptes Rendus des Séances de la Société de Biologie* **91,** 1254–1255.

Jayasri, M. and Parvateesam, M. (1982). *Cryptobia indica* n.sp. (Protozoa: Kinetoplastida) ectoparasite on the gills of *Puntius sarana* (Ham). *Current Science* **51,** 797–798.

Jones, S. R. M. and Woo, P. T. K. (1986). Acquired immunity against *Cryptobia salmositica* in rainbow trout, *Salmo gairdneri. Abstracts, Sixth International Congress of Parasitology, Brisbane, Australia.*

Jones, S. M., Woo, P. T. K. and Stevenson, R. M. W. (1986). Immunosuppression in *Salmo gairdneri* caused by the haemoflagellate *Cryptobia salmositica. Journal of Fish Diseases* **9**, 431–438.

Katz, M. (1951). Two new hemoflagellates (genus *Cryptobia*) from some western Washington teleosts. *Journal of Parasitology* **37,** 245–250.

Katz, M., Woodey, J. C., Becker, C. D., Woo, P. T. K. and Adams, J. R. (1966). Records of *Cryptobia salmositica* from sockeye salmon from the Fraser River drainage and from the State of Washington. *Journal of the Fisheries Research Board of Canada* **23,** 1965–1966.

Keysselitz, G. (1906). Generations und Wirtswechsel von *Trypanoplasma borreli* Laveran und Mesnil. *Archiv für Protistenkunde* **7,** 1–74.

Khaibulaev, K. Kh. and Guseinov, M. A. (1982). [Experimental study on the biology of some flagellates from the genera *Trypanosoma* Gruby 1841 (Trypanosomidae Doflein, 1911) and *Cryptobia* Leidy 1846 (Bodonidae Stern 1878).] *Izvestiya Akademii Nauk Azerbaidzhanskoi SSR, Biologicheskie Nauki* No. 2, 87–91.

Khaibulaev, K. Kh. and Guseinov, M. A. (1985). [Development of *Trypanosoma* and *Cryptobia* of carp and tench in the leech *Piscocola geometra*.] *Parazitologia* **19,** 75–77.

Khan, R. A. and Noble, E. R. (1972). Taxonomy, prevalence, and specificity of *Cryptobia dahli* (Mobius) (Mastigophora: Bodonidae) in lumpfish, *Cyclopterus lumpus. Journal of the Fisheries Research Board of Canada* **29,** 1291–1294.

Khan, R. A., Moyles, D. and Bal, A. K. (1980). Observations on the fine structure of a flagellated protozoan, *Cryptobia dahli. Proceedings of 7th Annual Meeting, Microscopical Society of Canada* **7,** 50–51.

Kipp, H. (1968). "Untersuchungen zum Vorkommen, zur Artsspezifität und Pathogenität der Cryptobien und Trypanosomen bei der Schleie (*Tinca tinca* L.)." Inaugural-Dissertation, Tierärztliche Fakultät der Ludwig Maximilians Universität, München.

Knittel, M. D. (1981). Susceptibility of steelhead trout *Salmo gairdneri* Richardson to redmouth infection *Yersinia ruckeri* following exposure to copper. *Journal of Fish Disease* **4,** 33–40.

Krettli, A. U. and Pereira, F. E. L. (1981). Immunosuppression in protozoal infections. *In* "Biochemistry and Physiology of Protozoa", edition 2 (M. Levandowsky and S. H. Hutner, eds), Vol. 4, pp. 431–462. Academic Press, New York.

Kozloff, E. N. (1948). The morphology of *Cryptobia helicis* Leidy, with an account of the fate of the extranuclear organelles in division. *Journal of Morphology* **83,** 253–279.

Laird, M. (1961). Parasites from northern Canada: II. Haematozoa of fishes. *Canadian Journal of Zoology* **39,** 541–548.

Laird, M. and Bullock, W. H. (1969). Marine fish hematozoa from New Brunswick and New England. *Journal of the Fisheries Research Board of Canada* **26,** 1075–1102.

Laudan, R., Stolen, J. S. and Cali, A. (1985). The immune response of a marine teleost, *Pseudopleuronectes americanus* (winter flounder), to the protozoan parasite *Glugea stephani. Abstracts, International Meeting on Fish Immunology, Sandy Hook, New Jersey*, p. P2.

Laveran, A. (1904). Trypanoplasme et trypanosome du varion. *Comptes Rendus des Séances de la Société de Biologie* **57,** 250–251.

Laveran, A. and Mesnil, F. (1901). Sur les flagellés à membrane ondulante des poissons (genres *Trypanosoma* Gruby et *Trypanoplasma* n.gen.). *Comptes Rendus Hebdomadaires des Séances de l'Académie des Sciences, Paris* **133,** 670–675.

Laveran, A. and Mesnil, F. (1902a). Sur le mode de multiplication des trypanosomes des poissons. *Comptes Rendus Hebdomadaires des Séances de l'Académie des Sciences, Paris* **134,** 1405–1409.

Laveran, A. and Mesnil, F. (1902b). Des trypanosomes des poissons. *Archiv für Protistenkunde* **1,** 475–498.

Laveran, A. and Mesnil, F. (1912). "Trypanosomes et Trypanosomiases", edition 2. Masson, Paris.

Léger, L. (1904a). Sur la morphologie du *Trypanoplasma* du varions. *Comptes Rendus Hebdomadaires des Séances de l'Académie des Sciences, Paris* **138,** 824–825.

Léger, L. (1904b). Sur la structure et les affinités des trypanoplasmes. *Comptes Rendus Hebdomadaires des Séances de l'Académie des Sciences, Paris* **138,** 856–859.

Léger, L. (1904c). *Trypanoplasm varium,* n.sp., parasite du sang de *Cobitis barbatula* L. *Comptes Rendus des Séances de la Société de Biologie* **57,** 345–347.

Léger, L. (1905). Sur la presence d'un *Trypanoplasma* intestinal chez les poissons. *Comptes Rendus des Séances de la Société de Biologie* **58,** 511–513.

Leidy, J. (1846). Description of a new genus and species of Entozoa. *Proceedings of the Academy of Natural Sciences of Philadelphia* **3,** 100–101.

Leidy, J. (1847). *Cryptobia* changed to *Cryptoicus. Proceedings of the Academy of Natural Sciences of Philadelphia* **3,** 239 [in Secretary's abstract].

Lom, J. (1971). Experimental infection of goldfish with blood flagellates. *Progress in Protozoology, Proceedings of the 4th International Congress on Protozoology*, p. 255.

Lom, J. (1979). Biology of the trypanosomes and trypanoplasms of fish. *In* "Biology of the Kinetoplastida" (W. H. R. Lumsden and D. A. Evans, eds), Vol. 2, pp. 269–337. Academic Press, London.

Lom, J. (1980). *Cryptobia branchialis* Nie from fish gills: ultrastructural evidence of ectocommensal function. *Journal of Fish Disease* **3,** 427–436.

Lom, J. and Nohynkova, E. (1977). Surface coat of the bloodstream phase of *Trypanoplasma borelli. Journal of Protozoology* **24,** 52A.

Lowe-Jinde, L. (1979). Some observations of rainbow trout, *Salmo gairdneri* Richardson, infected with *Cryptobia salmositica. Journal of Fish Biology* **14,** 297–302.

Lowe-Jinde, L. (1980). Observations of rainbow trout, *Salmo gairdneri* Richardson, infected with *Cryptobia salmositica. Journal of Fish Biology* **17,** 23–30.

Makeyeva, A. O. (1956). On one of the factors of prespawning mortality of pink salmon in rivers. *In* "Pacific Salmon", pp. 18–21. Israel Program for Scientific Translation, Jerusalem (1961); Office of Technical Service, U.S. Department of Commerce, Washington, D.C.

Martin, C. H. (1910). Observations on *Trypanoplasma congeri.* Part1. The division of the active form. *Quarterly Journal of Microscopical Science* **55,** 485–496.

Martin, C. H. (1913). Further observations on the intestinal trypanoplasmas of fishes, with a note on the division of *Trypanoplasma cyprini* in the crop of a leech. *Quarterly Journal of Microscopical Science* **59,** 175–195.

Mavor, J. M. (1915). On the occurrence of a trypanoplasma, probably *Trypanoplasma borreli* Laveran et Mesnil, in the blood of the common sucker *Catostomus commersoni*. *Journal of Parasitology* **2,** 1–6.

Migala, K. (1967). [A *Cryptobia* (*Trypanoplasma*) infection in the blood of *Ctenopharyngodon idella* Val. bred in the carp from ponds.] *Wiadomosci Parazytologiczne* **13,** 275–278.

Migala, K. (1971). [Observations on the infection by protozoa from the genus *Cryptobia* (*Trypanoplasma*) in the blood–vascular system of grass carp (*Ctenopharyngodon idella* Val.) bred in carp ponds.] *Roczniki Nauk Rolniczych* **93,** 65–73.

Minchin, E. A. (1909). Observations on the flagellates parasitic in the blood of freshwater fishes. *Proceedings of the Zoological Society of London* **1,** 2–31.

Möbius, K. (1888). Bruchstücke einer Infusorienfauna der Kieler Bucht. *Archiv für Naturgeschichte* **54,** 81–116.

Naumova, A. M. (1969). [Parasitism of *Cryptobia branchialis* on carps.] *In* "Rybovodstvo i Bolezni Ryb", pp. 253–254. Kolos, Moscow.

Noble, E. R. (1968). The flagellates in two species of deep sea fishes from the eastern Pacific. *Journal of Parasitology* **54,** 720–724.

Newman, M. W. (1978). Pathology associated with *Cryptobia* infection in a summer flounder (*Paralichthys dentatus*). *Journal of Wildlife Diseases* **14,** 299–304.

Nigrelli, R. F., Pokorny, K. S. and Ruggieri, C. D. (1975). Studies on parasitic kinetoplastids. II. Occurrence of a biflagellate kinetoplastid in the blood of *Opsanus tau* (toadfish) transmitted by the leech (*Piscicola funduli*). *Journal of Protozoology* **22,** Supplement, 43A.

Nowicki, E. (1940). Zur pathogenität der *Trypanoplasma cyprini*. *Zeitschrift für Parasitenkunde* **11,** 468–473.

Nohynkova, E. (1984). A new pathogenic *Cryptobia* from freshwater fishes: a light and electron microscope study. *Protistologica* **20,** 181–195.

Obradovic, J. and Fijan, N. (1979). [Attempted treatment of cryptobiosis in the carp by methylene blue and pirovet.] *Veterinarski Archiv* **49,** 99–102.

Paterson, W. B. and Woo, P. T. K. (1983). Electron microscopic observations of the bloodstream form of *Cryptobia salmositica* Katz 1951 (Kinetoplastida: Bodonina). *Journal of Protozoology* **30,** 431–437.

Paterson, W. B. and Woo, P. T. K. (1984). Ultrastructural studies on mitosis in *Trypanosoma danilewskyi* (Mastigophora: Zoomastigophorea). *Canadian Journal of Zoology* **62,** 1167–1171.

Plehn, M. (1903). *Trypanoplasma cyprini* nov. sp. *Archiv für Protistenkunde* **3,** 175–180.

Plehn, M. (1924). "Praktikum der Fischkrankheiten". E. Schweizerbartische Verlagsbuchhandlung, Stuttgart.

Ponselle, A. (1913a). *In vitro* culture de trypanosomes et trypanoplasmes. *Compte Rendu Hebdomadaire des Séances de la Société de Biologie* **74,** 339.

Ponselle, A. (1913b). Culture *in vitro* de *Trypanoplasma varium*. *Compte Rendu Hebdomadaire des Séances de la Société de Biologie* **74,** 685–688.

Putz, R. E. (1972a). *Cryptobia cataractae* sp. n. (Kinetoplastida: Cryptobiidae) a hemoflagellate of some cyprinid fishes of West Virginia. *Proceedings of the Helminthological Society of Washington* **39,** 18–22.

Putz, R. E. (1972b). Biological studies on the hemoflagellates *Cryptobia cataractae* and *Cryptobia salmositica*. *Technical Papers of the Bureau of Sport, Fisheries and Wildlife* **63,** 3–25.

Qadri, S. S. (1962). *Trypanoplasma willoughbii* sp. n. from British freshwater fish, *Salvelinus willoughbii. Rivista di Parassitologia* **23,** 1–9.

Rijkers, G. T., Teunissen, A. G., van Oosterom, R. and van Muiswinkel, W. B. (1980). The immune system of cyprinid fish. The immunosuppressive effect of the antibiotic oxytetracycline in carp (*Cyprinus carpio*). *Aquaculture* **19,** 177–189.

Robertson, M. (1911). Transmission of flagellates living in the blood of freshwater fishes. *Philosophical Transactions of the Royal Society of London, Series B* **202,** 29–50.

Sawyer, R. T., Lawler, A. R. and Overstreet, R. M. (1975). Marine leeches of the eastern United States and the Gulf of Mexico with a key to the species. *Journal of Natural History* **9,** 633–667.

Shul'man, S. S. (1984). ["Keys to parasites of freshwater fish". Vol. I: "Parasitic Protozoa"] (Abstract no. 4144 in *Protozoological Abstracts* **8,** 465.)

Sloan, N. A., Bower, S. M. and Robinson, S. M. C. (1984). Cocoon deposition on three crab species and fish parasitism by leech *Notostomum cyclostoma* from deep fjords in northern British Columbia. *Marine Ecology* **20,** 51–58.

Strout, R. G. (1962). A method for concentrating hemoflagellates. *Journal of Parasitology* **48,** 110.

Strout, R. G. (1965). A new hemoflagellate (genus *Cryptobia*) from marine fishes of northern New England. *Journal of Parasitology* **51,** 654–659.

Swezy, O. (1916). The kinetonucleus of flagellates and the binuclear theory of Hartman. *University of California Publications in Zoology* **16,** 185–240.

Swezy, O. (1919). The occurrence of *Trypanoplasma* as an ectoparasite. *Transactions of the American Microscopical Society* **38,** 20–24.

Sypek, J. P. and Burreson, E. M. (1983). Influence of temperature on the immune response of juvenile flounder, *Paralichthys dentatus*, and its role in the elimination of *Trypanoplasma bullocki* infections. *Developmental and Comparative Immunology* **7,** 277–286.

Sypek, J. P. and Howe, A. B. (1985). *Trypanoplasma bullocki*: natural infections in winter flounder, *Pseudopleuronectes americanus. Abstracts, International Meeting on Fish Immunology, Sandy Hook, New Jersey*, p. P3.

Tanabe, M. (1924). Studies on the hemoflagellata of the loach, *Misgurnus anguillicaudatus. Kitasato Archives of Experimental Medicine* **6,** 121–128.

Taylor, A. E. R., Edwards, Y. H., Smith, V., Baker, J. R., Woo, P. T. K., Lanham, S. M. and Pennick, N. C. (1982). *Trypanosoma* (*Schizotrypanum*) species from insectivorous bats (Michrochiroptera): characterization by poplypeptide profiles. *Systematic Parasitology* **4,** 155–168.

Tripathi, Y. R. (1954). Studies on parasites of Indian fishes III. Protozoa 2 (Mastigophora and Ciliophora). *Records of the Indian Museum (Calcutta)* **52,** 221–230.

Vickerman, K. (1971). Morphological and physiological considerations of extracellular blood protozoa. *In* "Physiology and Ecology of Parasites" (A. M. Fallis, ed.), pp. 59–91. Toronto University Press, Toronto.

Vickerman, K. (1977). DNA throughout the single mitochondrion of a kinetoplastid flagellate: observations of the ultrastructure of *Cryptobia vaginalis* (Hesse, 1910). *Journal of Protozoology* **24,** 221–233.

Vickerman, K. (1978). The free-living trypanoplasma: description of three species of the genus *Procryptobia* n. g. and redescription of *Dimastigella trypaniformis* Sandon, with notes on their relevance to the microscopical diagnosis of disease in man and animals. *Transactions of the American Microscopical Society* **97,** 485–502.

Wahul, M. A. (1985). Four new species of trypanoplasms from freshwater fishes of the genus *Mystus* in Maharashtra. *Proceedings of the Indian Academy of Sciences, Animal Sciences* **94,** 25–35.
Wales, J. H. and Wolf, H. (1955). Three protozoan diseases of trout in California. *California Fish and Game* **41,** 183–187.
Wehnert, S. D. and Woo, P. T. K. (1980). *In vivo* and *in vitro* studies on the host specificity of *Trypanoplasma salmositica. Journal of Wildlife Diseases* **16,** 183–187.
Wehnert, S. D. and Woo, P. T. K. (1981). The immune response of *Salmo gairdneri* during *Trypanoplasma salmositica* infection. *Bulletin of the Canadian Society of Zoologists* **12,** 100. [Abstract.]
Wenrich, D. H. (1931). A trypanoplasm on the gills of carp from the Schuylkill River. *Journal of Parasitology* **18,** 133.
Wenyon, C. M. (1926). "Protozoology". Vol. 1. Baillière, Tindall and Cox, London.
Woo, P. T. K. (1969). The haemocrit centrifuge for the detection of trypanosomes in blood. *Canadian Journal of Zoology* **47,** 921–923.
Woo, P. T. K. (1978). The division process of *Cryptobia salmositica* in experimentally infected rainbow trout (*Salmo gairdneri*). *Canadian Journal of Zoology* **56,** 1514–1518.
Woo, P. T. K. (1979). *Trypanoplasma salmositica*: experimental infections in rainbow trout, *Salmo gairdneri. Experimental Parasitology* **47,** 36–48.
Woo, P. T. K. (1981). *Trypanosoma danilewskyi*: a new multiplication process for *Trypanosoma* (Protozoa: Kinetoplastida). *Journal of Parasitology* **67,** 522–526.
Woo, P. T. K. and Bartlett, C. M. (1982). *Trypanosoma ontarioensis* n.sp. and *T. paddae* from *Corvus brachyrhynchos brachyrhynchos* in Ontario, Canada, with notes on the biology of *T. ontarioensis* n.sp. *Canadian Journal of Zoology* **60,** 2107–2115.
Woo, P. T. K. and Black, G. A. (1984). *Trypanosoma danilewskyi*: host specificity and host's effects on morphometrics. *Journal of Parasitology* **70,** 788–793.
Woo, P. T. K. and Bogart, J. P. (1984). *Trypanosoma* spp. (Protozoa: Kinetoplastida) in Hylidae (Anura) from eastern North America, with notes on their distributions and prevalences. *Canadian Journal of Zoology* **62,** 820–824.
Woo, P. T. K. and Bogart, J. P. (1986). Trypanosome infection in salamanders (order: Caudata) from eastern North America, with notes on the biology of *Trypanosoma ogawai* in *Ambystoma maculatum. Canadian Journal of Zoology* **64,** 121–127.
Woo, P. T. K. and Rogers, D. J. (1974). A statistical study of the sensitivity of the haematocrit centrifuge technique in the detection of trypanosomes in blood. *Transactions of the Royal Society of Tropical Medicine and Hygiene* **68,** 319–326.
Woo, P. T. K. and Wehnert, S. D. (1983). Direct transmission of a hemoflagellate, *Cryptobia salmositica* (Kinetoplastida: Bodonina) between rainbow trout under laboratory conditions. *Journal of Protozoology* **30,** 334–337.
Woo, P. T. K. and Wehnert, S. D. (1986). *Cryptobia salmositica*: susceptibility of infected rainbow trout, *Salmo gairdneri*, to environmental hypoxia. *Journal of Parasitology* **72,** 392–396.
Woo, P. T. K., Grant, D. R. and McLean, L. (1980). Trypanosomes of small mammals in southern Ontario. *Canadian Journal of Zoology* **58,** 567–571.
Woo, P. T. K., Wehnert, S. D. and Rodgers, D. (1983). The susceptibility of fishes to haemoflagellates at different ambient temperatures. *Parasitology* **87,** 385–392.
Woo, P. T. K., Baker, J. R. and Selden, L. F. (1985). DNA buoyant densities of *Trypanosoma* (*Schizotrypanum*) species from bats in Ontario, Canada. *Systematic Parasitology* **6,** 75–79.

Woo, P. T. K., Leatherland, J. F. and Lee, M. S. (in press). *Cryptobia salmositica*: cortisol increases the susceptibility of *Salmo gairdneri* fry to experimental cryptobiosis. *Journal of Fish Diseases*.

Woodcock, H. M. and Lodge, O. (1921). Protozoa. Part I. Parasitic Protozoa. *British Antarctic ("Terra Nova") Expedition, 1910, Natural History Report, Zoology* **6,** 1–24.

The Nature and Action of Host Signals

R. I. SOMMERVILLE AND W. P. ROGERS

Department of Zoology, University of Adelaide, Australia and Department of Plant Physiology, Waite Agricultural Research Institute, Glen Osmond, South Australia

ADVANCES IN PARASITOLOGY VOL. 26
ISBN 0-12-031726-5

*Copyright © 1987 Academic Press Inc. (London) Ltd.
All rights of reproduction in any form reserved.*

I. Introduction

In this paper we discuss firstly those features of the environment that act as the signals, or stimuli, which govern the development and behaviour of parasites within the host, and secondly, the mechanisms by which the signals provoke these responses. This is a wide field and its literature, though voluminous, generally gives only fragmentary information from which it is difficult, as yet, to provide satisfying generalizations. We have therefore directed our attention chiefly to one aspect with which we are most familiar: the natural history and physiology of host signals that govern the development of early parasitic stages of nematodes which infect animals *per os*. Host signals which affect other parasites are considered more briefly. This is not an exhaustive review of a whole field. Rather, we have examined one aspect in some detail in an attempt to obtain generalizations, some highly speculative, which may stimulate further work.

II. The Natural History of Host Signals

The environments of animals strongly influence the processes which govern development, reproduction and behaviour. Generally, animals live in environments which do not vary greatly. Except in the embryonic stages, for which especially stable environments are needed, their complex organization normally permits adaptations to meet most diurnal and seasonal changes. The environment thus provides signals to which the organism responds in an adaptive manner.

Within limits, the intensity of the response is related to the intensity of the signal and it starts and stops roughly in step with this signal. These changes are generally mediated via complex endocrine and nervous systems. They are confined largely to physiological changes; morphological responses are minimal, temporary, and reversible. Thus, they are most apparent in animals with simple, direct life cycles. In contrast, the more marked changes seen in animals which, during the post-embryonic life of the individual, move, for example, from an aquatic to a terrestrial environment, or from a free-living to a parasitic habitat, are governed by signals which usually induce more far-reaching modifications or metamorphoses. The most profound changes of this sort are seen in animals with complex life cycles, such as the arthropods. Here, adaptations to different environments occur in well defined, specific stages of the life cycle.

It is difficult to generalize on the nature of the signals which govern the changes from one stage of these life cycles to another. Some may be innate; others come from the external environment, as seen in the life cycles of the

Trematoda. In this group of parasites profound morphological changes occur when the infective stage enters the proper host; the ciliated miracidium becomes the sporocyst and the cercaria or metacercaria becomes the young adult. In the absence of the host, the miracidia and cercariae die, the former after a few hours, although metacercariae may live for months. Clearly the host provides an environment essential for further development as well as the signal which induces the physiological and morphological changes necessary for the exploitation of that environment. The form of the host's signal is not obvious. The changes it initiates give little indication of its nature—physical or chemical, simple or complex? Its effects are rapid, irreversible, and specific.

In addition to signals which induce development of early parasitic stages, hosts must provide the signals which affect some other aspects of development and behaviour, e.g. the development of later stages, and migration in host tissues. Some signals that affect these processes, however, may be innate, or may result from the secretion of pheromones (Bone, 1982).

This article is primarily concerned with host signals and their effects in starting the development of early parasitic stages. This is because we believe that these changes—from the free-living infective stage to parasite, or from parasitic infective stage in one host to parasite in another, different species of host—are fundamental in the development of parasitism. We have chosen to write chiefly about nematodes because we have studied this group most, and because it provides the opportunity to compare life cycles of entirely free-living species with those which are partly, or entirely, parasitic.

III. Host Signals and Oral Infection with Nematodes

Nematodes as a group show relatively minor morphological changes throughout their life cycles. Like the apterygote insects, they do not undergo a classical metamorphosis so the early stages are juveniles, not larvae (Hyman, 1951; Poinar, 1983). The form of the life cycle (egg, four juvenile instars or stages, and an adult, consistently punctuated by four moults) strongly suggests a rigidly controlled pattern of development in which the growth profile is correlated with the moults (Wilson, 1976).

In this article we refer to the freeing of the cuticle, or sheath, from the underlying hypodermis, as apolysis, and its subsequent casting as exsheathment or ecdysis. In the life cycle of a parasite, we regard the term "stage" as equivalent to "instar". Each moult involves changes in the hypodermis (Bird, 1971) and apolysis. Ecdysis may be an early feature in the development of the next instar (Rogers and Petronijevic, 1982). Unlike many other parasites, the stages of the life cycle which are infective vary with different species of nematode.

The infective stage is the agent by which the parasite moves from one environment to another. Thus adaptation to a parasitic life involves an infective stage with two main features: (a) it must survive long enough to allow sufficient opportunity for contacting the host, and (b) it must have the capacity to develop rapidly into a stage suitable for a different environment — that is different in temperature, nutrients, availability of water or oxygen, and so on. Juveniles of nematodes are "pre-adapted" to suit these conditions. Thus, the change from one juvenile stage to the next may involve a period of "modest dormancy", i.e. a hypometabolic state in which cells await conditions suitable for continued growth (Busa and Nuccitelli, 1984), and which is ended by an innate or external stimulus. The prolonging of this dormancy by increasing the threshold for the action of the stimulus may provide a stage in the life cycle in which the endocrine system which controls ecdysis and hatching is inactive, thus causing the retention of protective coverings. Furthermore, the gene set of the next stage which is suited to new environment is present, but inactive (Rogers and Petronijevic, 1982).

Ecdysis or hatching of an infective stage is a relatively rapid process, usually completed within a few hours and often in less than an hour. On the other hand, the early morphological changes of development are more difficult to detect and usually become evident only after several days. For this reason most studies on the nature of host signals for infection have been based on the success or failure to elicit ecdysis or hatching. This, in some instances, has given misleading results (see Section III B).

A. HOST SIGNALS AS PHYSIOLOGICAL TRIGGERS

Exposure to the signal for periods of less than an hour *in vitro* or *in vivo* is sufficient to induce an irreversible response which can often be maintained in simple media in the absence of the signal. The signal then, acts as a stimulus, a first messenger, or as a "physiological trigger" (Rogers and Sommerville, 1963). It switches on mechanisms that produce diverse results which, with our present knowledge, cannot be related directly to the nature of the signal. Once the system is switched on, factors in the environment other than the signal determine the success or otherwise of the processes of development.

The capacity to respond to the signal which initiates development of the early parasitic stage of nematodes must occur during the period when one stage of development has been terminated and the next has not yet commenced. This is true of many other parasites as well. It seems reasonable to suppose, then, that the signals and their systems of response which determine infection may be related to those processes which occur during the life cycles of unspecialized, free-living species when they pass from one instar to the next.

B. THE NATURE OF THE STIMULUS FOR ORAL INFECTION

This problem has been studied mostly by experiments *in vitro*, but authors generally relate the conditions they use to those which prevail *in vivo*. One action of the stimulus is to induce the secretion of ecdysial and hatching enzymes (Rogers, 1982). The ecdysial enzyme, in its action on its natural substrate, is exposed to substances in the medium which may inactivate it. Such experiments may therefore give false negative results. Generally, however, this procedure gives reasonable results; the measure of exsheathment or hatching as an indication of the efficiency of a stimulus seems reasonable.

The infective stages of some 22 species of nematodes (trichostrongylids, ascarids, trichurids and one oxyurid: Lackie, 1975) have been used to examine the stimulus for exsheathment and hatching of the parasites of homeothermic animals. Unfortunately, much of this work has been concerned with limited sets of conditions which do not assist greatly in establishing generalizations (Rogers and Sommerville, 1968). Salt solutions of appropriate osmotic pressure, usually at pH values near neutrality, 38° C, and gas phases of CO_2/air or CO_2/N_2 have been used. Studies with parasites which are stimulated to start development in the stomach of the host have been carried out using HCl, pH 2–3, in the medium (Christie and Charleston, 1965). Less common additives to the medium include sodium borate, pepsin and carbonic anhydrase.

1. *The role of H_2CO_3*

Of the infective stages which have been studied, most responded to CO_2 in the gas phase (some exceptions are discussed below). Generally, activity has been related to pCO_2 (Taylor and Whitlock, 1960; Smales and Sommerville, 1977) and sometimes to the concentration of dissolved gaseous CO_2 plus undissociated H_2CO_3 (Rogers, 1960; Bailey, 1968). That other components in the aqueous phase generated by CO_2 in the gas phase ($CO_2 + H_2O \rightleftarrows H_2CO_3 \rightleftarrows H^+ + HCO_3^- \rightleftarrows 2H^+ + CO_3^{2-}$) might act as the stimulus seems unlikely. Thus, although dissolved gaseous CO_2 and undissociated H_2CO_3 generally pass freely through biological membranes, the major hydration products of CO_2, namely protons, bicarbonate and carbonate ions, have a low permeability (Roos and Boron, 1981) and this applies to the nematode cuticle, which has a low permeability to ions generally (Wright and Newall, 1976; Marks *et al.*, 1968). Moreover bicarbonate ions do not act as a stimulus (Rogers, 1960; Petronijevic *et al.*, 1985). Nevertheless it is the physical chemistry of the overall system which is important in assessing the biological roles of the components.

In sodium chloride solutions at 38° C more than 99% of the dissolved CO_2 from the gas phase is in its original form; the H_2CO_3 plus HCO_3^- and CO_3^{2-} constitute less than 1% of the dissolved material. And over a wide range of pH values, the molal ratio, dissolved gaseous CO_2/H_2CO_3, is about 400/1 (Lindskog *et al.*, 1971). Thus, the concentration of undissociated H_2CO_3 is very low. The pK for the overall reaction is 6.06 at 38° C in 100 mM NaCl and the $pK_{H_2CO_3}$ is about 3.7. The rate constants are also important. The process of hydration of CO_2 and dehydration of H_2CO_3 require appreciable time ($k_{H_2CO_3}$ = 89/second, k_{CO_2} = 0.131/second), so much so that they are of critical importance in many biological processes (Roughton, 1941; Edsall and Wyman, 1958). However, the reaction $H_2CO_3 \rightleftharpoons H^+ + HCO_3^-$ is very fast and provides a source of "readily available", undissociated H_2CO_3 which can be further increased in the presence of carbonic anhydrase (k_{cat} for bovine carbonic anhydrase = 10^6/second; Kernohan, 1965). Sodium borate (as $H_2BO_3^-$) also catalyses the hydration of CO_2 (Roughton and Booth, 1938). The fact that this substance increased the effect of CO_2 in the gas phase as a stimulus led to the initial suggestion that the undissociated acid might be the important factor (Taylor and Whitlock, 1960).

Other considerations suggest that the "readily available" H_2CO_3 (or $H_2CO_3 + H^+ + HCO_3^-$) may provide a better basis for estimating the activity of the stimulus (Petronijevic *et al.*, 1986). This proposal provides explanations for a number of observations: (a) CO_2 in the gas phase may produce an effective stimulus over much of the pH range 2–8; (b) low pCO_2 values may be effective when the pH is low; (c) at higher pH values a given pCO_2 becomes more effective as the pH rises, and (d) catalysts of the reaction $CO_2 + H_2O \rightleftharpoons H_2CO_3$ increase the efficiency of CO_2 in the gas phase, especially when both pH and pCO_2 are low. The proposal that "readily available" H_2CO_3 is the active agent in the stimulus may also explain the differences in the effects of pH on the activity of the stimulus for infective juveniles and infective eggs (Rogers, 1960). Thus, with infective juveniles of *Haemonchus contortus* and *Trichostrongylus axei* the effect of a given concentration of $CO_2 + H_2CO_3$ increased as the pH was raised, and at a given pH the effect increased with increasing $[CO_2 + H_2CO_3]$ until a constant level of activity was reached. However, with eggs of *Ascaris suum* there was an optimum $[CO_2 + H_2CO_3]$ for an effective stimulus at a given pH. Beyond this optimum, increases in $[CO_2 + H_2CO_3]$ inhibited. This feature of the stimulus seems characteristic of eggs rather than of species (Rogers, 1979). With infective eggs, the entry of H_2CO_3 would rapidly release protons in the vitelline fluid. As the concentration of the "readily available" H_2CO_3 was increased, the buffering capacity of the fluid would be overcome and the pH would fall. At some point this falling pH would affect the activity of the hatching enzymes (pseudocollagenase, lipase and chitinase; Rogers, 1982) released by the ovic juveniles as a result of the stimulus. Thus, the peaks in hatching activity at different pH values may represent concentrations of "readily available" H_2CO_3 at which decreases in enzyme activity would be sufficient to inhibit hatching rather than an optimum value of the stimulus.

The argument that "readily available" H_2CO_3 is the important component of the stimulus rather than CO_2 comes mostly from studies with the infective juveniles of *Nematospiroides dubius* and *H. contortus* (Petronijevic *et al.*, 1985). It seems reasonable to suppose, however, that other species activated by CO_2 in the gas phase would act similarly.

2. *H_2CO_3 compared with other acids*

HCl, at pH 2–pH 3, may be an effective stimulus for the development of juveniles which normally exsheath in the stomach of the host. Thus, Christie and Charleston (1965) showed that HCl at low pH values stimulated exsheathment of *Nematodirus battus* and that CO_2 in the gas phase was unimportant. And Sommerville and Bailey (1973) obtained similar results with *N. dubius*, although the presence of CO_2 in the gas phase increased activity considerably. More recent experiments (Petronijevic *et al.*, 1985) showed that HCl, pH 2.03, with a $[CO_2]^{tot}$ in the medium of $< 2.2 \times 10^{-9}$ mM caused appreciable exsheathment though it was significantly increased when $[CO_2]^{tot}$ was raised to 7.4×10^{-3} mM. However, even at the low $[CO_2]^{tot}$, inhibition of the carbonic anhydrase within the infective stage decreased activity considerably. Moreover, infective stages of *N. dubius* which had been exposed to an inhibitor of the enzyme failed to infect mice though the reversal of inhibition restored infectivity (Rogers, 1966). Evidently H_2CO_3 is an important stimulus for *N. dubius in vivo*.

Infective juveniles of *H. contortus* and *N. dubius* may be stimulated to exsheath at appropriate concentrations of "readily available" H_2CO_3 over the range pH 2–7. The failure of Christie and Charleston (1965) to obtain exsheathment of *H. contortus* at low pH values was due, it seems, to the sensitivity of its exsheathing enzyme, pseudocollagenase, to acid. The similar exsheathing enzyme of *N. dubius* was not affected. Exposure of infective juveniles of *H. contortus* to high concentrations of "readily available" H_2CO_3 in 10 mM HCl for 3–25 minutes followed by incubation at pH 7 at a low $[CO_2]^{tot}$ caused ecdysis (Petronijevic *et al.*, 1986). Indeed, Sommerville and Murphy (1983) showed that, although CO_2 in the gas phase at low pH values apparently did not stimulate ecdysis, it did induce development of the fourth stage. Unlike *N. dubius*, however, HCl alone, even at a concentration of 200 mM, did not act as a stimulus for exsheathment in *H. contortus* (Petronijevic *et al.*, 1986).

The relative sensitivity of the two species to HCl as a stimulus was found to apply to other acids. Thus, relative percent ecdysis of *H. contortus*/*N. dubius* at pH 7 was "readily available" H_2CO_3, 0.18 mM, 0/28; and at 1.8 mM, 23/86 (Petronijevic *et al.*, 1986). In accordance with this, *N. dubius* responded, albeit slowly and at appropriate pH values, to a variety of undissociated organic acids while *H. contortus* did not. *N. dubius* responded rapidly to inorganic acids (HCl, H_2SO_4, HNO_3) at pH 2. Presumably, the very small amounts of undissociated acid available at this pH would be rapidly taken up and replaced by the highly concentrated products of dissociation (Petronijevic *et al.*, 1986).

3. *Bases as the stimulus for development*

Meza-Ruis and Alger (1968) found that 84% of 11-week-old infective juveniles of *H. contortus* exsheathed within 20 minutes in Earle's salt solution at pH 6, 38° C. The addition of 20 mM NH_4Cl to this medium increased ecdysis by 13%. Slocombe and Whitlock (1969) who used 14-day-old juveniles obtained no activity under the same conditions. These contradictory results may be explained: the ease of inducing ecdysis at 38° C increases with the age of the juveniles (although infectivity may decrease; Rogers, 1940). Because some organic acids induced exsheathment only after some 20 hours incubation (Petronijevic *et al.*, 1986), similar periods have been used in tests with bases (Petronijevic and Rogers, 1986).

NH_4Cl at pH 8, 10 mM, induced ecdysis in *H. contortus* after 20–30 hours incubation. Development of the fourth stage was not so markedly slowed; all exsheathed juveniles and some which had not exsheathed had the characters of the fourth stage after 78 hours incubation. Ecdysis did not occur earlier when the [NH_4Cl] was raised to 50 and 100 mM. Activity at pH 6 was lower than that at pH 8 and no activity was obtained at 5 mM. NH_4Cl also induced ecdysis or hatching with infective stages of *N. dubius* and *A. suum*. Similar results were obtained with NH_2CH_3, 50 mM, at pH 9. The pK values of ammonia and methylamine are 9.2 and 10.6 respectively, so the higher activity obtained with bases at higher pH values suggests that the undissociated base was the active agent.

4. *Other components of the stimulus*

In vitro tests showed that the activity of a stimulus rose from zero, at temperatures below about 25° C, to a maximum at 38–40° C. In contrast, the activity of exsheathing and hatching fluids, dependent upon enzyme action, rose steadily from about 14° C to 38–40° C (e.g. see Rogers and Sommerville, 1968). The steep rise in activity of the stimulus, associated with a small increase in temperature, suggests the involvement of "heat shock" genes (van der Ploeg *et al.*, 1985), or more likely, changes in membrane lipids (Thompson and Huang, 1980).

Although balanced salt solutions of differing compositions may influence the survival and development of parasitic stages formed by exposing infective stages to the stimulus, there is no definite evidence that any particular salt is required for the action of the stimulus itself. Certainly, ecdysis of *H. contortus* can be induced in high grade distilled water with CO_2 in the gas phase.

Reducing agents may increase the activity of the stimulus with some species. Though variable results have been obtained with *H. contortus*, reducing conditions consistently increased the hatching of eggs of *A. suum* (Rogers, 1957; Fairbairn, 1961; Hurley and Sommerville, 1982). There is little to indicate the mechanisms whereby reducing agents might affect the action of the stimulus. That they were most effective when $[H_2CO_3]$ was low and affected both eggs (e.g. *A. suum*) and juveniles (e.g. *T. axei*) suggests that they affected the efficiency of the stimulus rather than the substrates of exsheathing and hatching fluids (Rogers, 1960). Inhibition of carbonic anhydrase in infective stages may influence the efficiency of H_2CO_3 as a stimulus, especially at low concentrations of "readily available" H_2CO_3 (Rogers, 1980; Petronijevic *et al.*, 1985). Oxidation of the enzyme, which inactivates it, can be reversed by reducing agents (Kiese and Hastings, 1940), so it is possible that reducing conditions can influence the stimulus in this way.

Various substances, including cysteine, ascorbic acid, H_2S, SO_2 and sodium dithionite have been used as reducing agents. As well as serving this function in suitable media, they may provide weak acids in aqueous solution which, at appropriate pH values, may themselves act as a stimulus. Thus H_2S–water (pK_1, 7.0; pK_2, 12.0), about 100 mM, induced some 90% ecdysis of *N. dubius* in 30 minutes, pH 2.03, although it was less effective at high pH values. And ascorbic acid, 100 mM, induced exsheathment of *N. dubius* and *H. contortus* after some 20 hours incubation (Petronijevic *et al.*, 1985, 1986).

Silverman and Podger (1964) argued that pepsin was an essential factor of the stimulus for ecdysis of *Dictyocaulus viviparus*. However, later work showed that seven enzymes (six proteases and chitinase) each at its optimum pH caused exsheathment (Parker and Croll, 1976). Exposure to these enzymes led to the shedding of the "cap" of the sheath, typical of the process of ecdysis induced by a stimulus, and so it was argued that the host's proteolytic enzymes were responsible for exsheathing *in vivo*. Parker and Croll did not, however, test this hypothesis using isolated sheaths as substrates.

The eggs of *Aspiculuris tetraptera*, which normally hatch in the hind gut of the mouse, were found to hatch *in vitro* at 37° C, pH 7.3–7.4, under air (Anya, 1966). Under 5% CO_2/N_2 hatching was halved, and it was decreased further under N_2. Anya concluded that the process was aerobic and that temperature and pH were important.

5. *The stimulus for infection* in vivo: *the host signals*

For species of nematodes which infect homeothermic animals *per os* the major components of the host signal appear to be a temperature of 38° C, "readily available" H_2CO_3 (pH 2–7), and less important, HCl (pH 2–3). Acids, it appears, are taken up rapidly in the undissociated form, although the presence of a high concentration of the ionized components is important for replacing the undissociated acid as it is absorbed. One factor which may explain the effectiveness of the CO_2 produced by the host as a stimulus for development of the parasitic stage is the pK values of the system $CO_2 + H_2O \rightleftarrows H_2CO_3 \rightleftarrows H^+ + HCO_3^-$ which provides "readily available" H_2CO_3 over a wide range of pH values and thus varied sites for infection in the alimentary canal.

C. THE ACTION OF THE STIMULUS FOR DEVELOPMENT

Based on results obtained with three species it has been proposed that the action of the stimulus for the development of the parasitic stage from the infective stage activates (a) an endocrine system, set up in the previous instar, which controls ecdysis and hatching, and (b) the DNA transcription of the gene set of the next, parasitic stage (Petronijevic and Rogers, 1983; Fig. 1). Presumably, at the end of each instar, free-living or parasitic, a block in development, due to the inactivity of the systems (a) and (b), occurs. A stimulus, innate or environmental, would then be required to initiate development of the next stage. Generally, there is no prolonged halt in development between instars, so a stimulus, if such is needed, would have a low threshold. There is evidence that the spontaneous hatching of the non-infective eggs of *H. contortus* is inhibited at a $[CO_2]^{tot}$ of $< 2 \times 10^{-7}$ mM at pH 6 and 37° C (Rogers, 1980). Insect juvenile hormone can raise this threshold so that a stimulus, similar to that required for the hatching of infective eggs of *A. suum*, is necessary (Rogers, 1979; see Section III B). Furthermore, Dennis (1976) found that juvenile hormone inhibited the final moult of *N.*

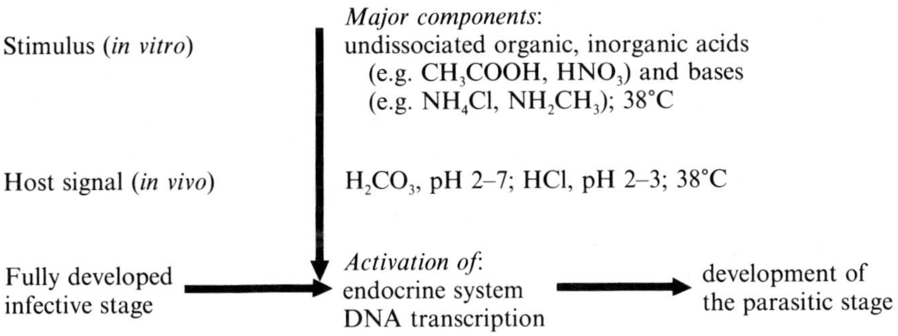

FIG. 1. The overall process for the induction of development of the parasitic stage from the infective stage of nematodes which enter homeothermic hosts *per os*. (For references see text.)

dubius. On the other hand, a number of analogues of juvenile hormone had no effect on the moulting of *Neoaplectana glaseri* (Hansen and Buecher, 1971). Does juvenile hormone, at least in some species, prolong "dormancy" by raising the threshold of the stimulus? How does the stimulus switch on an endocrine system and DNA transcription? Little is known about the process by which development of the parasitic stage from the infective stage is induced by the stimulus from the homeothermic animal host. Some results obtained largely from infective juveniles of *H. contortus* (Petronijevic and Rogers, 1986) suggest that the process may be similar, in some respects, to that seen in the parthenogenic activation of eggs of marine invertebrates (for reference see Epel, 1978; Shen, 1983; Dubé and Epel, 1986).

1. *Intracellular pH*

Despite earlier concepts, pH_i (the average internal pH of many compartments within a cell or group of cells), may vary considerably, 0.1–1.6 pH units, during marked metabolic or developmental changes (Busa and Nuccitelli, 1984). However, changes in pH_i caused by external acids and bases are often toxic (Thomas, 1974; Roos and Boron, 1981) , and bases are toxic to free-living and parasitic stages of nematodes. Infective stages, however, are more resistant (Petronijevic and Rogers, 1986). This, together with the acidic and basic nature of agents which stimulate development suggests that changes in the pH_i of infective stages may have a special significance.

The efficiency of H_2CO_3 as a stimulus depends upon a rapid uptake (see Section III B) and a rapid release of protons in the intracellular fluid (Rogers, 1980; Petronijevic *et al.*, 1985). Indeed, measurements with DMO (5,5-

dimethyl-2,4-oxazolidinedione) indicated that H_2CO_3 caused a rapid fall in pH_i followed by a rapid rise which overshot the initial pH_i. The pH_i then returned to near the initial level. These diphasic changes were not dependent upon a Na^+ influx (Petronijevic and Rogers, 1987). Undissociated bases, NH_4Cl and NH_2CH_3, also caused, slowly, within 20–30 hours, the development of the parasitic stage (see Section III B) and caused a rise in pH_i.

2. *The role of Ca^{2+}*

Calcium is involved in the hatching of eggs of *Globodera rostochiensis*, a parasite of potatoes, for which the host signal is the root diffusate (Perry and Clarke, 1981). It is also essential for the action of H_2CO_3 as the stimulus for ecdysis of infective juveniles of *H. contortus*. In the presence of the ionophore A23187, ecdysis was inhibited and this inhibition was reversed by Ca^{2+}. However, the ionophore in a medium high in Ca^{2+} did not induce ecdysis. In contrast with the action of H_2CO_3 which induced a diphasic change in pH_i, NH_4Cl, which induced the rise only, was not Ca^{2+}-dependent (Petronijevic and Rogers, 1986).

The activation of marine invertebrate eggs by acids and bases is similar, in terms of its Ca^{2+} relationships, to the action of acidic and basic stimuli on infective stages (Petronijevic and Rogers, 1986). The introduction of Ca^{2+} into marine eggs, however, is in itself sufficient for activation.

3. *Metabolic effects of the stimulus*

Though anoxic conditions at pH 6 were not toxic to infective juveniles of *H. contortus* at 38° C, incubation for periods longer than a few hours at pH 8 caused immobilization. This effect was reversed within an hour under air at 25° C. In alkaline media there was a considerable rise in the pH_i of the juveniles; at pH 6 the effect was less. It was therefore suggested that a homeostatic mechanism governing pH_i may require more energy at alkaline pH values, and that this energy is normally available to muscle cells from catabolism involving molecular oxygen. Exposure to CO_2/N_2 or, to a lesser degree, NH_4Cl under air, provided protection against anoxia; the stimulated juveniles retained their activity for at least 20 hours under a gas phase of N_2. It was proposed (Petronijevic and Rogers, 1986) that the action of the stimulus involved the activation of protein kinases (e.g. phosphorylase b kinase, phosphofructokinase).

4. *The endocrine system, ecdysis and hatching*

The secretion of exsheathing and hatching fluids by infective stages is under the control of an endocrine system. This system, set up in the previous stage, is activated by the stimulus so that ecdysis and hatching are early features of the development of the parasitic stage. The studies of K. G. Davey and his colleagues (Davey, 1976; Davey and Goh, 1984; Goh and Davey, 1984) with the infective fourth-stage juvenile of *Phocanema decipiens*, have provided the basic features of the system. Davey's results, and those obtained with infective juveniles and non-infective eggs of *H. contortus*, can be used to describe a series of events which link exposure to the stimulus with the breakdown of sheaths and egg capsules (Fig. 2).

The initial action of H_2CO_3 as the stimulus, probably a diphasic change in pH_i, induced a mobilization of Ca^{2+}. During the period when this occurred, < 1 hour, the noradrenaline content rose 2–9 times (Rogers and Head, 1972); during the second hour, exsheathment reached a maximum. NH_4Cl-induced development was not, however, Ca^{2+}-dependent (see Section III B) and ecdysis was delayed 20–30 hours. As it seems likely that the production of

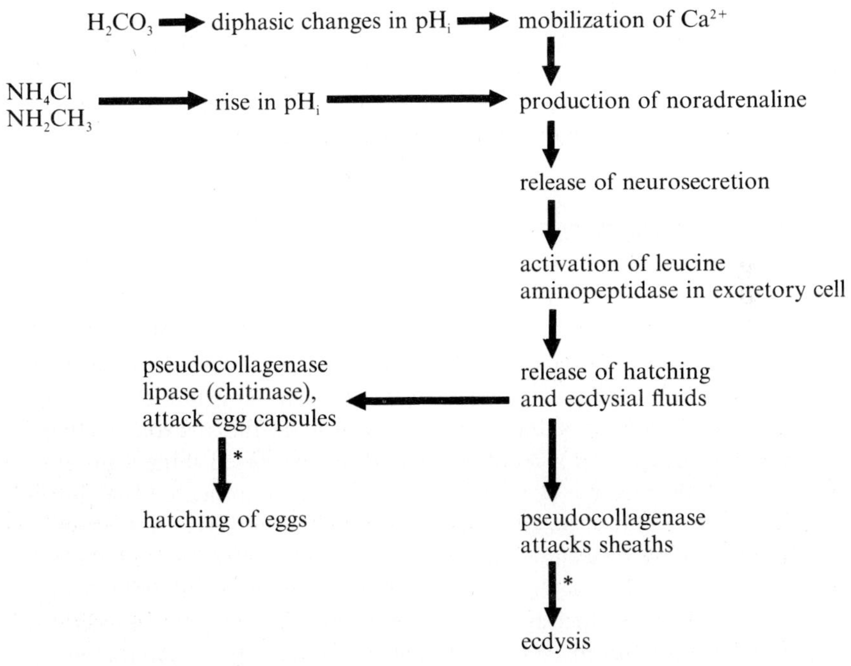

*Inhibitors: 1,10-phenanthroline, EGTA

FIG. 2. Suggested sequence of events linking the stimulus for development with the hatching and ecdysis of infective stages of nematodes. (For references see text.)

noradrenaline from a precursor was associated with changes in [Ca^{2+}] and activation of a protein kinase (Joh *et al.*, 1978) this delay in ecdysis may have been due to a different route for the production of noradrenaline. The possible sequence of the links, noradrenaline, neurosecretion, activation of leucine aminopeptidase in the excretory cell, release of ecdysial and hatching enzymes (pseudocollagenase, lipase, and in some ascarid eggs, chitinase) has been discussed previously (Rogers, 1982; Rogers and Petronijevic, 1982).

It should be emphasized that it was not considered that these enzymes were "induced" by the action of the stimulus (Justus and Ivey, 1969); rather, it was proposed that the stimulus led to the release of the fluids containing the preformed enzymes. Leucine aminopeptidase is now seen as the agent for the breakdown of cellular membranes (Lote and Weiss, 1971; Weiss *et al.*, 1971), with the consequent release of hatching and ecdysial fluids (Rogers, 1982).

5. *The stimulus and DNA transcription*

As yet there is no indication of how the initial events in the stimulation of development of the parasitic stage induced by H_2CO_3, NH_4Cl or NH_2CH_3, finally activates DNA transcription. The processes in marine invertebrate eggs, which follow fertilization or parthenogenic activation (Epel, 1978; Shen, 1983; Dubé and Epel, 1986) show similarities, in some respects, to the changes which are induced by the stimulus, and so provide useful hypotheses for future work.

6. *The role of juvenile hormone*

The possible action of juvenile hormone on the development of nematodes has been discussed elsewhere (Rogers and Petronijevic, 1982) and will be considered only briefly here. K. G. Davey and his colleagues, who have studied the action of the hormone using *P. decipiens*, consider that its action is fortuitous—it disrupts the normal function of the nervous system in nematodes (Davey, 1976). Another view has been based largely on experiments with non-infective eggs of *H. contortus*; these indicated that juvenile hormone and several of its analogues induced, or prolonged, a dormancy at the end of the development of the ovic juvenile. This effect could be reversed by a stimulus similar to that required for the hatching of infective eggs. Because a substance which has the action of juvenile hormone in insects was found in considerable amounts (200 Tenebrio units/g dry wt) in the infective stage of *H. contortus*, it has been suggested that the hormone might act by inducing or prolonging dormancy in the fully developed infective stage by raising the threshold for the action of the stimulus. However, high concentrations of juvenile hormone in the medium, 1–0.1 mM, were necessary to inhibit hatching. As the hormone permeates freely and reaches high concentrations in nematodes, its action may not be part of a normal physiological process (Jones *et al.*, 1983). Results obtained by Dennis (1976) showing that juvenile hormone, 2.2×10^{-8} mM, inhibited the fourth ecdysis of *N. dubius* may, however, suggest otherwise.

IV. Host Signals for Cutaneous Infection and Migration of Nematodes

There is at present no indication that cutaneous infection is governed by host signals similar to those which affect oral infection. Indeed, temperature and nonspecific mechanical factors are most important regulators of skin penetration (Lee, 1972; Matthews, 1972). A comprehensive theoretical account of where environmental stimuli may act in the life cycle of parasites has been given by MacInnis (1976). Experimental studies on chemotaxis (Bone, 1982), and factors affecting migration and location of parasitic nematodes in their hosts (Despommier, 1982; Wilson, 1982) have been reviewed.

V. Trematoda: Signals for Excystation and Transformation

Here, we have elected to examine signals from the host which are concerned in excystation of metacercariae and the transformation of cercariae of schistosomes to schistosomulae.

A. EXCYSTMENT OF METACERCARIA

1. *Introduction*

In the digenetic trematodes some cercariae reach the definitive host by forming a metacercaria, either on vegetation or within an intermediate host (Smyth and Halton, 1983). Most metacercariae are encysted and, when they are eaten, they excyst. We are concerned here with the stimuli from the host which are responsible for the release of the juvenile trematode.

2. *The metacercarial cyst*

Cysts may be simple structures, sometimes formed entirely by the host (Bogtish, 1961) or multilayered structures of great complexity, synthesized by host and parasite or by parasite alone. The composition too, is very varied and it is difficult to make any generalizations (Erasmus, 1972; Smyth and Halton, 1983), although species which encyst in the open have cysts of greater complexity than those which encyst within tissues (Dixon, 1975).

The cyst is often referred to as "protective"; it isolates the enclosed juvenile from the external environment and presumably protects it from microorganisms, and from adverse reactions when it is within an intermediate host. When the cyst is eaten, profound changes take place, often called "activation", and these conclude with the breakdown of part of the cyst wall and the escape of the juvenile trematode.

3. *The study of excystment*

Our understanding of the mechanisms of excystment is principally derived from an examination of the reactions of cysts *in vitro*; only rarely have these experiments been coupled with observations *in vivo*, such as those of Asanji and Williams (1974) for example. A feature of many of these experiments is the provision of a succession of environments. Cysts are first exposed to components which represent features of the gastric environment and, subsequently, the intestinal environment. This sequence had its genesis in the earlier physiological studies of trematodes, made more than 60 years ago by S. Yokogawa (Yokogawa *et al.*, 1960) on excystation of *Paragonimus westermani*. The principle has been applied with appropriate modifications to other species, and has led to our present understanding of the mechanism of excystment in species like *Fasciola hepatica* and *Echinoparyphium serratum* (Dixon, 1964, 1966; Howell, 1970).

The features of the gastric environment to which metacercariae are commonly exposed are pepsin at a pH near 2 and a balanced salt solution. This is sometimes called "pretreatment", and is followed by exposure to an "excystment medium", usually containing trypsin or bile salts or both, at an alkaline pH. Sometimes cysts are accorded a second pretreatment, by immersion in a reducing agent, before exposure to trypsin and bile. The experiments are usually made at the body temperature of the definitive host, where excystation would normally take place.

4. *The stimuli for excystment*

(a) Introduction. The important components of the stimulus are believed to include (1) temperature, (2) pepsin, (3) reducing agents, (4) trypsin and bile, and (5) pH. Table 1 lists the requirements for excystment of some metacercariae, related to the site in the host where excystment normally takes place.

TABLE 1

*Requirements for excystation of a variety of metacercariae. Key: Yes = necessary; * = may help, but not necessary; No = an adverse effect, or none; — = not tested*

Site of excystment	Species	Host	Temp. (°C)	CO_2	pH2	Pepsin pH2	pH > 7	Trypsin	Bile salts	References
Anterior to stomach	*Philophthalmus gralli*	Birds	> 35	—	—	No	—	No	—	Cheng and Thakur, 1967
	Philophthalmus hegeneri	Birds	> 35	—	—	—	—	—	—	Fried, 1981
	Clinostomum tilapiae	Birds	40	—	—	—	—	—	—	Asanji and Williams, 1975
Stomach	*Posthodiplostomum nanum*	Birds	10–40	—	Yes	*	—	—	—	Asanji and Williams, 1975
Small Intestine	*Fasciola hepatica*	Ruminants	39	Yes[a]	*	*	—	No	Yes	Dixon, 1964, 1966
	Parorchis acanthus	Birds	39	—	No	Yes	No	Yes	*	Asanji and Williams, 1975
			42	—	—	*	—	Yes	Yes	Fried and Roth, 1974
	Holostephanus luehei	Birds	37	—	Yes	*	—	Yes	Yes	Erasmus and Bennett, 1965
	Cyathocotyle bushiensis	Birds								
	Bucephaloides gracilescens	Gadoid fish								
	(a) Thin-walled cysts[b]		10	No	—	Yes	Yes	No	—	Johnston and Halton, 1981
	(b) Thick-walled cysts[b]		10	No	Yes	—	—	No	Yes	
	Posthodiplostomum sp.	Birds	40	—	No	Yes	Yes	No	*	Asanji and Williams, 1975
	Posthodiplostomoides leonensis	Birds	40	—	No	Yes	Yes	No	*	Asanji and Williams, 1975
	Sphaeridiotrema globulus	Birds	37	—	—	—	—	Yes	Yes	Fried and Huffman, 1982
	Echinoparyphium serratum	Birds	39	No	Yes[a]	*	—	Yes	Yes	Howell, 1970

[a] with reducing agent

[b] cysts from the cranial cavity have a thinner wall than those from the orbital and nasal regions

(b) Stimuli and site of excystment. The more anterior the site of excystment, the more simple is the signal from the host. Species like *Clinostomum tilapiae*, *Philophthalmus gralli* and *Philophthalmus hegeneri*, which excyst in the mouth or oesophagus, do so in response to the high and constant body temperatures of the host. *Posthodiplostomum nanum* excysts in the stomach; in addition to temperature, a high concentration of hydrogen ions is required. It is those species which excyst in the intestine which apparently have the most complex requirements, involving stimuli from rumen or stomach and intestine.

It should not be inferred, however, that every part of the gut along which the cyst travels provides a necessary part of the stimulus for excystment. For example, the components of the signals for excystment of *F. hepatica* come from the rumen and intestine; the stomach makes no necessary contribution (Dixon, 1964, 1966).

(c) Temperature. If the definitive host is a bird or mammal, metacercariae will not excyst *in vitro* unless the temperature of the media is similar to that of the host (Asanji and Williams, 1975; Thompson and Halton, 1982). If the body temperature of the host is lower, as with fish, then experiments like those with *Bucephaloides gracilescens* can be conducted at 10° C. However, as is clear from Table 1, for most species the correct temperature is a necessary but not a sufficient condition for excystment *in vitro.* A temperature difference of 4° C may be sufficient to yield quite different results, as for example in *Sphaeridiotrema globulus* (Table 1).

(d) Exogenous enzymes and bile salts. We are concerned here with pepsin and trypsin. The latter is commonly associated with bile salts in experiments on excystment *in vitro*.

(i) Pepsin. The presence of pepsin at a high [H^+] in the stomach of the definitive host has been taken to imply that this enzyme is likely to be important in excystment. This notion is supported by observation *in vivo* which show that the outer layers of cysts of several species are removed when the cysts are in the stomach (Asanji and Williams, 1974), and by observations *in vitro*, which show that outer parts of cysts are frequently degraded in the presence of pepsin (Macy *et al.*, 1968). Yet this activity of pepsin may conceal a more important and fundamental stimulus, namely [H^+]. In many of the species listed in Table 1, a salt solution at pH 2 is a potent part of the stimulus. This is true of *P. nanum*, *E. serratum*, *Holostephanus luehei*, *Cyathocotyle bushiensis*, and even for the thick-walled cysts of *B. gracilescens*, where pepsin is needed if a high proportion of juveniles are to be freed from the cyst. However, there seems to be a clear requirement for peptic activity in some species like *Posthodiplostomoides leonensis* and *Posthodiplos-*

tomum species, which have thick-walled cysts, the two outer layers of which are degraded in the stomach (Asanji and Williams, 1974).

On the other hand, although *S. globulus* loses a thin outer layer of the cyst on exposure to pepsin *in vitro*, excystment can be obtained if the cysts are exposed directly to trypsin and bile (Fried and Huffman, 1982). Pepsin is not needed.

It can be concluded that in many species exposure of cysts to a high concentration of hydrogen ions is an important part of the stimulus leading to excystment *in vitro*. Pepsin may contribute by eroding parts of the cyst, but even this activity can sometimes be taken over by trypsin, so that an absolute requirement for pepsin is rare.

(ii) Trypsin and bile salts. Trypsin at pH values of about 8, is usually combined with a variety of bile salts, and may either offer an additional stimulus to cysts which must be first exposed to acid pepsin or to high [H^+], as in *H. luehei* or *E. serratum* (Table 1). However, in other species, in which pretreatment is not needed, trypsin and bile may supply the whole stimulus for excystment, as for example with *S. globulus* and *P. acanthus* (Table 1).

In many experiments on excystation *in vitro*, trypsin and bile are commonly used together, without testing to see whether both are necessary or whether a salt solution alone, at the same pH and temperature, is effective. Both *P. leonensis* and a species of *Posthodiplostomum* (Table 1) excyst readily in salt solutions at pH 8 to about 60%. Addition of bile increased this proportion to 80% (Asanji and Williams, 1975), but is not an absolute requirement.

Bile salts or trypsin can sometimes be used alone; for example, *F. hepatica* does not require the presence of bile salts (Table 1) and trypsin alone suffices for excystment of *Himasthla quissetensis* (Kirschner and Bacha, 1980). Most commonly they must be used together. A series of elegant experiments (Howell, 1970; Table 1) has shown that cysts of *E. serratum* after appropriate pre-treatment, fail to excyst in media containing either sodium cholate or trypsin. If after an hour the missing component is added, excystment follows. In this experiment, it is clear that trypsin attacks and breaks down a capsule of host tissue which surrounds the cyst. The effect of adding sodium cholate is that the juvenile trematodes escape from the cyst wall; without the aid of trypsin they cannot escape from the host capsule.

(iii) Roles played by exogenous enzymes. So far it seems that pepsin, trypsin and sometimes "pancreatin" affect the course of excystment non-specifically, by breaking down the cyst wall. Is there any evidence that the entire cyst wall is broken down in this way? On the limited data available the answer must be no. In all those species listed in Table 1 as excysting in the small intestine (except *F. hepatica* for which neither trypsin nor pepsin are needed), these enzymes do not break down all layers of the cyst; most commonly an innermost single layer (as seen under the light microscope) is apparently not affected.

Although we have emphasized the role of exogenous enzymes in breaking down the wall of the cyst, they may also have an important function in altering the permeability of the cyst, a step which may be necessary for excystment.

(iv) The role of bile. There are numerous observations that the addition of bile is followed by vigorous activity of the juvenile trematode, for example in *Cotylurus variegatus* (Thompson and Halton, 1982), *Acanthoparyphium spinulosum* (Bass and LeFlore, 1984), *F. hepatica* (Dixon, 1964, 1966) and *E. serratum* (Howell, 1970). Perhaps the bile penetrates the cyst wall, or changes the permeability of the wall, eventually leading to internal changes and so to excystment. In one species the need for bile seems to be related to the thickness of the cyst wall. More than 90% of thin-walled cranial cysts of *B. gracilescens* will excyst after pretreatment if washed in Hanks' salt solution at pH 7.2. Thick-walled cysts will also break down in salt solution, but sodium tauroglycocholate must be added if 90% excystment is to be obtained (Johnston and Halton, 1981). Here it seems possible that the bile salt acts by changing the cyst wall. As yet however, there is no "single model to explain the action of bile salts" (Thompson and Halton, 1982).

(e) Reducing agents. Although excystment of *F. hepatica* takes place in the absence of reducing agents, it is greatly enhanced if they are provided (Dixon, 1964, 1966). Some species like *Zygocotyle lunata* and *A. spinulosum* (Fried *et al.*, 1978; Bass and LeFlore, 1984) will not excyst unless pretreated with sodium dithionite, while excystment of other species is either enhanced or not affected. In some species, reducing agents seem to be substantially effective only when used after high $[H^+]$, in place of acid pepsin (Howell, 1970; Kirschner and Bacha, 1980).

We do not have any good experimental evidence as to what reducing agents actually do. Moreover, many experiments which incorporate reducing agents are difficult to interpret because it is not always clear that they have been handled so as to avoid oxidation. Some reports mention that cysts become "sticky" (Kirshner and Bacha, 1980; Bass and LeFlore, 1984) after exposure to sodium dithionite. The significance of this observation for normal excystment is not clear. A strong solution of sodium dithionite could have profound effects on the structure of the cyst *in vitro*, which might be entirely irrelevant to the biology of excystment *in vivo*. This is further discussed in Section VIII C.

(f) Carbon dioxide as a stimulus. Carbon dioxide is an important component of the stimulus for excystment of *F. hepatica*, but has no effect on

B. gracilescens or *E. serratum* (Table 1). Work with nematodes which exsheath or hatch in response to "readily available" H_2CO_3 has shown that both the pH of the medium and the pCO_2 of the gas phase are important (Section III B), and the same may be true of excystment, so that tests should be performed at different concentrations and pH values. Moreover, in nematodes which respond to carbon dioxide, the response can be blocked by inhibitors of carbonic anhydrase (Section III B) and experiments with these where carbon dioxide is suspected to be important, might be valuable.

5. *What is the mechanism for excystment?*

In the early parasitological literature, it was often assumed that exsheathing, excystment or hatching of various infective stages was brought about by the non-specific action of digestive enzymes and perhaps the movement of ingesta. While there is no doubt that digestive enzymes can erode some membranes in which these stages are encapsulated, and sometimes the stress of mastication will detach and break up parts of the cyst wall, as in *F. hepatica* (Dixon, 1966), this relatively simple view seems to have been largely discarded. Many studies of excystment describe the process as an "active" one, i.e. the participation of the juvenile trematode is required. There are at least two views on the way in which this participation is achieved, and these are not necessarily exclusive. One involves intense activity on the part of the trematode, the other postulates the release of enzymes by the trematode, commonly accompanied by movement.

There is no doubt that the enclosed juvenile becomes intensely active prior to excystment. Movement in species such as *S. globulus*, *H. quissetensis* and *C. variegatus* (Macey *et al.*, 1968; Kirschner and Bacha, 1980; Thompson and Halton, 1982) is not however sufficient to ensure excystment. For example, *H. quissetensis* in a medium containing bile salts but devoid of trypsin becomes very active but does not excyst. However, vigorous movements of most species are needed to squeeze out of the cyst after the wall has broken.

Although the possible involvement of endogenous enzymes in excystment has been suggested many times (Dixon, 1965, 1966; Howell, 1970; Irwin *et al.*, 1984), little attention has been paid to this hypothesis. Circumstantial evidence which favours it includes the observation that excystment of some species can take place in media devoid of exogenous enzymes, that in many instances, although some layers of the cyst may be removed by pepsin or trypsin, there remains an apparently unaltered layer, and some reports show clearly that changes in the innermost membranes precede those in the outer membranes.

While it is unlikely that all metacercariae excyst in the same way, it seems reasonable to suppose that excystment involves the receipt of signals from the host, and that these signals set in train events which govern the initiation of development on the one hand, and on the other, mechanisms for breaking out of the cyst. Two of these mechanisms are probably the release of enzymes from the juvenile fluke, and vigorous movements.

6. *Temperature and pH as signals for excystment*

Cysts of species which live in homeothermic hosts most commonly require temperatures close to the host's body temperature. Under these conditions, temperature is a component of the signal from the host, but how it acts in this role is not known. The possibility that pH, or a *change* in pH, may be an important trigger for excystation has been suggested (Macy *et al.*, 1968; Johnston and Halton, 1981) but received little attention.

Posthodiplostomum nanum excysts in the stomach and *in vitro* in salt solutions at pH 2 (Asanji and Williams, 1974, 1975). As already discussed, several species which seem to have a requirement for pretreatment in pepsin, will respond to high $[H^+]$ alone, and subsequently excyst in appropriate media. Yet other species like *P. leonensis* or the thin-walled cranial cysts of *B. gracilescens* (Table 1), after appropriate pretreatment in acid medium, will excyst when transferred to alkaline salt solutions.

The exposure first to acid and then to alkaline media induces violent activity in both *B. gracilescens* and *S. globulus* (Macy *et al.*, 1968; Johnston and Halton, 1981) and in these two species the change in pH may be important. However, *S. globulus* will excyst when placed directly into alkaline media, without pretreatment (Fried and Huffman, 1982). Simple exposure of cysts to acid or alkaline pH values, alone or in succession, does not necessarily produce excystment of species like *Cryptocotyle lingua* (McDaniel, 1966). If pH is important, it may only be so when modulated by other requirements, such as exogenous enzymes, bile salts and perhaps reducing agents.

7. *General comments*

Much of the investigation of excystment has a narrow conceptual framework, probably because the goal is often to get as many excysted juveniles as possible, rather than to understand the mechanism. Commonly a sequence of treatments, acid then alkaline, with enzymes and bile is employed, and there may be no attempt to analyse the contribution of individual components. Often, too, there is no attempt to relate the results to what happens in the host, so it is not always clear that the components used are supplying the natural signal from the host. For example, excystation might be produced by a medium which supplied some intermediate, or set in train some intermediate reaction in the normal sequence of events between stimulus and excystation. The real nature of the stimuli would then be obscured.

The functions of bile are not clear. Its requirement varies greatly, and sometimes seems to be related to the thickness of the cyst wall; in these instances it may alter the properties of the cyst membranes. However, it could also have an effect on the juvenile trematode, because many records make it clear that violent activity follows exposure to bile. It has not been possible to separate the direct effects of bile on the trematode from any indirect effects it may produce by altering the cyst wall. Moreover much of this work is hampered by uncertainty about the composition of "bile" or even "bile salts" (Smyth and Haslewood, 1963) and the great complexity of the chemistry of bile acids and their salts. The topic is discussed further in Section IX.

Information on excystment is very incomplete. One reason for this lack of information is that the cysts are hard to work with, and it is difficult to separate the action of such components as pH, bile and exogenous enzymes on the cyst from their effects on the enclosed juvenile. It would help if the stimulus could be separated from the response by brief exposure to the former, or by withholding part of the stimulus. For example, cysts of *F. hepatica* which have been treated with carbon dioxide will remain quiescent for many hours until supplied with bile. This circumstance seems to offer good opportunities for further analysis.

Very little information is available about the permeability of the metacercarial cyst and the changes during treatments which ultimately lead to excystation. The lead given by Halton and Johnston (1982) seems not to have been exploited.

B. TRANSFORMATION FROM CERCARIA TO SCHISTOSOMULUM

1. *Introduction*

In some trematodes, for example the Schistosomatidae, the cercaria does not form a metacercaria, but infects the final host directly, usually by penetrating the skin. This act is associated with transformation from a cercaria to a stage called the schistosomulum. The transformation is rapid and profound; the problem we address here is the nature of the signals from the host which trigger these changes. Most of the work has been done on *Schistosoma mansoni*. The literature is very abundant indeed, and we have relied heavily upon reviews by Clegg (1972) and Stirewalt (1966, 1974).

2. *Natural history of invasion*

The exploration and penetration of the skin by cercariae of *S. mansoni* is a complex phenomenon (Stirewalt, 1966; Matthews, 1977) and here we can only indicate briefly the nature and sequence of events. When the cercariae encounter the skin of a suitable host, they receive a stimulus which sets in train a series of changes in behaviour and activity (Gordon and Griffiths, 1951) commonly called the "penetration response" (Stirewalt, 1971). The events are irreversible and, when completed, the cercaria is transformed into a schistosomulum.

The invasive mechanisms of *S. mansoni* (Stirewalt, 1966) involve a succession of behavioural states shown by the movement of the cercariae over, into and through the skin, and they include the orderly and sequential release of secretions from the acetabular glands. Penetration is along the line of least resistance in the skin. Obviously movement of the schistosomulum is critical, but the extent to which enzymes and perhaps other secretions help is not entirely certain.

It is generally believed that initial entry into the skin is mechanical. The schistosomulum makes vigorous movements of the muscular oral region and the tail. Secretions from the post-acetabular glands are sticky, and give the organism some degree of purchase. The secretions are also alkaline, and this may soften and degrade the barrier (Stirewalt, 1966), provided the pH is high enough. However, McKerrow *et al.* (1983) believe that initial invasion of the skin is probably facilitated by a proteinase from the pre-acetabular gland, i.e. both mechanical and enzymatic activity are involved. Whatever the mechanism, the process is quick; on human skin less than 0.5 minutes was involved in "exploration" and entry was accomplished in about 7 minutes (Stirewalt and Hackey, 1956).

Once the schistosomulum is beneath the horny outer layer, the pre-acetabular glands secrete copiously. Their secretions (Stirewalt, 1978) contain a serine proteinase, resembling vertebrate chymotrypsin (Landsperger *et al.*, 1982) which is active against the peptide core of cartilage proteoglycan, but has no effect on soluble or fibrillar collagen. It seems, however, to be slowly replaced as invasion proceeds, by a metalloproteinase, which is unique to the schistosomulum, and is the dominant enzyme activity detected after 24 hours (Keene *et al.*, 1983). This enzyme has little activity against elastin and collagen, but degraded, trypsin-labile glycoprotein in the connective tissue matrix is used as substrate.

Probably not enough is known about the migration of the schistosomulum to assess the roles and significance of these two enzymes. In any event the pre-acetabular gland also contains calcium as calcium carbonate (Gordon and Griffiths, 1951; Dresden and Asch, 1977; Davies, 1983): Ca^{2+} could help disaggregate anionic proteoglycan (Landsperger *et al.*, 1982), so that migration might be assisted by at least two components of the pre-acetabular gland, one proteolytic, the other cationic. Ca^{2+} is also necessary for the action of some metalloproteinases.

The contents of the acetabular glands are exhausted within the first hour of infection, when small numbers of cercariae penetrate, and although distal portions of the ducts retain secretions for several hours (Stirewalt, 1963) it seems likely that these glands do not contribute to later events. It is not clear how subsequent migration takes place. Crabtree and Wilson (1985) have proposed that secretions from the head glands together with the head spines might be important, and Salafsky *et al.* (1984a) have suggested that cercarial prostaglandins might promote penetration by release of histamine.

3. *Conversion of cercaria to schistosomulum*

(a) Introduction. As soon as the cercaria begins to invade the skin it undergoes a conversion or "transmogrification" into a schistosomulum. This involves very extensive irreversible and progressive changes which are the first steps in, and are essential to, infection. Until a cercaria has transformed it cannot develop *in vitro* (Clegg, 1965) or, presumably, *in vivo*. There seems to be no information on how these changes are regulated or controlled, but it is clear that many of them take place very quickly, within an hour of invasion of the skin. They do not involve cell growth, multiplication or division (Stirewalt, 1974).

(b) The changes involved in transformation. Stirewalt (1974) has tabulated some 20 characters which change during transformation, and more recently others have been added (Stirewalt *et al.*, 1983; Cousin *et al.*, 1986b). The changes include:
(i) Water tolerance. Cercariae can survive in water, but schistosomula cannot;
(ii) Replacement of the trilaminate plasma membrane of the cercaria with a heptalaminate "double membrane" in the schistosomulum;
(iii) Migration of coiled membranous inclusions from the tegumentary cell body through the cytoplasmic bridges into the epidermal syncytium;
(iv) Loss of the glycocalyx early in transformation;
(v) Loss of the "cercarienhüllen reaktion" which results from the interaction of the glycocalyx with antibodies in antischistosome serum;
(vi) Development of a capacity to survive after freezing and fast thawing. Cercariae invariably die when so treated;
(vii) Migration of granules from glands to cells lining the lumen of the oesphagus;

(vii) Change of nuclei from a heterochromatic to a euchromatic state.

(c) Rate of change. Many of these changes take place quickly. For example the replacement of the trilaminate surface membrane with a heptalaminate one requires about 60 minutes (Hockley and McLaren, 1973). At the same time, microvilli form on the surface and are then lost within 90 minutes. These and similar early developments are probably too quick to be accounted for by protein synthesis induced by contact with skin (McLaren and Hockley, 1976) and indeed, the requirement for DNA-dependent RNA synthesis is very low initially, but slowly increases after about 5 hours (Nagai *et al.*, 1977). It seems reasonable to suppose therefore that these changes rely on transcription from a gene set during the sporocyst phase in the molluscan intermediate host.

4. *The trigger for conversion of cercaria to schistosomulum*

(a) Role of skin lipids. It has long been known that lipids on the surface of the skin set in train what Stirewalt (1974) has called "a series of progressive and interrelated steps", the "penetration response" (Wagner, 1959; Clegg, 1969; Stirewalt, 1971; reviewed by Stirewalt, 1974).

On the skin of the chicken the active fraction for *Austrobilharzia terrigalensis* is cholesterol (Clegg, 1969), but for *S. mansoni* and *Schistosomatium douthitti* the unsaturated fatty acid fraction seems to be important. This is so whether the cercarial response is tested on animal membranes (Austin *et al.*, 1972; Gilbert *et al.*, 1972) or on agar containing the appropriate lipid fraction (MacInnis, 1969; Shiff *et al.*, 1972). A piece of skin, an inert membrane coated with lipid, or a glass slide coated with skin lipid will evoke the penetration response. Although temperature is important for the initial steps in penetration, it is clear that the primary element is provided by skin lipid (Stirewalt, 1971). If the temperature of the surface is suitable, then in the absence of lipid, the cercariae of *S. mansoni* seem limited to attachment and creeping or "exploring" (Haas, 1976; Haas and Schmitt, 1978). Ultimately they swim away.

Haas and Schmitt (1982a) have examined a wide range of substances for their capacity to evoke a penetration response when made up in agar. Penetration into the agar was stimulated only by aliphatic hydrocarbon chains with a hydrophilic as well as a lipophilic end group. While saturated substances were effective at chain lengths between 10 and 15 carbon atoms, unsaturated molecules were effective at longer (C-16, C-18) chain lengths. Moreover, their effectiveness was enhanced when the number of double bonds in the *cis* position was increased. Active substances were lethal, even at very low concentrations, apparently because they reacted with specific receptor sites (Haas and Schmitt, 1982b) in the cercariae and set in train events which led to changes in the tegument. These were manifested as an incapacity to survive in water and a reduction in the "cercarienhüllen reaktion".

It is particulary interesting to note that free fatty acids are especially abundant on the human skin. Moreover, their chemical characteristics correspond to those which Haas and Schmitt (1982a) showed are needed for an effective penetration response. This observation is important. Just as the metacercaria of *F. hepatica* and the infective juvenile of *H. contortus* utilize particular and special characteristics of the ovine alimentary tract to initiate infection, so it seems does *S. mansoni* on the human skin, and we can accept with some confidence that we are concerned with the natural signals, and not with artefacts.

(b) Eicosanoid production and the penetration response. The synthesis of arachidonate metabolites, including prostaglandins, leukotrienes and hydroxyeicosatetraenoic acids is referred to as "ecosanoid production" (Fusco *et al.*, 1985). Salafsky *et al.* (1984a) have drawn attention to the role of some essential fatty acids in ecosanoid production, and more particularly, prostaglandin synthesis. Fatty acids of the octadecatrienoic (linolenic) and octadecadienoic (linoleic) groups can be converted to intermediates which give rise to physiologically active prostaglandins. These same fatty acids are potent stimulants of the penetration response (Austin *et al.*, 1972; Shiff *et al.*, 1972; Haas and Schmitt, 1978, 1982a).

Compounds which inhibit eicosanoid synthesis change the behaviour of cercariae in response to octadecatrienoic and octadecadienoic acids and inhibit penetration of isolated rat skin (Salafsky *et al.*, 1984b). Cercariae produce a wide range of eicosanoids when stimulated to initiate the penetration response by octadecadienoate. While it is too early to assess the full significance of this research, it seems that eicosanoid production is necessary for successful penetration of skin (Fusco *et al.*, 1985).

However, if fatty acids are required for the synthesis of eicosanoids in penetrating cercariae, then some mechanism for uptake of lipid is needed. Moreover, the schistosomule cannot synthesize its own lipid *de novo*, and presumably substantial amounts of lipid would have been needed to synthesize the double trilaminate membrane, leaving insufficient for other requirements. Rumjanek *et al.* (1983) have identified a serum-induced receptor in schistosomulae on which serum lipoproteins can be absorbed and presumably internalized and degraded.

(c) Temperature as a trigger for conversion. Methods are available for the production of schistosomula from cercariae *in vitro*. These do not depend

upon the presence of skin lipids, but involve a variety of systems, some of which seem to be purely physical, e.g. centrifugation or passage through a syringe, followed by incubation. These techniques, although known for some time, have recently been re-evaluated, partly because they offer a means of producing large numbers of schistosomula for experimental work (Cousin *et al.*, 1986b). Stirewalt *et al.* (1983) have concluded that the only treatment common to all techniques was incubation in a culture medium at 37° C for about 2 hours or more. They have proposed that "an isotonic but nonlethal environment, which is undoubtedly stressful for the cercariae and is warmer than the cercarial water medium, both triggers and supports the cercaria-to-schistosomule conversion".

The most simple media now available are physiological saline and phosphate-buffered saline. Although transformation is slower than in more favourable media, it clearly takes place here in the absence of lipid (Cousin *et al.*, 1986a).

(d) Evaluation of schistosomula produced by in vitro *techniques.*

(i) Techniques employed. Some methods for production of schistosomula involve passage through dried rat skin or incubation in serum or lactalbumin hydrolysate. In others, cercariae are treated in a variety of ways, including centrifugation, alternation of low and high temperatures and needle-passage, and subsequent incubation for various intervals. These details have been summarized by Stirewalt *et al.* (1983), who modified the different procedures only by providing a uniform incubation medium, containing lactalbumin hydrolysate in Earle's solution. Further evaluation has been carried out by Cousin *et al.* (1986b), who incubated the transforming cercariae in a similar medium, with the addition of 10% pooled human serum, presumably containing lipids in some form, together with antibiotics.

(ii) Comparison of schistosomula *in vivo* and *in vitro*. In Table 2 we have summarized some of the results obtained by Stirewalt *et al.* (1983) and Cousin *et al.* (1986a,b). The time taken for some selected characteristics of schistosomula to appear is compared with the times for transformation *in vivo*, using earskin of anaesthetized mice.

Some events associated with transformation are almost as quick *in vitro* as *in vivo* (Table 2). They include the development of intolerance to water, formation of the double surface membrane and the appearance of granules from certain glands in the cells lining the lumen of the oesophagus. Because these events, both *in vitro* and *in vivo*, take place very quickly, it seems they must be ones for which the transforming cercaria is well prepared. For example, the synthesis of the components for the new membranes is presumably carried out when the cercaria is developing in the sporocyst within the molluscan host. The appearance of granules in the cytoplasmic

TABLE 2

Comparison of the time taken for transformation in vitro *of cercaria of* Schistosoma mansoni *to schistosomulum, compared with the time taken* in vivo

Production of schistosomula *in vitro* by	Time of incubation (hr) *in vitro* to attain stages comparable with schistosomula *in vivo* 1 hr				
	Intolerant of water	Double surface membrane extensively developed	Granules in mucosal epithelium	Glycocalyx lost	Euchromatic nuclei
Dried rat skin	3	3	1	1–3	6–24
Centrifuged/vortexed	1.3	1.3	1–3	3–6	24–48
Syringe-passaged	2	2	1–3	6–24	24–48
Omnimixed	3	3	1–3	6–24	24–48
Centrifuged/incubated	3	3	1–3	6–24	24–48
Serum (50% in Earle's salt solution)	3	3	1	3–6	6–24
Lactalbumin hydrolysate (0.5% in Earle's salt solution)	3	3	1–3	6–24	24–48
Physiological saline	3	3	3	6–24	48–72
Production of schistosomula *in vivo*	1	1	1	1	1

SOURCES:
Stirewalt *et al.*, 1983: Data on reaction to water; presence of double membrane; changes *in vivo* (except granules in mucosa).
Cousin *et al.*, 1986b: Data on granules in mucosa; loss of glycocalyx; euchromatic nuclei.
Cousin *et al.*, 1986a: All data on schistosomulae in saline.
Cousin *et al.*, 1981: Data on granules in mucosa *in vivo*.

bridges leading to the surface syncytium is a very early event (Hockley and McLaren, 1973), and these are presumably precursors in the formation of new membrane. As McLaren and Hockley (1976) suggest, the changes associated with the formation of the double membrane are too quick to be accounted for by protein synthesis initiated by the experimental treatment.

Other events must similarly be pre-arranged. The granules which appear in the oesophageal epithelial cells for example, are probably connected with the need for the onset of feeding and digestion (Cousin *et al.*, 1986b) and are presumably synthesized in the glands long before the cercaria encounters a real or substitute host.

If the hypothesis that temperature is the stimulus for conversion to schistosomule is correct, it may mean that many different cells are independently activated so that various products already present can be secreted or polymerized. Alternatively, temperature may act on a single cell or group of cells which then regulate and control the diverse and complex events which go to make the transformation, an hypothesis which implies the existence of an endocrine system. In any event, the early events are too quick to be induced by the action of temperature on "heat shock genes" (van der Ploeg *et al.*, 1985).

Not all the events described in Table 2 are as quick *in vitro* as *in vivo*. In particular, the development of euchromatic nuclei is for the most part 24 to 48 times slower than *in vivo*. Euchromatic nuclei are probably those in which selected genes have become activated, and begin to direct the development of the adult fluke. It seems that these products start to become important in the adult fluke after 6 hours from commencement of conversion (Nagai *et al.*, 1977).

Perhaps *Schistosoma* responds to contact with the host in much the same way as the nematode parasite, *Haemonchus*. The first steps in the association involve events which must take place quickly, and in *Haemonchus* and related species these are controlled by an endocrine system (Section III C). At the same time, the gene set which controls development of the parasite must become active. Perhaps in *Schistosoma* as in *Haemonchus*, transformation involves two separate events. One, short-term and very urgent, concerns immediate events in transformation. The other is slow, because it requires the activity of particular gene sets, and is a preparation for future development.

If this view is correct for *Schistosoma*, some of the short-term events at least can clearly be triggered by temperature. Presumably it is the lack of a suitable medium which delays those schistosomula *in vitro* compared with those *in vivo*. This delay can be very great, as with the loss of the glycocalyx (Table 2); however, temperature seems particularly ineffective in converting nuclei to the euchromatic state. Is this because something more than temperature is required? Do skin lipids play an important role here?

Although it is clear that the schistosomules produced by some or all of these *in vitro* techniques eventually resemble those produced by passage through the skin of a living animal, it seems that they might be deficient in two ways. First, they are apparently denied for many hours the products of gene activity stimulated by normal invasion. Second, in some of these techniques, they would not encounter lipid or lipoprotein from serum or any other source. Presumably then, eicosanoid synthesis would be deficient.

5. *Conclusions*

It is clear that, at least for *S. mansoni*, temperature is critical, and that even in very simple *in vitro* systems at a suitable temperature, some aspects of transformation can proceed. However, other aspects of transformation are delayed substantially compared with *in vivo* schistosomula, particularly the development of euchromatic nuclei. This implies that some additional components are needed, perhaps skin lipid.

Clearly it is not possible to make any generalizations about the penetration of skin by cercariae from one species alone, and much more information is needed about other species. This is particularly true about species which penetrate the integument of poikilotherms, for example the invasion of fish by cercariae of *Diplostomum spathaceum* (Haas, 1974a,b; 1975).

VI. Cestoda

A. Introduction

In cyclophyllidean cestodes, a strobilate form occurs in the definitive host and a metacestode, variously a cysticercus, cysticercoid or hydatid cyst, in the intermediate host. The link between the strobilate form and the metacestode is a capsule or "egg" containing an infective embryo, called an oncosphere or hexacanth embryo, which must be eaten by the intermediate host. The definitive host becomes infected when it eats the metacestode. We are here concerned with the ways in which oncospheres and metacestode are released from their enveloping membranes and prepared for development in their respective hosts. Space prevents a detailed analysis of this subject, and we have referred to a few papers only, which illustrate aspects we believe are especially important.

B. Emergence of the Taeniid Oncosphere

The taeniid "egg" is strictly a capsule and the so-called "shell" is composed of embryonic membranes (Ubelaker, 1980). Emergence of the oncosphere, or "hatching of eggs" of pseudophyllidean cestodes has been thoroughly reviewed by Lethbridge (1980), and we therefore confine ourselves mainly to a discussion of his conclusions.

Emergence *in vitro* of the oncosphere requires somewhat similar stimuli to those for excystation of some metacercarial and coccidial oocyts. The event involves two processes. In the first, enzymes like trypsin disaggregate the blocks of which the outermost layer or embryophore is composed. The oncosphere apparently makes no contribution to these events. In the second process, bile from the host changes the permeability of an inner membranous lamina and at the same time, the oncosphere becomes active. It is not clear whether this activity is a consequence of changed permeability of the membranous lamina, or of direct action of bile on the embryo. However, movement of the embryo, particularly of its hooks, may be responsible for rupture of the membrane (Huffman and Jones, 1962). This pattern, with minor variations, prevails for all species so far examined.

It is clear that the stimuli for emergence *in vitro* are also present in the alimentary tract of the host. If we make some assumptions about their concentration and time of exposure, then we might conclude that these stimuli are indeed the signals which operate *in vivo*. Emergence then, would simply be a consequence of removal of the embryonic envelopes, aided minimally by movement of the oncosphere itself. Many questions are not yet answered; in particular we do not know the mechanisms which switch the oncosphere to an actively growing metacestode.

C. EMERGENCE OF OTHER CYCLOPHYLLIDAE

There is insufficient information about the emergence of oncospheres of non-taeniid species to enable any general conclusions to be made (Lethbridge, 1980). Most information which is available relates to the hymenolepid spp., in which the intermediate hosts are arthropods. The first step in emergence is mechanical removal or disruption of the egg shell, or embryonic envelope, by the arthropodal mandibles. Only after this treatment can the embryo become active and emerge. Lethbridge (1980) has proposed that the changes in the embryos, or "activation", involve a change in the balance of ions and water, but no experimental evidence is available. It is clear, however, that even in the activated oncosphere, breakdown of the inner envelope and embryophore is quick, and the process is passive; the oncosphere contributes nothing, as tests with dead eggs have shown.

D. EXCYSTMENT AND EVAGINATION OF CYCLOPHYLLIDEAN METACESTODES

1. *Introduction*

Most metacestodes are encysted in a cyst wall of their own formation, but others may be encapsulated in host tissue, or even both. Within the cyst, the scolex is commonly invaginated, and the metacestode shows little or no movement. Signals from the host ultimately determine or trigger both excystment and evagination, and also ensure that the dormant metacestode becomes very active. Excystment and evagination are separate processes, but as Smyth (1969) has pointed out, they follow one another so closely as to be indistinguishable.

It is usual to distinguish the cysticercus or "bladder worms" found in mammalian intermediate hosts and the cysticercoid, with a more complex and massive wall, found in invertebrate hosts. This difference is not superficial; its genesis can be discerned in the pattern of embryological development (Freeman, 1973; Slais, 1973; Ubelaker, 1983).

2. *Evagination of the cysticercus*

Campbell (1963) showed that the evagination of the cysticercus of *Taenia pisiformis* was a response to a range of surface-active compounds, and pointed out a correlation between evagination and surface tension (air–water interface). *In vitro* the surface-active properties of bile salts were sufficient to induce evagination. This proposal suggests a rather different role for bile, which is more commonly believed to denature and to disrupt biological membranes and envelopes of cestodes and trematodes. The histological pattern of the cysticerci of the species of *Taenia* is similar (Voge, 1967) and the idea seems worth exploring more widely.

3. *Excystation of the cysticercoid*

The stimuli which produce excystation and evagination of cysticerci *in vitro* are like those which are important for the emergence of oncospheres. The principal components are bile, enzymes, temperature and pH (Smyth, 1969). However, the requirement for these varies greatly between different species. For example, young cysts of *Hymenolepis diminuta* require only bile at the appropriate temperature to excyst, whereas *Hymenolepis nana*, *Hymenolepis citelli* and *Hymenolepis microstoma* require trypsin in addition (Rothman, 1959; Goodchild and Davis, 1972). On the other hand, as cysts of *H. diminuta* age, trypsin becomes necessary, and this is associated with occlusion of the anterior canal which is closed in the former species and becomes obstructed with age in the latter. Evidently, the requirement for this enzyme is linked with the complexity of the envelopes around the metacestode.

(a) Role of pepsin. Pepsin, at high $[H^+]$ speeds up excystation in some species *in vitro* (Rothman, 1959; Davis, 1975). Probably pepsin and $[H^+]$ have the same effect *in vivo* because old cysts, which excyst slowly *in vitro* in the absence of pepsin pretreatment, are as effective as young cysts in parasitizing mice (Davis, 1975). This sort of experiment is valuable because it helps to link observations *in vitro* with what happens in the host. Unfortunately, it is also rather rare.

(b) Role of bile and bile salts. Bogitsh (1967) suggested that bile salts released lysosomal acid hydrolases from the cysticercoid wall, which would disrupt the wall from within. Although this hypothesis is not supported by the observation that bile salts alone fail to produce excystation of *Hymenolepis microstoma* (Goodchild and Davis, 1982; Lippens-Mertens and De Rycke, 1973) it is important, because it is the first suggestion that the metacestode may make a positive contribution to excystment, other than by movement.

One way to study the role of bile in excystation is to examine microscopically cysticercoids before and after exposure. For example, Caley (1975) has shown that exposure to bile *in vitro* resulted in profound changes to the wall of the cystercoid of *H. nana*. The outer epidermal syncytium was eroded and cell membranes in the cyst wall became indistinct. Caley concluded that although bile salts were not directly responsible for activation of the scolex, they changed the permeability of the cyst. This might allow the diffusion inwards of an activating substance, or loss of an inhibitor (Caley, 1975). This hypothesis is similar to that proposed for the effect of bile on the activity of the oncosphere of taeniid eggs (Lethbridge, 1980). Perhaps the movement of ions or water is important. An investigation of the effects of bile on the movements of ion and water would be worthwhile.

E. CONCLUSIONS

The nature of the stimuli which induce emergence or excystation *in vitro* are well known for some species and satisfactory methods have been developed, for example in the preparation of cysticercoids for *in vitro* cultivation (Evans, 1980). Yet there is no general hypothesis to explain emergence or excystation, and how it happens *in vivo*. It is true that for a few species we can see what trypsin or bile does in a general way, but precise information is lacking. The oncosphere or metacestode, enclosed in its membranes, is usually inactive. There is no growth, no differentiation. Once the various envelopes have been removed, what restarts growth and differentiation? It seems unlikely to be trypsin or bile, which are concerned with the envelopes. It cannot be temperature alone. Clearly there is a fundamental gap in our understanding.

VII. Acanthocephala

A. Introduction

Members of this phylum have a complex life cycle. Adults live in the alimentary tract of vertebrates, and juvenile stages in an invertebrate, usually an arthropod (Crompton, 1970). We are concerned here with two species, *Moniliformis dubius*, adults of which live in rats and intermediate stages in cockroaches, and *Polymorphus minutus*, which lives in ducks and in species of *Gammarus*, a freshwater amphipod. Both species have two infective stages. The "egg" or shelled acanthor is released into the host's intestine and may be found in the faeces; it is infective for the intermediate host. The cystacanth, an encysted "resting stage", found in the body cavity of the intermediate host, is infective for the definitive host, in which it excysts.

B. Hatching of the Eggs of *Moniliformis dubius*

Eggs of *M. dubius* hatch *in vitro* in solutions of a number of electrolytes, of which the most effective is a 0.25 M solution of sodium (or potassium) chloride containing 0.02 M bicarbonate ion, which is more effective than phosphate ion (Edmonds, 1966). Greatest hatching was obtained in solutions of molarity 0.2–0.35 and at pH values above 7.5. At any given pH, the addition of CO_2 enhanced hatching. The stimulus was not needed all the time; brief exposure to the electrolytes was sufficient to trigger the hatching mechanism, so that hatching continued in the absence of the stimulus. While Edmonds (1966) could not be certain that the stimulus provided in these solutions was the same as signals in the gut of the cockroach, the timing of events was similar to that *in vivo*, and as Crompton (1970) has pointed out, the physico-chemical components of the medium would have been present in the alimentary tract of the cockroach. Whether other components in the gut, absent from Edmonds' media, were important is not known. Chitinase is present in the gut, but exogenous chitinase had no effect on eggs. On the other hand, chitinase was released from the eggs when they hatched;

presumably its natural substrate would be the third of the four major egg envelopes, which contains chitin (Wright, 1971).

When eggs were exposed to the stimulus, the acanthor began to move vigorously, and these movements, aided by the rostellar hooks and chitinase were important in hatching. The principal components of the stimulus are pH and the molar concentration of the salt solution; the optimum molarity was about 0.4 M, and hatching was reduced in solutions of lower (0.2) or higher (0.6) molarity. Eggs failed to hatch in solutions of sucrose, and it seemed that ionic rather than osmotic effects were the more important. The egg membranes in *M. dubius* are complex and we know little about their permeability and nothing about the exact nature of the stimulus which penetrates to the enclosed acanthor.

C. ACTIVATION OF THE CYSTACANTH

In both *M. dubius* and *P. minutus* the cystacanth is surrounded by a very thin membrane and the thorny proboscis is withdrawn into the body wall (Crompton, 1970). In the definitive host, the enclosed worm is said to become activated, which involves rapid evagination and invagination of the proboscis. This alone may be sufficient to tear the outer membrane.

The requirements for activation of both *M. dubius* (Graff and Kitzman, 1965) and *P. minutus in vitro* (Lackie, 1974) are similar. Temperatures must be near the body temperature of the host. In balanced salt solutions at neutral to alkaline pH, *P. minutus* is activated, and the effect is enhanced if bile or bile salts are added. On the other hand, *M. dubius* must have bile or bile salts for activation and, unlike *P. minutus*, it responds to the presence of CO_2.

The effect on *P. minutus* of bile salts (as sodium taurocholate) at different pH values was interesting; at high $[H^+]$ immersion in the bile salt had no visible effect, but on transfer to a balanced salt solution without bile, cysts were immediately activated. Lackie (1974) was successful in obtaining activation of *P. minutus* with both saponin and sodium fusidate, compounds with a structure not unlike bile salts and both able to act as biological surfactants. The results obtained with these and sodium taurocholate led Lackie (1974) to suggest that steroid configuration might be important. Further analyses using a variety of detergent-like substances may be profitable.

VIII. Excystation of Coccidia

A. INTRODUCTION

Excystation of coccidian oocysts of the genus *Eimeria* (Order Eucoccidiorida, subphylum Apicomplexa) has been studied in considerable detail. It is clear that there are close parallels between excystation of these organisms and comparable events in infective stages of platyhelminths and nematode parasites. The subject has been reviewed by Hammond (1973), Ryley (1973), Lackie (1975), Todd and Ernst (1977) and Wang (1982). We have drawn on these papers as a source of much of the literature.

B. THE GENERAL HYPOTHESIS OF EXCYSTMENT

It is now firmly established that, at least *in vitro*, excystation is a consequence of two separate and successive stimuli, a hypothesis originally formulated by Jackson (1962). The "primary phase" (Ryley, 1973) requires CO_2. The "secondary phase" is induced by crude preparations of trypsin and bile.

1. *Events in the primary phase*

The consequences of exposure to CO_2 are profound (Table 3). There are extensive changes to the wall of the oocyst, which becomes permeable so that a variety of stains can stain the inner wall, the sporocysts are no longer immune to osmotic shock and the contents as well as the oocyst wall are quickly destroyed in sodium hypochorite. More importantly, the oocysts can now respond by excysting when placed in trypsin and bile.

Eimeria arlongi, the species with which Jackson (1962) worked, would encounter high concentrations of CO_2 in the sheep's rumen. The redox potential of the ruminal contents is low, ranging from -210 to -260 mV (Dewey, Lee and Marston, 1958) and Jackson found that *in vitro*, the addition of reducing agents generally increased the effectiveness of the stimulus. However, it seems clear that the essential part of the stimulus is provided by CO_2. Temperature is also of great importance, and the stimulus was not effective below about 30° C. More recent work suggests that many species of *Eimeria* respond to CO_2 in much the same way as *E. arlongi* (Ryley, 1973; Todd and Ernst, 1977).

2. *Events in the secondary phase*

When exposed to trypsin and bile *in vitro*, cysts which have been pretreated

TABLE 3
The effect of exposure to CO_2 on the coccidian oocyst

Changes in oocyst after exposure to CO_2	References
Micropyle damaged	Jackson, 1962; Nyberg and Hammond, 1964; Nyberg *et al.*, 1968
Cysts become fragile	Bunch and Nyberg, 1970
Inner wall becomes thin and buckled	Jackson, 1964
Oocyst becomes permeable	Jackson, 1962, 1964; Nyberg and Hammond, 1964; Jensen *et al.*, 1976
Oocyst now responds to trypsin and bile	Jackson, 1962; Nyberg *et al.*, 1968
Stieda body of sporocysts altered	Hibbert, L. E., 1969 quoted in Hammond, 1973

with carbon dioxide undergo two obvious changes. First, the sporozoites become active within the sporocyst (Jackson, 1962; Nyberg and Hammond, 1964; Nyberg *et al.*, 1968). Second, the Stieda body and, where present, a substiedal body disintegrate (Jackson, 1962; Nyberg and Hammond, 1964; Hammond *et al.*, 1970). The Stieda body is a thickening at one end of the sporocyst and lies in a hole in the wall. Loss of this structure is necessary if the enclosed sporozoites are to make their way out of the sporocyst and eventually out of the oocyst.

C. MECHANISM OF THE PRIMARY PHASE

1. *The role of CO_2*

There are three major hypotheses on the role of CO_2 in excystment (Table 4). One holds that CO_2 leads to the production or activation of an enzyme(s) in the oocyst, the source of the enzyme variously being proposed as the sporozoites (Hibbert and Hammond, 1968) or the residual body (Ryley, 1973). The second proposes that reducing agents are important, with CO_2 acting in a secondary role, and the third hypothesis argues that in some species, the host's gizzard is more important than CO_2 in weakening the oocyst wall.

There is no direct evidence for the involvement of an enzyme in the changes which oocysts undergo in the primary phase. Hibbert and Hammond (1968) concluded from an examination of the relationship between

TABLE 4
Principal hypotheses on the mechanism of the primary phase of excystment of coccidian oocysts

Hypothesis	References
Carbon dioxide leads to release or activation of an enzyme(s) from within the cyst, which is responsible for changes in the permeability of the oocyst wall	Jackson, 1962 Hibbert and Hammond, 1968 Ryley, 1973 Jolley and Nyberg, 1974
Carbon dioxide acts directly on the oocyst wall to expose disulphide bonds which can then be cleaved by reducing agent	Jolley and Nyberg, 1974 Jensen *et al.*, 1976
Oocysts of species parasitic in gallinaceous birds are mechanically broken in the gizzard; this effect is enhanced because CO_2 makes oocysts fragile	Farr and Doran, 1962 Bunch and Nyberg, 1970

temperature and velocity of excystation, that CO_2 stimulated activation of an enzyme or an enzymatic rate-limiting step. The complexity of excystment may, however, be such that this conclusion is not warranted. Perhaps all that can be concluded is that some action is involved in which rate increases exponentially with temperature.

In other experiments, fluid in which oocysts had excysted was found to contain a heat-labile component, presumably an enzyme, which effectively completed the primary phase of excystment (Hammond, 1971). Jolley and Nyberg (1974) were unable to repeat a similar experiment with a different species, but if an enzyme is present it might be inactivated by trypsin used in the secondary phase, or may simply be very unstable. There now seem to be no grounds for the proposal that leucine aminopeptidase is involved in excystment (Wang and Stotish, 1978; Wang, 1982).

An alternative proposal for the role of CO_2 is that it acts on the oocyst wall to make the molecules more susceptible to the action of reducing agents (Jensen, *et al.*, 1976; Jolley *et al.*, 1976). This mechanism could account for the substantial increase in sulphydryl groups which follows treatment with CO_2.

It is not clear how relevant this hypothesis is to the events in the gut of the host. If the hypothesis was correct, it might be expected that treatment with reducing agent and CO_2 would induce the same changes in oocysts of unsporulated or incompletely sporulated oocysts as it does in mature ones, but this does not happen (Jackson, 1964); only viable sporulated oocyts respond.

The use of reducing agents in experiments with oocysts probably derived from Jackson's demonstration that in sheep they enhanced the effect of CO_2. Even so, reducing conditions were not obligatory. *In vitro*, strong solutions of reducing agents might be expected to disrupt oocyst walls. While it is clear that parts of the alimentary tract such as the rumen and intestine have reducing tendencies (Dewey *et al.*, 1958; Metrick and Podesta, 1974) measurements of Eh are not an estimate of the amounts of reducing substances present. It does not necessarily follow that strong solutions of reducing agents *in vitro*, which might have profound and widespread effects on oocyts, reproduce conditions found in the gut.

Carbon dioxide can be replaced *in vitro* with nitric oxide or H_2S, although these gases are less effective (Jensen *et al.*, 1976). Their effect might be related to their status as reducing agents. But H_2S can also substitute for CO_2 as a stimulus for exsheathment of the nematode *N. dubius* (Section III, B). While it may well have a direct effect on the oocyst wall, it may also act as an undissociated acid and have more fundamental effects on excystation (Petronijevic *et al.*, 1985).

2. *Mechanical stress and CO_2*

Sporcysts of poultry coccidia are liberated when the oocysts pass through the gizzard (Farr and Doran, 1962). Although these species clearly respond to the presence of CO_2, much quicker excystation is obtained *in vitro* when oocysts are first mechanically damaged and then incubated in bile and trypsin (Hibbert and Hammond, 1968). These observations support the idea that mechanical stress on the oocyst is an important part of the process of excystation in gallinaceous birds (Doran and Farr, 1962; Bunch and Nyberg, 1970). There seems to be no direct evidence that oocysts are damaged in this way in the gizzard, for example by examination of dead oocysts or unsporulated oocysts after passage through the gizzard. Yet excystation of *Eimeria acervulina* is very quick (Doran and Farr, 1962) and while it seems very probable that mechanical crushing is important, if it is not, there must be an alternative and most potent stimulus. This might involve CO_2 at particular and critical pH values.

D. MECHANISM OF THE SECONDARY PHASE

1. *Hypotheses*

The principal hypotheses about the action of exogenous enzymes, commonly "trypsin", together with bile or bile salts in the secondary phase of excystment are shown in Table 5. In species in which the cap over the micropyle lifts or splits, there seems no reason to doubt that enzymes and bile gain entrance to the oocyst and are in contact with the sporocyst. In other species, in which it seems that the cap over the micropyle merely becomes thinner, it is assumed that they enter. Perhaps bile in these instances does facilitate entry of enzymes as Hibbert *et al.* (1969) proposed, but we have no direct information. There is however, much evidence that oocysts are permeable to a variety of molecules after passing through the primary phase, and these may include proteins and bile salts or acids. Certainly, circumstantial evidence suggests that both may gain entrance to the oocyst; many investigators have shown that the response of mechanically isolated sporocysts to bile and trypsin is the same as that seen within oocysts after appropriate treatment and exposure to bile and enzymes. For example, within the oocyst the Stieda body disappears and the sporozoites become active in *E. arlongi* (Jackson, 1962); these changes are similar in principle to those seen in mechanically isolated sporocysts of *E. acervulina* or *Eimeria utahensis* immersed in comparable media (Doran and Farr, 1962; Hammond *et al.*, 1970).

It does not of course necessarily follow that because sporocyts recovered mechanically excyst in exogenous enzymes and bile, these same agents operate within the oocyst in the host's gut. But evidence on the location of excystation *in vivo* (Doran and Farr, 1962; Nyberg and Hammond, 1964) clearly supports the hypothesis that the host's bile and enzymes are critical for excystment. Moreover, normal excystment is not possible when oocysts are enclosed within dialysis tubing and placed in the host's gut (Jackson,

TABLE 5

Hypotheses proposed to account for the involvement of enzymes and bile in the secondary phase of excystment of coccidial oocyts

Hypothesis	References
Enzyme and bile enter oocyst where bile alters the surface of the Stieda body so that the enzyme can act on it.	Doran and Farr, 1962
Bile facilitates entrance of enzymes through the altered micropyle.	Hibbert, *et al.*, 1969
Enzymes and bile trigger release of enzymes by sporozoites.	Doran, 1966
Enzymes and bile enter sporocyst and induce activity in sporozoites.	Farr and Doran, 1962 Nyberg and Hammond, 1964

1962), but subsequent exposure to enzyme and bile induces excystment (Nyberg and Hammond, 1964). Whether, as Doran (1966) suggests, the sporozoites themselves produce enzymes which aid in their release is unknown.

2. *Roles of bile and bile salts*

Bile, or salts of bile, are needed in the secondary phase of excystment for all species so far examined, except perhaps, the sporocysts of *Eimeria bovis* (Hibbert *et al.*, 1969; Table 6). However, bile alone is without effect; it works in conjunction with trypsin. Bile can be replaced by surface-active agents, including Tween 80 (Doran and Farr, 1962; Jackson, 1962). One role proposed is that it breaks down protein or lipoprotein membranes (Table 5), although there seems to be no direct evidence that it does so in excystation. Another role for bile is induction of activity in sporozoites (Table 5). There is good evidence that sporozoites become very active when either oocysts which have been treated with CO_2, or sporozoites which have been mechanically released, are exposed to bile or bile salts. This effect is probably direct, i.e. the bile passes into the sporocyst (Table 5). Certainly direct application of bile to merozoites of *Eimeria* spp. in tissue culture has a dramatic effect on motility (Speer *et al.*, 1970). Speer (1983) has proposed that bile may enhance motility by altering the permeability of membranes. If an influx of calcium ions followed, this might enhance microtubular sliding, and hence motility.

The induction of activity seems likely to be an important aspect of excystation, because it is necessary if sporozoites are to escape from sporocyst and oocyst. It might also be necessary if any enzymes are to be discharged from sporozoites.

3. *Enzymes*

Trypsin of varying degrees of purity is commonly used in conjunction with bile salts to produce excystation in the secondary phase (Table 6). Almost without exception, specific inhibitors have not been used to check the assumption that trypsin itself is important. At least for *Eimeria tenella*, and probably other species, chymotrypsin is the enzyme involved in the secondary phase (Wang and Stotish, 1975). Chymotrypsin, or crude trypsin, is not effective against most species unless it is accompanied by bile; only with *E. acervulina* does a significant proportion excyst with enzyme alone (Table 6). The substrate on which the enzyme acts presumably includes the Stieda body, which usually swells and disappears. Whether it acts anywhere else is not known.

TABLE 6

Requirement for bile and enzyme, separately or together, for excystment of species of Eimeria

Species	OO–Oocyst SP–Mechanically released sporocysts	Treatment and % Excystment			Reference
		Bile only	Enzyme[a] only	Bile and Enzyme[a]	
E. acervulina	SP	None	Variable: usually <2%	>85%	Doran and Farr, 1962
E. arlongi	OO	None	None	>85%	Jackson, 1962
E. bovis	SP	Not tested	Excysted (%?)	>80%	Hibbert and Hammond, 1968
E. bovis	OO	None	6%	>90%	Hibbert *et al.*, 1969
E. callospermophili	SP	None	Excysted (%?)	54%	Roberts *et al.*, 1970
E. larimerensis	SP	None	Excysted (%?)	83%	Roberts *et al.*, 1970

[a] Commonly, impure preparations of trypsin.

E. SUMMARY AND CONCLUSIONS

It is clear that excystations *in vitro* of the coccidia so far examined involves two steps, in the first of which CO_2 is important, and the second, in which an external source of chymotrypsin and surface-active agents are required. However, the details of the mechanism of excystment are not clear. We do not know how the presence of CO_2 changes the permeability of the oocyst wall. We do not know whether CO_2 does anything to the sporozoite or sporocyst; the circumstance that mechanically-released sporocysts readily excyst under appropriate conditions without the necessity for high concentrations of, or perhaps any, CO_2 suggests it does not.

Circumstantial evidence suggests that the substrate in which chymotrypsin acts is the Stieda body, but whether the enzyme has other roles we do not know. Similarly, the role of bile is ill-defined, although it does seem that the induction of activity is important—but how is this brought about?

The techniques available to excyst oocysts are, for many species, very efficient. If CO_2 is, as it seems to be, a fundamental stimulus, then efficiency might be enhanced if more attention was given, not so much to increasing the time of exposure and amount of CO_2 in the gas phase, but rather to the pH of the medium, which is rarely stated or apparently, controlled. The pH determines the proportion of the different carbonate species in solution, which may be of greater significance than the partial pressure of CO_2 in the gas phase (see also Section V A).

Although high numbers of excysted sporocysts can be obtained with a particular technique, this does not necessarily mean that all the signals supplied by the host are reproduced *in vitro*. Jackson (1962) found it necessary to wash oocysts in water or dilute buffers between the primary phase and the secondary phase, a step which implies a deficiency in the methods he used. Commonly, oocysts are exposed to a strong solution of L-cysteine. Does this reflect a general deficiency in the technique, or a counterpart of strongly reducing conditions in ruminant and non-ruminant alike? It seems that we have only a very general outline of excystment, and that we do not understand the details. Yet the problem seems to have been put aside; the most recent relevant reference we have found is dated 1983.

IX. DISCUSSION

The signals which induce development of the early stages of parasites are best understood in nematodes. Here, those infective stages which have been closely studied have ceased development after apolysis and before ecdysis. Both free-living and parasitic nematodes moult. The infective stage is different only in that development is delayed, and is resumed on a signal from the host. This sets in train an immediate and urgent event like ecdysis and activates the gene set governing the next developmental stage.

While the infective stages of parasitic nematodes do not differ greatly from their free-living relations, the trematodes, cestodes and acanthocephalans have profoundly specialized infective stages. The membranes or cysts which envelop them are not seen at any other stage of the life cycle. There seems to be an increasing reliance for escape from these membranes on direct action by the host, using enzymes, bile or mechanical means to break them open. In the cestodes particularly, loss of the enveloping membranes seems to be almost entirely "passive", in that the enclosed juvenile plays no part. Signals from the host act directly on the membranes. Some coccidia and trematodes may be like this too, but the evidence suggests that others may rely both on direct action from the host and may also themselves contribute enzymes for the same purpose.

All the parasites we have examined undergo immediate and profound structural changes when they enter the host. But what signal turns on the appropriate gene set for the ensuing developmental stage? In nematodes one signal leads to both structural change, namely ecdysis, and switches on the gene set. In the cercaria of *S. mansoni* temperature induces immediate change, and we have speculated that free fatty acids might be part of a signal which initiates transcription. In the cestodes it may be enough to remove the enveloping membranes; transcription in the juvenile may be triggered by a profound change in the ionic environment which follows their loss.

No clear hypothesis has emerged about the way bile acts. Surface-active agents are well known to be capable of denaturing proteins (Attwood and Florence, 1983) and this property may lead to changes like those described in cysticercoids of *H. nana* after exposure to bile (Caley, 1975). But bile salts and other classes of surface-active agents can alter the permeability of membranes (Attwood and Florence, 1983). Changes in permeability of cysts or surface membranes of enclosed organisms might be important triggers for emergence or for inducing transcription. These ideas are foreshadowed in the views of the action of bile held by Caley (1975), Lethbridge (1980) and Speer (1983).

Space has not allowed us to examine other important systems of host signals. These include the signals involved in penetration of a molluscan host by miracidia and subsequent metamorphosis to a sporocyst; these events may have much in common with the attachment and metamorphosis of the oncomiracidium of *Entobdella* on its host (Kearn, 1967). A second area of interest concerns the signals from the roots of host plants to which nematode parasites respond.

Very little work is now being done on the nature of host signals and their effects. Yet the subject is one of great significance for our understanding of parasitism. Moreover, considerable information can be obtained from simple experiments and with basic apparatus. For these reasons alone, and with financial constraints now so common, this area of research may experience a resurgence of activity.

ACKNOWLEDGEMENTS

One of us (W.P.R.) wishes to acknowledge assistance given by grants from the Australian Research Grants Committee and the UNDP/WHO special programme for Research and Training in Tropical Diseases (ID 850199). We gratefully acknowledge secretarial help from Miss S. H. Lawson, Mrs H. Kimber and Mrs S. Thomas. We are especially grateful to Dr C. E. Cousin, Dr M. A. Stirewalt, Dr C. E. Dorsey and Dr L. P. Watson, for allowing us to quote from their unpublished manuscripts.

REFERENCES

Anya, A. O. (1966). Experimental studies on the physiology of hatching of eggs of *Aspiculuris tetraptera* Schulz (Oxyuridea: Nematoda). *Parasitology* **56,** 733–744.

Asanji, M. F. and Williams, M. O. (1974). Studies on the excystment of trematode metacercaria *in vivo*. *Journal of Helminthology* **48,** 85–91.

Asanji, M. F. and Williams, M. O. (1975). Studies on the excystment of trematode metacercariae *in vitro*. *Zeitschrift für Parasitenkunde* **47,** 151–163.

Attwood, D. and Florence, A. T. (1983). "Surfactant systems". Chapman and Hall, London.

Austin, F. G., Stirewalt, M. A. and Danziger, R. E. (1972). *Schistosoma mansoni*: stimulatory effect of rat skin lipid fractions on cercarial penetration behaviour. *Experimental Parasitology* **31,** 217–224.

Bailey, M. A. (1968). The role of the host in initiation of development of the parasitic stage of *Trichostrongylus retortaeformis* (Nematoda). *Comparative Biochemistry and Physiology* **26,** 897–906.

Bass, H. S. and LeFlore, W. B. (1984). *In vitro* excystment of the metacercaria of *Acanthoparyphium spinulosum* (Trematoda: Echinostomatidae). *Proceedings of the Helminthological Society of Washington* **51,** 149–153.

Bird, A. F. (1971). "The Structure of Nematodes". Academic Press, New York.

Bogitsh, B. J. (1961). Histological and histochemical observations on the nature of the cyst of *Neoechinorhynchus cylindratus* in *Lepomis* sp. *Proceedings of the Helminthological Society of Washington* **28,** 75–81.

Bogitsh, B. J. (1967). Histochemical localization of some enzymes in cysticercoids of two species of *Hymenolepis*. *Experimental Parasitology* **21,** 373–379.

Bone, L. W. (1982). Chemotaxis of parasitic nematodes. *In* "Cues that Influence Behaviour of Internal Parasites" (W. S. Bailey, ed.), pp. 52–66. Agricultural

Research Service (Southern Region), U.S. Department of Agriculture, New Orleans.

Bunch, T. D. and Nyberg, P. A. (1970). Effects of carbon dioxide on coccidian oocysts from 6 host species. *Journal of Protozoology* **17,** 364–370.

Busa, W. B. and Nuccitelli, R. (1984). Metabolic regulation via intracellular pH. *American Journal of Physiology* **246,** R409–R438.

Caley, J. (1975). A comparative study of the two alternative larval forms of *Hymenolepis nana*, the dwarf tapeworm, with special reference to the process of excystment. *Zeitschrift für Parasitenkunde* **46,** 217–235.

Campbell, W. C. (1963). The efficacy of surface-active agents in stimulating evagination of cysticerci *in vitro*. *Journal of Parasitology* **49,** 81–84.

Cheng, T. C. and Thakur, A. S. (1967). Thermal activation and inactivation of *Philophthalmus gralli* metacercariae. *Journal of Parasitology* **53,** 212–213.

Christie, M. G. and Charleston, W. A. G. (1965). Stimulus to exsheathing of *Nematodirus battus* infective larvae. *Experimental Parasitology* **17,** 46–50.

Clegg, J. A. (1965). *In vitro* cultivation of *Schistosoma mansoni. Experimental Parasitology* **16,** 133–147.

Clegg, J. A. (1969). Skin penetration by cercariae of the bird schistosome *Austrobilharzia terrigalensis*: the stimulatory effect of cholesterol. *Parasitology* **59,** 973–989.

Clegg, J. A. (1972). The schistosome surface in relation to parasitism. *In* "Functional aspects of Parasite Surfaces" *British Society for Parasitology Symposia 10*. pp. 23–40. Blackwells, Oxford.

Cousin, C. E., Stirewalt, M. A. and Dorsey, C. H. (1981). *Schistosoma mansoni*: ultrastructure of early transformation of skin and shear-pressure-derived schistosomules. *Experimental Parasitology* **51,** 341–365.

Cousin, C. E., Stirewalt, M. A. and Dorsey, C. H. (1986a). *Schistosoma mansoni:* transformation of cercariae to schistosomules in ELAC, saline and phosphate-buffered saline. *Journal of Parasitology* **72**, 609–611.

Cousin, C. E., Stirewalt, M. A., Dorsey, C. H. and Watson, L. P. (1986b). *Schistosoma mansoni*: comparative development of schistosomules produced by artificial techniques. *Journal of Parasitology* **72**, 606–609.

Crabtree, J. E. and Wilson, R. A. (1985). *Schistosoma mansoni*: an ultrastructure examination of skin migration in the hamster cheek pouch. *Parasitology* **91,** 111–120.

Crompton, D. W. T. (1970). "An Ecological Approach to Acanthocephalan Physiology". Cambridge University Press, Cambridge.

Davey, K. G. (1976). Hormones and hormonal effects in parasitic nematodes. *In* "Biochemistry of Parasites and Host–Parasite Relationships" (H. van den Bossche, ed.), North Holland Publishing Company, Amsterdam.

Davey, K. G. and Goh, S. L. (1984). Ecdysis in a parasitic nematode: direct evidence for an ecdysial factor in the head. *Canadian Journal of Zoology* **62,** 2293–2296.

Davies, T. W. (1983). *Schistosoma mansoni*: the structure and elemental composition of pre-acetabular gland cells secretion in pre-emergent cercariae. *Parasitology* **87,** 55–60.

Davis, B. O. (1975). *Hymenolepis microstoma* (Cestoda): Effects of cysticeroid age on morphology, excystation and establishment. *Acta Parasitologica Polonica* **23,** 229–236.

Dennis, R. D. (1976). Insect morphogenetic hormones and developmental mechanisms in the nematode, *Nematospiroides dubius. Comparative Biochemistry and Physiology* **53A,** 53–56.

Despommier, D. D. (1982). Behavioural cues in migration and location of parasitic nematodes with special emphasis on *Trichinella spiralis*. *In* "Cues that Influence Behaviour of Internal Parasites" (W. S. Bailey, ed.), pp. 110–126. Agricultural Research Service (Southern Region), U.S. Department of Agriculture, New Orleans.

Dewey, D. W., Lee, H. J. and Marston, H. R. (1958). Provision of cobalt to ruminants by means of heavy pellets. *Nature* (*Lond.*) **181,** 1367–1371.

Dixon, K. E. (1964). Excystment of metacercariae of *Fasciola hepatica* L. *in vitro*. *Nature* (*Lond.*) **202,** 1240–1241.

Dixon, K. E. (1965). The structure and histochemistry of the cyst wall of the metacercaria of *Fasciola hepatica* L. *Parasitology* **55,** 215–226.

Dixon, K. E. (1966). The physiology of excystment of the metacercaria of *Fasciola hepatica* L. *Parasitology* **56,** 431–456.

Dixon, K. E. (1975). The structure and composition of the cyst wall of the metacercaria of *Cloacotrema narrabeenensis* (Howell and Bearup, 1967) (Digenea: Philophthalmidae). *International Journal for Parasitology* **5,** 113–118.

Doran, D. J. (1966). Pancreatic enzymes initiating excystation of *Eimeria acervulina* sporozoites. *Proceedings of the Helminthological Society of Washington* **33,** 42–43.

Doran, D. J. and Farr, M. M. (1962). Excystation of the poultry coccidium, *Eimeria acervulina*. *Journal of Protozoology* **9,** 154–161.

Dresden, M. H. and Asch, H. L. (1977). Calcium carbonate content of the preacetabular glands of *Schistosoma mansoni* cercariae. *Journal of Parasitology* **63,** 163–165.

Dubé, F. and Epel, D. (1986). The relationship between pH and the rate of protein synthesis in sea urchin eggs and the existence of a pH-dependent event triggered by ammonia. *Experimental Cell Research* **162,** 191–204.

Edmonds, S. J. (1966). Hatching of the eggs of *Moniliformis dubius*. *Experimental Parasitology* **19,** 216–226.

Edsall, J. T. and Wyman, J. (1958). "Biophysical Chemistry", Academic Press, New York.

Epel, D. (1978). Mechanisms of activation of sperm and eggs during fertilization of sea urchin gametes. *Current Topics in Developmental Biology* **12,** 185–246.

Erasmus, D. A. (1972). "The Biology of Trematodes". Edward Arnold, London.

Erasmus, D. A. and Bennett, L. J. (1965). A study of some of the factors affecting excystation *in vitro* of the metacercarial stages of *Holostephanus lühei Szidar, 1936 and Cyathocotyle bushiensis* Khan, 1962 (Strigeidae: Trematoda). *Journal of Helminthology* **39,** 185–196.

Evans, W. S. (1980). The cultivation of *Hymenolepis in vitro*. *In* "Biology of the Tapeworm, *Hymenolepis diminuta*" (H. P. Arai, ed.), pp. 425–448. Academic Press, London, New York.

Fairbairn, D. (1961). The *in vitro* hatching of *Ascaris lumbricoides* eggs. *Canadian Journal of Zoology* **39,** 153–162.

Farr, M. M. and Doran, D. J. (1962). Comparative excystation of four species of poultry coccidia. *Journal of Protozoology* **9,** 403–407.

Freeman, R. S. (1973). Ontogeny of cestodes and its bearing on their phylogeny and systematics. *Advances in Parasitology* **11,** 481–557.

Fried, B., Robbins, S. H. and Nelson, P. D. (1978). *In vivo* and *in vitro* excystation of *Zygocotyle lunata* (Trematoda) metacercariae and histochemical observations on the cyst. *Journal of Parasitology* **64,** 395–397.

Fried, B. and Huffman, J. E. (1982). Excystation and development in the chick and on

the chick chorioallantois of the metacercaria of *Sphaeridiotrema globulus* (Trematoda). *International Journal for Parasitology* **12,** 427–431.
Fried, B. and Roth, R. M. (1974). *In vitro* excystment of the metacercaria of *Parorchis acanthus*. *Journal of Parasitology* **60,** 465.
Fried, B. F. (1981). Thermal activation and inactivation of the metacercaria of *Philophthalmus hegeneri* Penner and Fried, 1963. *Zeitschrift für Parasitenkunde* **65,** 359–360.
Fusco, A. C., Salafsky, B. and Kevin, M. B. (1985). *Schistosoma mansoni*: eicosanoid production by cercariae. *Experimental Parasitology* **59,** 44–50.
Gilbert, B., Da Rosa, M. N., Borojevic, R. and Pellegrino, J. (1972). *Schistosoma mansoni: in vitro* transformation of cercariae into schistosomula. *Parasitology* **64,** 333–339.
Goh, S. L. and Davey, K. G. (1984). Occurrence of noradrenaline in the central nervous system of *Phocanema decipiens* and its possible role in the control of ecdysis. *Canadian Journal of Zoology* **63,** 475–479.
Goodchild, C. G. and Davis, B. O. (1972). *Hymenolepis microstoma* cysticercoid activation and excystation *in vitro* (Cestoda). *Journal of Parasitology* **58,** 735–741.
Gordon, R. M. and Griffiths, R. B. (1951). Observations on the means by which the cercariae of *Schistosoma mansoni* penetrate mammalian skin, together with an account of certain morphological changes observed in the newly penetrated larvae. *Annals of Tropical Medicine and Parasitology* **45,** 227–243.
Graff, D. J. and Kitzman, W. B. (1965). Factors influencing the activation of acanthocephalan cystacanths. *Journal of Parasitology* **51,** 424–429.
Haas, W. (1974a). Analyse der Invasionsmechanismen der Cercariae von *Diplostomum spathaceum*—I. Fixation und Penetration. *International Journal for Parasitology* **4,** 311–319.
Haas, W. (1974b). Analyse der Invasionsmechanismen der Cercariae von *Diplostomum spathaceum*—II. Chemische Invasionsstimuli. *International Journal for Parasitology* **4,** 321–330.
Haas, W. (1975). Einfluss von CO_2 und pH auf das Fixationsverhalten der Cercariae von *Diplostomum spathaceum* (Trematoda). *Zeitschrift für Parasitenkunde* **46,** 53–60.
Haas, W. (1976). Die Anheftung (Fixation) der Cercarie von *Schistosoma mansoni*. *Zeitschrift für Parasitenkunde* **49,** 63–72.
Haas, W. and Schmitt, R. (1978). Chemical stimuli for penetration of *Schistosoma mansoni* cercariae. *Naturwissenschaften* **65,** 110.
Haas, W. and Schmitt, R. (1982a). Characterization of chemical stimuli for the penetration of *Schistosoma mansoni* cercariae. I. Effective substances, host specificity. *Zeitschrift für Parasitenkunde* **66,** 293–307.
Haas, W. and Schmitt, R. (1982b). Characterization of chemical stimuli for the penetration of *Schistosoma mansoni* cercariae. II. Conditions and mode of action. *Zeitschrift für Parasitenkunde* **66,** 309–319.
Halton, D. W. and Johnston, B. R. 1982. Functional morphology of the metacercarial cyst of *Bucephaloides gracilescens* (Trematoda: Bucephalidae). *Parasitology* **85,** 45–52.
Hammond, D. M. (1971). The development and ecology of coccidia and related intracellular parasites. *In* "Ecology and Physiology of Parasites. A symposium." (A. M. Fallis, ed.), pp. 3–20. University of Toronto Press, Canada.
Hammond, D. M. (1973). Life cycles and development of coccidia. *In* "The Coccidia"

(D. M. Hammond and P. L. Long eds.), pp. 45–79. University Park Press, Baltimore.

Hammond, D. M., Ernst, J. V. and Chobotar, B. (1970). Composition and function of the substiedal body in the sporocysts of *Eimeria utahensis*. *Journal of Parasitology* **56,** 618–619.

Hansen, E. L. and Buecher, E. J. (1971). Effect of insect hormones on nematodes in axenic culture. *Experientia* **27,** 859–860.

Hibbert, L. E. and Hammond, D. M. (1968). Effects of temperature on the *in vitro* excystation of various *Eimeria* species. *Experimental Parasitology* **23,** 161–170.

Hibbert, L. E., Hammond, D. M. and Simmons, J. R. (1969). The effects of pH, buffers, bile and bile acids on excystation of sporozoites of various *Eimeria* species. *Journal of Protozoology* **16,** 441–444.

Hockley, D. J. and McLaren, D. J. (1973). *Schistosoma mansoni*: changes in the outer membrane of the tegument during development from cercaria to adult worm. *International Journal for Parasitology* **3,** 13–25.

Howell, M. J. (1970). Excystment of the metacercariae of *Echinoparyphium serratum* (Tremadoda: Echinostomatidae). *Journal of Helminthology* **44,** 35–56.

Huffman, L. J. and Jones, H. W. (1962). Hatchability, viability, and infectivity of *Hydatigera taeniaeformis* eggs. *Experimental Parasitology* **12,** 120–124.

Hurley, L. C. and Sommerville, R. I. (1982). Reversible inhibition of hatching of infective eggs of *Ascaris suum* (Nematoda). *International Journal for Parasitology* **12,** 463–465.

Hyman, L. H. (1951). "The Invertebrates", Vol. 3. McGraw Hill Book Company, New York.

Irwin, S. W. B., McKerr, G., Judge, B. C. and Moran, I. (1984). Studies on metacercarial excystment in *Himasthla leptosoma* (Trematoda: Echinostomatidae) and newly emerged metacercariae. *International Journal for Parasitology* **14,** 415–421.

Jackson, A. R. B. (1962). Excystation of *Eimeria arlongi* (Marotel, 1905): stimuli from the host sheep. *Nature* (*Lond.*) **194,** 847–849.

Jackson, A. R. B. (1964). The isolation of viable coccidial sporozoites. *Parasitology* **54,** 87–93.

Jensen, J. B., Nyberg, P. A., Burton, S. D. and Jolley, W. R. (1976). The effects of selected gases on excystation of coccidian oocysts. *Journal of Parasitology* **62,** 195–198.

Joh, T. H., Park, D. H. and Reis, D. J. (1978). Direct phosphorylation of brain tyrosine hydroxylase by cyclic AMP-dependent protein kinase: mechanism of enzyme activation. *Proceedings of the National Academy of Science, U.S.A.* **75,** 4744–4748.

Johnston, B. R. and Halton, D. W. (1981). Excystation *in vitro* of *Bucephaloides gracilescens* metacercaria (Trematoda: Bucephalidae). *Zeitschrift für Parasitenkunde* **65,** 71–78.

Jolley, W. R. and Nyberg, P. A. (1974). Formation of a carbon dioxide–cystein complex in the incubation fluid used for excysting *Eimeria* species *in vitro*. *Proceedings of the Helminthological Society of Washington* **41,** 259–260.

Jolley, W. R., Burton, S. D., Nyberg, P. A. and Jensen, J. B. (1976). Formation of sulfhydryl groups in the walls of *Eimeria stiedae* and *E. tenella* oocysts subjected to *in vitro* excystation. *Journal of Parasitology* **62,** 199–202.

Jones, G. P., Petronijevic, T. and Rogers, W. P. (1983). The dynamics of the permeation of an analogue of juvenile hormone into nematodes. *Comparative Biochemistry and Physiology* **76A,** 289–293.

Justus, D. E. and Ivey, M. H. (1969). Chitinase activity in developmental stages of *Ascaris suum* and its inhibition by antibody. *Journal of Parasitology* **55,** 472–476.

Kearn, G. C. (1967). Experiments on host-finding and host-specificity in the monogenean skin parasite *Entobdella soleae. Parasitology* **57,** 585–605.

Keene, W. E., Jeong, K. H., McKerrow, J. H. and Werb, Z. (1983). Degradation of extracellular matrix by larvae of *Schistosoma mansoni.* II. Degradation by newly transformed and developing schistosomula. *Laboratory Investigation* **49,** 201–207.

Kernohan, J. C. (1965). The pH-activity curve of bovine carbonic anhydrase and its relation to the inhibition of the enzyme by anions. *Biochimica et Biophysica Acta* **96,** 304–317.

Kiese, M. and Hastings, A. B. (1940). Factors affecting the activity of carbonic anhydrase. *Journal of Biological Chemistry* **132,** 281–292.

Kirschner, K. and Bacha, W. J. (1980). Excystment of *Himasthla quissetensis* (Trematoda: Echinostomatidae) metacercariae *in vitro. Journal of Parasitology* **66,** 263–267.

Lackie, A. M. (1974). The activation of cystacanths of *Polymorphus minutus* (Acanthocephala) *in vitro. Parasitology* **68,** 135–146.

Lackie, A. M. (1975). The activation of the infective stages of endoparasites of vertebrates. *Biological Reviews* **50,** 285–323.

Landsperger, W. J., Stirewalt, M. A. and Dresden, M. H. (1982). Purification and properties of a proteolytic enzyme from the cercariae of the human trematode parasite, *Schistosoma mansoni. Biochemical Journal* **201,** 137–144.

Lee, D. L. (1972). Penetration of mammalian skin by the infective larva of *Nippostrongylus brasiliensis. Parasitology* **65,** 499–505.

Lethbridge, R. C. (1980). The biology of the oncosphere of cyclophyllidean cestodes. *Helminthological Abstracts* **49A,** 59–72.

Lindskog, S., Henderson, L. E., Kannan, K. K., Liljas, A., Nyman, P. O. and Strandberg, B. (1971). Carbonic anhydrase. *In* "The Enzymes" (P. D. Boyer, ed.), Vol. 5, pp. 587–665. Academic Press, New York.

Lippens-Mertens, F. and De Rycke, P. H. (1973). Excystation of *Hymenolepis microstoma.* II. Relative influence of proteolytic enzymes and bile salts. *Zeitschrift für Parasitenkunde* **42,** 61–67.

Lote, C. J. and Weiss, J. B. (1971). Identification of digalactosylcysteine in a glycopeptide isolated from urine by a new preparative technique. *FEBS Letters* **16,** 81–85.

MacInnis, A. J. (1969). Identification of chemicals triggering cercariae penetration responses of *Schistosoma mansoni. Nature* (*Lond.*) **224,** 1221–1222.

MacInnis, A. J. (1976). Host selection and its consequences. *In* "Ecological Aspects of Parasitology" (C. R. Kennedy, ed.), pp. 3–20. North Holland Publishing Company, Amsterdam.

Macy, R. W., Berntzen, A. K. and Benz, M. (1968). *In vitro* excystation of *Sphaeridiotrema globulus* metacercariae, structure of cyst, and the relationship to host specificity. *Journal of Parasitology* **54,** 28–38.

Marks, C. F., Thomason, I. J. and Castro, C. E. (1968). Dynamics of the permeation of nematodes by water nematocides and other substances. *Experimental Parasitology* **22,** 321–337.

Matthews, B. E. (1972). Invasion of skin by larvae of the cat hookworm *Ancylostoma tubaeforme. Parasitology* **65,** 457–467.

Matthews, B. E. (1977). The passage of larval helminths through tissue barriers. *British Society for Parasitology*. Symposia 15, 93–119.
McDaniel, J. S. (1966). Excystment of *Cryptocotyle lingua* metacercariae. *Biological Bulletin* **130,** 369–377.
McKerrow, J. H., Keene, W. E., Jeong, K. H. and Werb, Z. (1983). Degradation of extracellular matrix by larvae of *Schistosoma mansoni*. I. Degradation by cercariae as a model for initial parasite invasion of the host. *Laboratory Investigation* **49,** 195–200.
McLaren, D. J. and Hockley, D. J. (1976). *Schistosoma mansoni*: the occurrence of microvilli on the surface of the tegument during transformation from cercaria to schistosomulum. *Parasitology* **73,** 169–187.
Mettrick, D. F. and Podesta, R. B. (1974). Ecological and physiological aspects of helminth–host interactions in the mammalian gastro-intestinal canal. *Advances in Parasitology* **12,** 183–278.
Meza-Ruiz, G. and Alger, N. E. (1968). First parasitic ecdysis of *Haemonchus contortus in vitro* without stimulation by carbon dioxide. *Experimental Parasitology* **22,** 219–222.
Nagai, Y., Gazzinezzi, G., De Moraes, G. W. G. and Pellegrino, J. (1977). Protein synthesis during cercaria-schistosomulum transformation and early development of the *Schistosoma mansoni* larvae. *Comparative Biochemistry and Physiology* **57B,** 27–30.
Nyberg, P. A. and Hammond, D. M. (1964). Excystation of *Eimeria bovis* and other species of bovine coccidea. *Journal of Protozoology* **11,** 474–480.
Nyberg, P. A., Bauer, D. H. and Knapp, S. E. (1968). Carbon dioxide as the initial stimulus for excystation of *Eimeria tenella* oocysts. *Journal of Protozoology* **15,** 144–148.
Parker, S. and Croll, N. A. (1976). *Dictyocaulus viviparus*: the role of pepsin in the exsheathment of infective larvae. *Experimental Parasitology* **40,** 80–85.
Perry, R. N. and Clarke, A. J. (1981). Hatching mechanisms of nematodes. *Parasitology* **83,** 435–449.
Petronijevic, T. and Rogers, W. P. (1983). Gene activity and the development of early parasitic stages of nematodes. *International Journal for Parasitology* **13,** 197–199.
Petronijevic, T. and Rogers, W. P. (1986). Undissociated bases as the stimulus for the development of early parasitic stages of nematodes. *International Journal for Parasitology* (in press).
Petronijevic, T. and Rogers, W. P. (1987). The physiology of infection with nematodes: the role of intracellular pH in the development of the early parasitic stage. *Comparative Biochemistry and Physiology* (in press).
Petronijevic, T., Rogers, W. P. and Sommerville, R. I. (1985). Carbonic acid as the host signal for the development of parasitic stages of nematodes. *International Journal for Parasitology* **15,** 661–667.
Petronijevic, T., Rogers, W. P. and Sommerville, R. I. (1986). Organic and inorganic acids as the stimulus for exsheathment of infective juveniles of nematodes. *International Journal for Parasitology* **16,** 163–168.
Poinar, G. D. (1983). "The Natural History of Nematodes". Prentice-Hall, New Jersey.
Roberts, W. L., Speer, C. A. and Hammond, D. M. (1970). Electron and light microscope studies of the oocyst walls, sporocysts and excysting sporozoites of *Eimeria callospermophili* and *E. larimerensis*. *Journal of Parasitology* **56,** 918–926.

Rogers, W. P. (1940). The physiological ageing of the infective larvae of *Haemonchus contortus*. *Journal of Helminthology* **18,** 183–192.
Rogers, W. P. (1957). Physiology of the hatching of eggs of *Ascaris lumbricoides*. *Nature* (*Lond.*) **181,** 1410–1411.
Rogers, W. P. (1960). Physiology of infective processes of nematode parasites; the stimulus from the animal host. *Proceedings of the Royal Society* **152B,** 367–386.
Rogers, W. P. (1966). Reversible inhibition of a receptor governing infection with some nematodes. *Experimental Parasitology* **19,** 15–20.
Rogers, W. P. (1979). The interaction of insect juvenile hormone and carbon dioxide in the hatching of nematode eggs: its significance in the physiology of infective stages. *Comparative Biochemistry and Physiology* **64A,** 77–80.
Rogers, W. P. (1980). The action of insect juvenile hormone on the hatching of eggs of the nematode *Haemonchus contortus*, and its role in the development of infective and non-infective stages. *Comparative Biochemistry and Physiology* **64A,** 631–635.
Rogers, W. P. (1982). Enzymes in the exsheathing fluid of nematodes and their biological significance. *International Journal for Parasitology* **12,** 495–502.
Rogers, W. P. and Head, R. (1972). The effect of the stimulus for infection on hormones in *Haemonchus contortus*. *Comparative and General Pharmacology* **3,** 6–10.
Rogers, W. P. and Petronijevic, T. (1982). The infective stage and the development of nematodes. *In* "Biology and Control of Endoparasites" (L. E. A. Symons, A. D. Donald and J. K. Dineen, eds.), pp. 3–28. Academic Press, New York, London.
Rogers, W. P. and Sommerville, R. I. (1963). The infective stage of nematode parasites and its significance in parasitism. *Advances in Parasitology* **1,** 109–177.
Rogers, W. P. and Sommerville, R. I. (1968). The infectious process, and its relation to the development of early parasitic stages of nematodes. *Advances in Parasitology* **6,** 327–348.
Roos, A. and Boron, W. F. (1981). Intracellular pH. *Physiological Reviews* **61,** 296–434.
Rothman, A. H. (1959). Studies on the excystment of tapeworms. *Experimental Parasitology* **8,** 336–364.
Roughton, F. J. W. (1941). The kinetics and rapid thermochemistry of carbonic acid. *Journal of the American Chemical Society* **63,** 2930–2934.
Roughton, F. J. W. and Booth, V. H. (1938). CCLXVI. The catalytic effect of buffers on the reaction $CO_2 + H_2O \rightleftarrows H_2CO_3$. *Biochemical Journal* **32,** 2049–2069.
Rumjanek, F. D., McLaren, D. J. and Smithers, S. R. (1983). Serum-induced expression of a surface protein in schistosomula of *Schistosoma mansoni*: a possible receptor for lipid uptake. *Molecular and Biochemical Parasitology* **9,** 337–350.
Ryley, J. F. (1973). Cytochemistry, physiology and biochemistry. *In* "The Coccidia" (D. M. Hammond and P. L. Long, eds.), pp. 145–181. University Park Press, Baltimore.
Salafsky, B., Wang, Y-S., Kevin, M. B., Hill. H. and Fusco, A. C. (1984a). The role of prostaglandins in cercarial (*Schistosoma mansoni*) response to free fatty acids. *Journal of Parasitology* **70,** 584–591.
Salafsky, B., Wang, Y-S., Fusco, A. C. and Antonacci, J. (1984b). The role of essential fatty acids and prostaglandins in cercariae penetration (*Schistosoma mansoni*). *Journal of Parasitology* **70,** 656–660.
Shen, S. S. (1983). Membrane properties and intracellular ion activities of marine invertebrate eggs and their changes during activation. *In* "Mechanism and Control

of Animal Fertilization" (J. D. Hartmann, ed.), pp. 213–267. Academic Press, New York.

Shiff, C. J., Cmelik, S. H. W., Ley, H. E. and Kriel, R. L. (1972). The influence of human skin lipids on the cercarial penetration responses of *Schistosoma haematobium* and *Schistosoma mansoni*. *Journal of Parasitology* **58,** 476–480.

Silverman, P. H. and Podger, K. R. (1964). *In vitro* exsheathment of some nematode infective larvae. *Experimental Parasitology* **15,** 314–324.

Slais, J. (1973). Functional morphology of cestode larvae. *Advances in Parasitology* **11,** 395–480.

Slocombe, J. O. D. and Whitlock, J. H. (1969). Rapid ecdysis of infective *Haemonchus contortus cayugensis* larvae. *Journal of Parasitology* **55,** 1102–1103.

Smales, L. R. and Sommerville, R. I. (1977). Exsheathment of the infective larvae of *Labiostrongylus eugenii*, a nematode parasite of the Kangaroo Island wallaby *Macropus eugenii*. *International Journal for Parasitology* **7,** 205–209.

Smyth, J. D. (1969). "The Physiology of Cestodes". Oliver and Boyd, London.

Smyth, J. D. and Halton, D. W. (1983). "The Physiology of Trematodes". Cambridge University Press, Cambridge.

Smyth, J. D. and Haslewood, G. A. D. (1963). The biochemistry of bile as a factor in determining host specificity in intestinal parasites, with particular reference to *Echinococcus granulosus*. *Annals of the New York Academy of Sciences* **113,** 234–260.

Sommerville, R. I. and Bailey, M. A. (1973). *Nematospiroides dubius*: exsheathment of infective juveniles. *Experimental Parasitology* **33,** 1–9.

Sommerville, R. I. and Murphy, C. R. (1983). Reversal of order of ecdysis in *Haemonchus contortus* (Nematoda). *Journal of Parasitology* **69,** 368–371.

Speer, C. A. (1983). The Coccidia. *In* "*In Vitro* Cultivation of Protozoan Parasites" (J. B. Jensen, ed.), pp. 1–64. CRC Press, Florida.

Speer, C. A., Hammond, D. M. and Kelley, G. L. (1970). Stimulation of motility in merozoites of five *Eimeria* species by bile salts. *Journal of Parasitology* **56,** 927–929.

Stirewalt, M. A. (1963). Cercaria vs. schistosomule (*Schistosoma mansoni*): absence of the pericercarial envelope *in vivo* and the early physiological and histological metamorphosis of the parasite. *Experimental Parasitology* **13,** 395–406.

Stirewalt, M. A. (1966). Skin penetration mechanisms of helminths. *In* "Biology of Parasites" (E. J. L. Soulsby, ed.), pp. 41–59. Academic Press, New York.

Stirewalt, M. A. (1971). Penetration stimuli for schistosome cercariae. *In* "Aspects of the Biology of Symbiosis" (T. C. Cheng, ed.), pp. 1–23. University Park Press, Baltimore.

Stirewalt, M. A. (1974). *Schistosoma mansoni*: cercaria to schistosomule. *Advances in Parasitology* **12,** 115–182.

Stirewalt, M. A. (1978). Quantitative collection and proteolytic activity of preacetabular gland enzyme of cercariae of *Schistosoma mansoni*. *American Journal of Tropical Medicine and Hygiene* **27,** 548–553.

Stirewalt, M. A., Cousin, C. E. and Dorsey, C. H. (1983). *Schistosoma mansoni*: stimulus and transformation of cercariae to schistosomules. *Experimental Parasitology* **56,** 358–368.

Stirewalt, M. A. and Hackey, J. R. (1956). Penetration of the host skin by cercariae of *Schistosoma mansoni*. I. Observed entry into skin of mouse, hamster, rat, monkey and man. *Journal of Parasitology* **42,** 565–580.

Taylor, A. and Whitlock, J. H. (1960). The exsheathing stimulus for infective larvae of *Haemonchus contortus*. *Cornell Veterinarian* **50,** 339–344.

Thomas, R. C. (1974). Intracellular pH of snail neurones. *Journal of Physiology* **238,** 159–180.

Thompson, M. and Halton, D. W. (1982). Observations on excystment *in vitro* of *Cotylurus variegatus* metacercariae (Trematoda: Strigeidae). *Zeitschrift für Parasitenkunde* **68,** 201–209.

Thompson, T. E. and Huang, C. (1980). Dynamics of lipids in biomembranes. *In* "Membrane Physiology" (T. E. Andreoli, J. F. Hoffman and D. D. Fanestil, eds.), pp. 27–48. Plenum Medical Book Company, New York.

Todd, K. S. and Ernst, J. V. (1977). Coccidia of mammals except man. *In* "Parasitic Protozoa" (J. P. Kreier, ed.), Vol. III. pp. 71–99. Academic Press, New York, London.

Ubelaker, J. E. (1980). Structure and ultrastructure of the larvae and metacestodes of *Hymenolepis diminuta*. *In* "Biology of the Tapeworm *Hymenolepis diminuta*" (H. P. Arai, ed.), pp. 59–156. Academic Press, New York, London.

Ubelaker, J. E. (1983). Metacestodes: morphology and development. *In* "Biology of the Eucestoda" (C. Arme and P. W. Pappas, eds.), Vol. 1, pp. 139–176. Academic Press, New York, London.

van der Ploeg, L. H. T., Giannini, S. H. and Cantor, C. R. (1985). Heat shock genes: regulatory role for differentiation in parasitic protozoa. *Science* **228,** 1443–1445.

Voge, M. (1967). Developmental stages of cestodes. *Advances in Parasitology* **5,** 247–297.

Wagner, A. (1959). Stimulation of *Schistosomatium douthitti* cercariae to penetrate their host. *Journal of Parasitology* **45,** (Section 2): 16.

Wang, C. C. (1982). Biochemistry and physiology of coccidia. *In* "The Biology of Coccidia" (P. L. Long, ed.), pp. 167–228. Edward Arnold, London.

Wang, C. C. and Stotish, R. L. (1975). Pancreatic chymotrypsin as the essential enzyme for excystation of *Eimeria tenella*. *Journal of Parasitology* **61,** 923–927.

Wang, C. C. and Stotish, R. L. (1978). Multiple leucine aminopeptidases in the oocysts of *Eimeria tenella* and their changes during sporulation. *Comparative Biochemistry and Physiology* **61B,** 307–313.

Weiss, J. B., Lote, C. J. and Bobinski, H. (1971). New low molecular weight glycopeptide containing triglucosylcysteine in human erythrocyte-membrane. *Nature, New Biology* **234,** 25–26.

Wilson, P. A. G. (1976). Nematode growth patterns in the moulting cycle: the population growth profile. *Journal of Zoology* (*Lond.*) **179,** 135–151.

Wilson, P. A. G. (1982). Roundworm juvenile migration in mammals: the pathways of skin-penetration reconsidered. *In* "Aspects of Parasitology" (E. Meerovitch, ed.), pp. 459–485. Institute of Parasitology, McGill University, Montreal.

Wright, D. J. and Newall, D. R. (1976). Nitrogen excretion, osmotic and ionic regulation in nematodes. *In* "The Organization of Nematodes" (N. A. Croll, ed.), pp. 163–210. Academic Press, New York, London.

Wright, R. D. (1971). The egg envelopes of *Moniliformis dubius*. *Journal of Parasitology* **57,** 122–131.

Yokogawa, S., Cort, W. W. and Yokogawa, M. (1960). *Paragonimus* and Paragonimiasis. *Experimental Parasitology* **10,** 81–137.

Index

DATE DUE